ENGINEERING THERMODYNAMICS

An Introductory Text

BY

D. B. SPALDING

M.A., Ph.D., A.M.I.Mech.E., A.M.Inst.F.

PROFESSOR OF HEAT TRANSFER, MECHANICAL ENGINEERING DEPARTMENT,
CITY AND GUILDS COLLEGE,
IMPERIAL COLLEGE OF SCIENCE AND TECHNOLOGY, UNIVERSITY OF LONDON

AND

E. H. COLE

B.Sc.(Eng.), A.C.G.I., A.M.I.Mech.E., Wh.Sc.

LECTURER, MECHANICAL ENGINEERING DEPARTMENT,
CITY AND GUILDS COLLEGE,
IMPERIAL COLLEGE OF SCIENCE AND TECHNOLOGY, UNIVERSITY OF LONDON

LONDON
EDWARD ARNOLD (PUBLISHERS) LTD.

Printed in Northern Ireland at The Universities Press, Belfast

FOREWORD

by

Professor O. A. Saunders, M.A., D.Sc.(Eng.), M.I.Mech.E., F.Inst.P., F.Inst.F., F.R.Ae.S., F.R.S.

A thorough grounding in the fundamentals of thermodynamics has always been an essential part of engineering education and recent developments in power engineering and propulsion have emphasized this. Although the mechanical engineer is the most concerned, electrical, chemical and aeronautical engineers also need a sound preparation for their own later specialisations, and civil engineers must be familiar with the background of the subject.

In the past thermodynamics has been regarded as one of the more difficult subjects to teach and there has often been much confusion of thought in the presentation of the fundamentals. Many engineering text books treat the subject as the science of the heat engine, in the sense that the mechanical engineer understands the term, and this leaves many gaps in the knowledge of the young engineer which may handicap him in later years when he encounters broader applications such as high speed flow of fluids, the relation between chemical, thermal and mechanical energy, and electrical effects. These facts point strongly to the need for a clear exposition of the broad fundamentals of thermodynamics for all engineering students in their first year at University or Technical College and it is with this in mind that the present book has been written. The authors do not claim that the book covers the whole of engineering thermodynamics for any kind of engineer. Certainly mechanical engineers need to know a great deal more of internal-combustion engines, steam engines and refrigeration than is contained in this book, and such matters form a natural follow-up in the second and third years of a degree course. The same applies to other kinds of engineers, the majority of whom need to study the subject in their second year. The authors have, however, introduced some of the practical aspects of the subject by means of the numerous examples which show the essentials of the various kinds of calculations in which thermodynamics is applied in practice, and in the unworked problems given at the end of each chapter. Throughout the book the importance of a clear logical development of the argument starting with careful definitions of all terms used, has been stressed. The clear distinction between heat and work effects is fundamental to the approach used and many examples are given to bring this out. It is hoped that through this course the student may see thermodynamics in its proper relation to the other branches of engineering science.

The pioneer work in this kind of approach to thermodynamics teaching has of course been done by Professor J. H. Keenan of the Massachusetts Institute of Technology whose book has laid the foundations, and the present authors have obviously depended very largely on Keenan's work

iii

for their inspiration and guidance. There have, however, been very few books in this vein from British authors. For three years past, the First Year Common Course for engineers at Imperial College has now followed the lines indicated in this book and it is felt that as a result our students are better equipped at the end of their First Year to deal with the various specialised problems they may meet in later years.

PREFACE

This book is based on lectures given to first-year engineering students, by one of us (D. B. S.) at Cambridge University under Professor W. R. Hawthorne, and by both of us at the City and Guilds College under Professor O. A. Saunders. In both cases the lectures have been attended by students of mechanical, aeronautical, civil, and electrical engineering alike. Consequently the book is concerned with fundamentals rather than applications, although we have sought throughout to demonstrate the way in which the theoretical subtleties arise out of, and help to solve, practical engineering problems. We have added two chapters which are not included in our first-year lectures, namely those on Gaseous Mixtures and on Combustion; for these are also fundamental in character, and have to be dealt with early in the second year.

In the order and logic of our treatment, we have largely followed Keenan's *Thermodynamics*, and it is a pleasure to acknowledge the profound and healthy influence which this book has exercised on the teaching and practice of thermodynamics in the United Kingdom. We hold a rigorous development of the subject to be of the highest importance, and have no sympathy with the view that the engineer is a practical chap who merely needs a few formulae to help him deal with engines. Even if this view has done little obvious harm in the past, when engine design was relatively static, the speed of current developments, and in particular the increasing role of aerodynamics in power-plant practice, make a firm grasp of principles essential.

We regard it as equally important that the engineer should recognise thermodynamics as a body of theory that has arisen out of practical experience of engine performance, that has been moulded so as to permit clear analysis of engineering problems, and that is a simple and powerful tool for him to use. We have therefore striven to accompany the theoretical development by a commentary on its significance for the production of mechanical power, and by examples on its use in engineering calculations.

These two main aims have determined the order in which the various themes are handled. Logic demands that definitions of work, temperature and heat should precede treatment of the First Law. Before the latter can be used, the properties of systems have to be discussed. Then, however, a wide variety of engineering calculations can be carried out; in particular we spend some time discussing the application of the First Law to problems involving steady flow.

At this stage we only mention Ideal Gases in passing, preferring to use steam in most of the examples. There are two reasons. Firstly, steam is typical of practical fluids in exhibiting phase change, a critical point, variation of internal energy with pressure as well as temperature, and the necessity to have its properties tabulated *in extenso*: the Ideal Gases are exceptions, of unrepresentative simplicity. Secondly, it is a matter of

v

experience that the Ideal Gas formulae exercise a hypnotic effect on students: if not previously nourished on a diet of steam and general formulations, students easily become adept in Ideal Gas calculations but helpless when faced by a more irregular substance. This is the more serious, since the tendency of pressure and temperature ranges to widen in engineering practice brings the irregularities of even such relatively simple substances as air into greater prominence.

The First Law examples demonstrate that more information is needed before the maximum work output of machines can be determined. At this stage therefore we introduce the Second Law; Planck's formulation is given prominence because of its direct relevance to power production. The Absolute Temperature Scale and entropy are then introduced as part of an effort to express the maximum work output quantitatively, for non-cyclic processes as well as for cyclic ones.

With this body of theory established, we are able to deal with Ideal Gases. Boyle's and Joule's Laws are introduced as experimental relations which some substances obey rather closely. We then *deduce* that these substances must also obey the pressure-volume-temperature relation known as the Ideal Gas Rule. Our treatment of the Ideal Gas Rule thus differs in order from that of Keenan, who deduces Joule's Law from the Rule. Of course there is no essential difference in final result.

We have also departed from Keenan's procedures in a few other respects. Firstly we use the term *energy* where he uses *internal energy*; we restrict the latter term to the energy of a pure substance in the absence of gravitational, kinetic, and other effects. This distinction then corresponds to the use of the symbols E and U. Secondly, we have found it convenient to introduce the term *chemical substance* for a restricted but important class of systems capable of chemical reaction, and have introduced corresponding new symbols. Thirdly, we have used the system of units (lb_f, lb_m, ft, s) which is employed by most engineers in English-speaking countries; this requires the use of the symbol g_0 as the constant in Newton's Second Law of Motion. We believe that our procedure will make it easy for students to pass over to systems (e.g. lb_f, slug; or poundal, lb_m) which make g_0 equal to unity, wherever there is advantage in doing so.

We wish to thank Professor J. H. Keenan, Professor F. G. Keyes and Messrs. John Wiley and Sons, Inc., for permission to include abstracts from their *Thermodynamic Properties of Steam*. We are grateful to the following institutions and firms for the use of material:— The Science Museum, (Fig. 1.1 and Fig. 1.2); The General Electric Company Ltd., (Fig. 1.3); D. Napier and Son Ltd., (Fig. 1.4); Ruston and Hornsby Ltd., (Fig. 1.5); Hawker-Siddeley Group Ltd., (Fig. 1.6); Budenberg Gauge Co. Ltd. and the Society of Instrument Technology, (Fig. 2.5); Dobbie McInnes Ltd., (Fig. 3.9); Griffin and George Ltd., (Fig. 16.6 and Fig. 16.7).

We also wish to thank our colleagues and students at Cambridge and South Kensington for the discussions and criticisms which have deepened and enlarged our understanding of thermodynamics; we hope they will recognise their influence in the book. Particular gratitude is due to Dr. R. D. Tyler who has read much of the manuscript, made many

valuable comments, and contributed some of the examples, and to
Mr. F. W. James, Librarian, City and Guilds College, who has assisted in
the location and checking of references.

D. B. S.

E. H. C.

South Kensington, 1958.

CONTENTS

INTRODUCTORY SURVEY

HISTORICAL INTRODUCTION

Mechanical power as the basis of civilized life

Man is physically a weak animal; yet he dominates the globe. How has this come about? The answer lies in his ability to control forces far greater than those which his own muscles can exert. The need to do so was apparent as soon as agriculture and urban life were instituted; for water had to be pumped to irrigate the land and supply the towns; food and building materials had to be transported; corn must be ground and wood sawed. Later, when valuable ores were discovered beneath the surface of the earth, these too had to be transported and processed; the deeper the mines became, the more difficult grew the task of keeping them free of water. Man's ability to provide sufficient power for these and similar purposes set limits to the rate of growth of civilization, as indeed it still does. Provision of this power is nowadays one of the main tasks of the mechanical engineer.

Sources of power

Animals, wind and water. When civilization began, during the sixth millennium B.C., the only available sources of power were animal: heavy tasks were performed by gangs of slaves or by domestic animals. This organization and division of labour was a prerequisite for the establishment of collective life.

The power of the wind was the next source, at first used only for driving sailing vessels. Not until the 10th century A.D. however was the wind harnessed, by means of windmills, to mechanical tasks such as milling and sawing.

Water-wheels were invented earlier, probably in primitive form before the beginning of the Christian era. For centuries they remained man's main source of mechanical power. Animals are slow, winds uncertain; water power is not always found in the right places. Particularly for mining, more concentrated, reliable and disposable sources of power were needed and urgently looked for throughout the Middle Ages.

The beginnings of steam power. The seventeenth century in Europe saw the rise of modern science. Observations were recorded and communicated; experiments were planned purposively; above all, quantitative measurements were systematically made.

Much study was devoted to the properties of air and water. With the invention of the piston-and-cylinder air pump by von Guericke in Germany in 1654, the properties of gas under pressure, and of vacua, could be investigated. Notable discoveries were made by Boyle and Hooke in England. Even earlier, Porta in Italy and de Caus in France had shown

1

how steam could be made to raise water by pressure or by condensation. By the end of the century Savery had managed to combine these processes into a practical means of pumping water.

A most important advance was made by Newcomen in 1712: he combined the piston and cylinder of the air pump with the use of steam. A vertical cylinder was filled with steam from a boiler; cold water was then injected into the cylinder, causing the steam to condense and its pressure to fall; the atmospheric pressure pushing on top of the piston forced it down into the cylinder, thereby moving a beam which drove a water pump, (Fig. 1.1). This was the first practical steam engine. Its immediate effect was to solve the problem of draining the mines; of more far-reaching significance however was that man now had a source of power of unprecedented magnitude, dependent neither on flesh and blood nor on the vagaries of weather and geography.

Power developments in the eighteenth century. The importance of the Newcomen engine was soon recognised throughout the western world, and engineers worked strenuously both to improve its functioning and to use it for other tasks than the pumping of water.

Most notable among the improvements was Watt's invention of the *separate condenser* in 1769. Instead of condensing the steam within the cylinder, Watt connected the cylinder, at the appropriate point of the piston movement, to another vessel which was kept cool the whole time and held at a low pressure by means of an *air-pump* (Fig. 1.2). This brought about a notable saving of fuel, much of which had been wasted in the Newcomen engine in heating the cylinder again after each injection of cold water. Watt and his associates were also responsible for systematizing measurements of the power and fuel consumption of their engines. It was Watt, for example, who invented the *horse-power* unit.

Manufacturing industry benefited greatly from the existence of the new source of power. By the end of the 18th century, steam engines were driving spinning machinery, paper mills, winding-engines and many other plants. Experiments in applying steam power to transport were also being pursued.

Power developments in the nineteenth century. Because of the weight and bulk of the machinery, the most striking application of steam power to transport was in the driving of ships. Here the United States of America made notable contributions: the first commercial steam-boat was launched by Fulton on the Hudson River in 1807.

On land, after unsuccessful attempts to make steam engines travel over the inadequate roads of the time, the use of railways made possible the support, not only of the heavy engines themselves, but also of the long trains of goods and passengers which they could pull. Throughout the century networks of railways spread over the civilized regions of the world, transforming both the scenery and the mode of life of millions.

The reciprocating steam engine was not however to remain unchallenged. The improvements in manufacturing technique which it had made possible, together with the great spread of technical knowledge, had made engineers

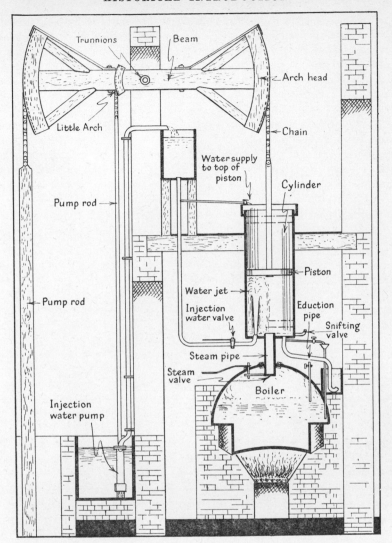

Fig. 1.1 Newcomen's pumping engine, 1712.

This diagram shows a typical atmospheric pumping engine, as made by Newcomen, in section, with the piston in the middle of the downward or working stroke. Steam is generated at atmospheric pressure in the boiler and fills the cylinder during the upward stroke of the piston. The steam valve is then closed and the steam is condensed by a jet of cold water, so reducing the pressure under the piston. The atmospheric pressure acting on the top of the piston forces it down, hence the name "atmospheric" engine, and this constitutes the working stroke. The piston is raised again by the overbalancing weight of the pump-rods.

(Reproduced by permission of The Science Museum)

Crown copyright reserved

look once more at an idea often mooted before but abandoned as impracticable: the elimination of steam as the intermediary between the fuel and the working piston. Already by 1678 Hooke had proposed the use of gunpowder within a cylinder operating a piston; a century later, Street

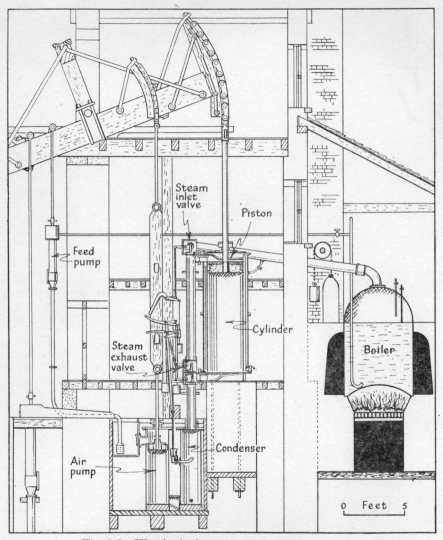

Fig. 1.2   Watt's single-acting pumping engine, 1788.
(Reproduced by permission of The Science Museum)
Crown copyright reserved

patented an internal combustion engine which was to explode vaporized turpentine and air. It was not however until the second half of the nineteenth century that commercial success was achieved. The *gas engine* using a gas derived from the partial combustion of coal, and the *petrol engine* using a vaporizable fuel, each employing either electrical or external-flame ignition, were both developed in this period; the former was primarily for static operation, the latter for transport. *Heavy-oil engines*, in which the fuel was ignited in the cylinder either by contact with a "hot-bulb" or as a result of the temperature rise of the compressed air, followed shortly after. French, German and British engineers were prominent in these developments.

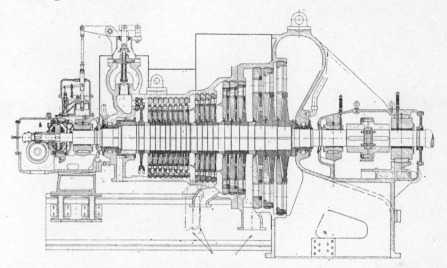

Fig. 1.3   Section through steam turbine.

So encouraging were the results obtained with the new prime movers, that it appeared as though steam power would soon cease to be important. Prophecies to this effect were falsified however by the successful combination by Parsons, in 1884, of the use of steam with the principles of the wind-mill. The new engine was the *reaction steam turbine* (Fig. 1.3), in which high-pressure steam from a boiler flowed steadily through alternate rows of fixed vanes projecting from the inner surface of a casing, and moving blades mounted on a rotating shaft. In this way very great powers were obtained from a small and smoothly running piece of machinery; moreover the fuel consumption was significantly lower than that of the reciprocating steam engine. The result was a new lease of life for the steam power plant, which, in its new form, retained for many years its dominance in the driving of ships, and which is still pre-eminent in the production of electrical power on land.

Power production in the first half of the twentieth century. The beginning of the twentieth century was remarkable more for the intensive development of the prime movers already discussed than for the introduction of new types. In the course of this development, the relative advantages of the various engines were gradually discovered, largely by trial-and-error, and their appropriate areas of employment became delineated. These however are always shifting as a consequence of minor improvements in performance.

From the start, the petrol engine has had a clear lead in propelling road vehicles, although the greater fuel economy of the heavy-oil (diesel) engine is making great inroads here. Reciprocating steam engines,

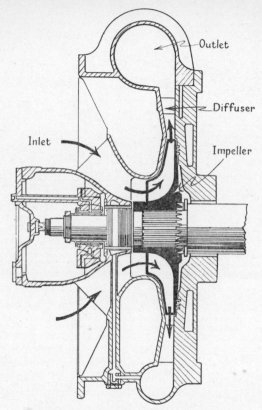

Fig. 1.4   Centrifugal compressor.

though still providing the major part of the power of the world's railways, are also giving way to diesel-powered locomotives or to electricity derived from central steam-turbine-driven power stations. The compression-ignition oil engine has made great advances also in the propulsion of ships, both large and small.

The gas engine was foiled of its expected future in central power stations by the advent of the steam turbine. Its use is now restricted mainly to regions where a ready supply of fuel gas is obtainable directly from wells in the earth. This field of application also is threatened by a relative newcomer: *the gas-turbine engine.*

The early years of the century saw the development of powered flight. From being a spectacular novelty, the aeroplane has become a major vehicle of transport, both commercially and militarily. Aero-engines must be both powerful and light; these requirements were until recently met only by the petrol engine. In the 1930's however development of the gas turbine engine in Switzerland, England and Germany, provided a new power plant with advantages which have greatly diminished the use of

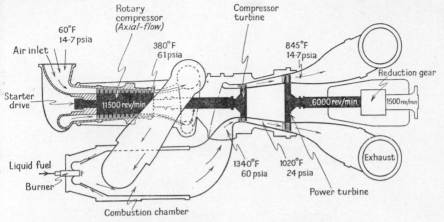

Fig. 1.5 Industrial gas-turbine engine.

the petrol engine. Once again, the idea had been proposed in the eighteenth century; but the means for realising it were not present until 150 years later.

The gas turbine employs the principle which Parsons used to such effect fifty years earlier: the reciprocating piston is dispensed with and the gases flow through rows of moving and stationary blades. Instead of water, however, air has first to be compressed in a rotary compressor (Fig. 1.4);

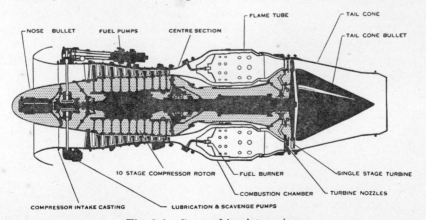

Fig. 1.6 Gas-turbine jet engine.

liquid or gaseous fuel is burnt in the compressed air stream, and the hot gases thereby produced flow out through the turbine. The power output is effected either through the shaft coupled to compressor and turbine or by way of the propulsive force of a jet (Figs. 1.5 and 1.6). Nowadays the gas turbine dominates aircraft propulsion; but its advance in competition with other modes of power production on land has been much slower. Here fuel consumption is often more important than the lightness and mechanical simplicity which the gas turbine has to offer; in this respect the older-established engines are still supreme.

Fuel consumption is all the more important because coal and oil have to be extracted from the mines and reservoirs beneath the earth. Not only is this extraction difficult and expensive, but the supplies there are not inexhaustible. Already the more far-sighted see serious grounds for anxiety in our present improvident use of the world's fuel resources. It is therefore fortunate that a new type of fuel has been discovered: uranium and its products. Whereas coal and oil are useful because they can undergo *chemical reaction*, uranium carries out a *nuclear reaction:* the nuclei of the atom become split and so release energy. Although still a mineral fuel, and very expensive to extract and process, uranium is relatively plentifully distributed in the earth's crust and may well supply at least part of man's power requirements for many generations; for the work obtainable from a ton of uranium is equivalent to that of $2\frac{3}{4}$ million tons of coal. Already it is making an important contribution to Britain's electricity supply.

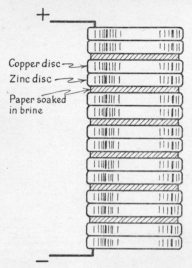

Copper disc

Zinc disc

Paper soaked in brine

Fig. 1.7   Volta's pile, 1800.

Despite the differences in its mode of reaction, nuclear fuel is still used in conjunction with steam turbine plants. Although it is likely that gas turbines will also find a part to play, there is no entirely new type of nuclear-driven power plant in prospect at the present time.

The role of electricity. Electrical effects were known in ancient times, but the starting point of modern knowledge and use of electricity may be said to be the discovery by Volta in 1799 of the possibility of producing an electrical current from a chemical reaction, namely that between paired discs of copper and zinc in brine (Fig. 1.7). Although developments of it are used for car accumulators and the batteries of flashlamps, Volta's discovery has not yet led to any large-scale production of electrical power; the reason is that on the one hand the substances with which it is easy to produce electricity are expensive, while on the other hand the chemical reactions undergone by common fuels are difficult to harness in this way, for technical reasons. Nevertheless the possibility is of great theoretical interest, as will be seen later in this book.

Modern use of electricity in power production derives from Faraday's discovery in 1831 of how electricity could be produced by moving an electrical conductor in a magnetic field, thus eventually making possible the convenient *transmission* of power. Dynamos and electric motors should therefore be thought of, not as prime movers, but as modern equivalents of the levers, gears, belts and pulleys which have been used for transmission since engineering began.

Power production in the future. Advances in the techniques of power production have been so swift that speculation as to future developments is hazardous. It can be said with certainty that chemical fuels will become increasingly scarce within relatively few generations unless drastic changes in their use are introduced. One such change would be the application of Volta's discovery to the production of electric power directly from the reaction of coal and oil with air, by the commercial development of a *fuel cell;* in this way about three times as much power could be produced per unit of fuel as at present. Although the difficulties are great, even more formidable ones have been overcome in the development of nuclear power.

A possibility of solving the power difficulties of mankind more permanently is currently engaging serious attention. This is the use of the nuclear *fusion*, as opposed to *fission*, reaction. In this, which is the essential process of the hydrogen bomb, the nuclei of the atoms of light elements combine to form heavier nuclei with a very great release of energy. Since hydrogen is extremely plentiful, no shortage of raw material need be feared. However it has not yet been demonstrated that the power consumed in processing the hydrogen to prepare it for the fusion reaction is less than that which can be released by the reaction. Moreover the reaction is only known to proceed at temperatures which are far above the present range of engineering experience. So far all that can be said is that the thermo-nuclear reaction is as likely to prove the saviour of mankind as its destroyer.

Summarising remarks about the means of power production

The choice of power plant. In our brief survey of the history of man's search for power, some important considerations have emerged which will now be recapitulated.

Firstly, the power plant should have sufficient *magnitude*. This requirement, coupled with the aims which man has set his heart on, has been the major stimulus to development.

Secondly, the *fuel consumption* should be low. This is as true of petrol engines and nuclear power plants as it was when the food for slaves and animals was the main item of current expenditure.

Often *concentration* of power is the prime requirement, as in aircraft propulsion. No matter how many oxen are available, and however rich and plentiful their fodder, they are incapable of exerting enough power to lift themselves off the ground.

Finally power sources must be *reliable* and *flexible*. It is for this reason that, though the winds are strong and cost nothing, we prefer to pay for fuel for our ships in order that they should "sail" with certainty, even when the wind is contrary or absent.

The elements of modern power plant. Finally we draw particular attention to some components of engines, which, as has been seen, have long been known to man, and which will greatly occupy our attention in the present book.

The first is the *bladed wheel*. The earliest form was the water-wheel; later it appeared as wind-mill, and finally as steam or gas turbine or as rotary compressor.

The second is the *piston-cylinder combination*, used first as a pump for water or air and later as the mechanism by which the pressure of steam or hot gases impels the motion of beams, shafts, propellers and motor-cars.

The third is the *Voltaic* cell, still the Cinderella of power sources, waiting for the glass slipper to be found.

Finally we note that, whereas solid shafts and gears often transmit the power, it is fluids which make the machines go round. Water and steam, air and combustion products: these are of prime concern to the power plant engineer. They will occupy much of our attention in subsequent chapters.

THE NATURE OF THERMODYNAMICS

The role of science in the development of power plants

Observation, speculation, experiment; abstraction of essentials, prediction: these have always been man's most characteristic activities. Nowhere are they more noticeable than in the way he has striven for power over his environment. To most men, however, the first three come more easily; yet the last two characteristics must be superadded before man's activity can be called truly scientific. This fact also is illustrated by the history of engineering.

The first systematic *observation* of nature in the seventeenth century, particularly the study of the properties of fluids, led to *speculation* about the production of power from steam and fire. After many failures, *experiment* showed that such engines could indeed be made and used. The pragmatic approach was amply justified. Continued experiment produced continued improvement in performance, particularly in the amount of water which could be pumped with the consumption of a fixed amount of fuel.

It is questionable however whether *science* made much contribution before Watt, realising what was "really" going on in the Newcomen cylinder, and interpreting the processes in the light of Black's discovery of the "latent heat" of steam, *predicted* that the provision of a separate condenser would reduce the fuel consumption. This step required a high degree of abstract thought.

Yet deeper questions remained: could the fuel consumption be reduced indefinitely and if not, why not? In providing the answers, the science of *thermodynamics* was born.

Nowadays these questions and many others can be answered by engineering students before the end of their first year of study. Attention is paid to them, not primarily because of the intellectual exercise which they provide, but because *experiments are expensive*. "Bright ideas" about new engineering devices are easy to think up, yet, if they are to be tested in practice, raw material must be bought, machines diverted from other production, and the testing personnel must be paid. No one is willing to authorise this expenditure until the proposals have been examined as to their concordance with known scientific principles, and until the best possible prediction of their outcome has been made. Experiment and trial-and-error development can seldom be dispensed with entirely, but a case for the new idea must be made out "on paper" before the first order is placed on the workshop.

The discovery of the laws of thermodynamics

At the beginning of the nineteenth century the questions about the fuel consumption of engines were being thought of in terms of two abstractions: *work*, the thing that the engineer wanted to get; and *heat*, the thing that, via the burning of fuel, he had to employ to get it. What were the laws governing the conversion of heat into work?

A partial answer was provided by Carnot in France in 1824. By a brilliant feat of abstract thought, he perceived that *temperature* provided the key. He used the fruitful method of arguing by analogy. It was known that water, flowing from a high level to a low one, could do an amount of work which increased in proportion to the differences of level. Could not heat, then, be in this respect like water, the temperatures at which the heat was supplied (in the boiler) and rejected (in the condenser) being the counterparts of the levels of the water? This thought, and its development in the hands of Carnot himself and of others, is embodied in what is now known as the *Second Law of Thermodynamics*.

In one respect Carnot was wrong; moreover it was the argument by analogy which misled him. For whereas the same amount of water flows away from a water-wheel as flows to it, less heat is rejected by an engine than is supplied to it. Carnot can hardly be blamed for not noticing this: the heat "lost" amounted to less than ten per cent even in the best engines of his time.

Carnot's work attracted little attention until more than twenty years later. Meanwhile the Englishman Joule was following a different track. In a long series of careful experiments he showed what had happened to the "lost" heat: it had "turned into" work. This was not, of course, quite the way in which the matter appeared to him; his experiments were not made on engines but on specially designed apparatus. But his discovery, published in 1850, has this import among many others. It is now known as the *First Law of Thermodynamics*.

The reconciliation of Carnot's and Joule's principles soon followed, and in a few years the main structure of classical thermodynamics was established. Kelvin in Scotland and Clausius in Germany were outstanding in this work, which has proved to be significant far beyond the boundaries of power-plant engineering: physicists, chemists, biologists and even philosophers must nowadays be familiar with the First and Second Laws.

The establishment of the laws of thermodynamics did not of course render further observation and experiment unnecessary. Rather it stimulated them; for now a theoretical framework was available into which the new experimental data could be fitted; and by showing what was possible and what was not, the efforts of the experimenters could be directed towards the most fruitful ends. This book will be largely concerned with the results of their experiments and with an account of the two laws which give them meaning.

The content of thermodynamics

Definition. Thermodynamics is the science of the relations between heat, work and the properties of systems.

The words *heat, work, property* and *system* will all be the subject of precise definition below. For the moment we can substitute *matter* for *system* and attribute to the other terms their meanings in ordinary speech.

Fig. 1.8

Thermodynamics then relates the changes which matter undergoes to the influences to which it is subjected: for example, it tells how the pressure and temperature of the steam in an engine depend on the extent to which the steam is heated and the amount of work which is extracted.

A characteristic feature of thermodynamics is that these relations can often be stated in complete ignorance of the *details* of the process in question. The following parlour puzzle, which appears in many forms, will serve as illustration.

Problem: Two equal tumblers are each half full, one with white wine, the other with red. A teaspoonful of the white wine is taken from the first tumbler and transferred to the second, the contents of which are then thoroughly mixed; then a teaspoonful of the mixture in the second tumbler is transferred back to the first tumbler, which is similarly stirred. *Question:* Which of the two resultant mixtures is the more pure?

Solution: (This should not be read until attempts have been made to follow the process in detail, noting that pure white wine is transferred to the second tumbler but that some of it returns when the second transference occurs. Noting further that the first teaspoonful of white wine is mixed with half a tumbler of red wine, whereas the second teaspoonful is mixed with a smaller quantity, algebra arises of sufficient complexity to make mistakes and conflicting answers abound.)

The thermodynamicist's approach is as follows:—

1. Draw a *diagram*, enclosing each tumbler by an imaginary boundary, Fig. 1.8. (Later these boundaries will be called *control surfaces*.)

2. Consider the *net* transfer of wine across one of the boundaries. Since one teaspoonful of wine (regardless of colour) travels in each direction, the net transfer of wine is zero.

3. Consider the *net* transfer of *white* wine *out of* the first tumbler. Let this quantity have the volume x. Then since there is zero net transfer of wine, an equal volume x of *red* wine must have been transferred *into* the first tumbler, and *out of* the second.

4. *Conclusion.* The net process is symmetrical: *the two final mixtures are equally pure (or impure).*

This economical proof, though hardly belonging to engineering thermodynamics, has features which are typical of many which will be found in this book.

Thermodynamics as the scourge of inventors

Another important feature of thermodynamics is that it furnishes simple tests of whether an inventor's proposal for a new power plant is possible.

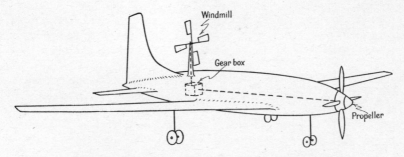

Fig. 1.9   Invention 1.   Proposal for aircraft propulsion.

Usually the inventions which are submitted for development are so complicated that to attempt to follow the proposals in detail is to get lost in a maze in which fact and supposition are impossible to disentangle. Often however the thermodynamicist can sit back and, by proofs as elegant as the above, demonstrate that a fallacy must exist somewhere. This rarely satisfies the inventor, it must be admitted. The following examples will indicate the sort of problems which arise, although we cannot follow out their solutions here.

Invention 1. Most schoolboys destined to be engineers, soon after learning the function of (a) windmills, and (b) propellers for aircraft, hit on the idea of combining them in the way shown in Fig. 1.9. A windmill, mounted near the tail is rotated by the air rushing past; this windmill is connected by shafts to the propeller and so serves to drive the aircraft forward without the need of an engine. The more sophisticated young inventors recognise that friction in the bearings may be a draw-back and so insert step-up gearing in the transmission. Launching by catapult is usually recommended in order that the propulsion system should get under way.

Discussion: Unfortunately it has not been found possible to make this scheme work in practice, even with step-up gearing! Most readers will accept this without recourse to thermodynamics, but a strict proof is only possible with the help of its laws.

Invention 2. Acquaintance with the workings of the filter pump (jet pump) used in school chemistry laboratories sometimes inspires the proposal for pumping water shown in Fig. 1.10. Water from reservoir A flows through the jet pump into reservoir B where the water is at the same level (A and B could in fact be the same reservoir; friction has to be ignored). The mixing region of the jet pump is connected to a third reservoir C at a lower level. Water from C is drawn into the pump and so flows up to B with the main stream.

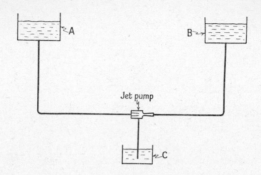

Fig. 1.10   Invention 2. A proposal for pumping water.

Discussion: The reasons why this invention will not work are too obvious to mention. It has only been introduced because of its similarity to a rather more subtle proposal, which now follows.

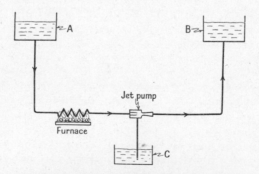

Fig. 1.11   Invention 3. Another proposal for pumping water.

Invention 3. The arrangement is the same as that of *invention 2*, except that the water flowing from A to the jet-pump first passes through a coiled pipe exposed to a flame (Fig. 1.11); there it is vaporised so that it enters the pump in the form of steam. Water from C is drawn into the pump and flows up to B as before. Will this system work?

Discussion: The answer is "Yes", provided that the temperature of the water in C is below that of the steam; indeed it will even work if B is higher than *both* the other reservoirs. The reasons are too complicated to discuss here, but it is interesting to note that it was invented by Giffard in 1858, and has been widely used for pumping fresh water into the boilers of railway locomotives. It has recently been re-invented, in another form, under the name *aerothermopressor*, as a device for driving supersonic wind-tunnels.

Concluding remarks. The fallacies of the first two inventions were easy to discern, because only mechanical considerations were involved. Some readers may have supposed that *invention 3* was likewise a vain attempt to "lift oneself up by the bootstraps". Evidently however, when heat is involved, a correct decision is harder to reach. It is in these cases that the laws of thermodynamics require specific application.

What thermodynamics leaves out

Rate processes. We have already implied that thermodynamics is concerned with the "before" and "after" of a process and often ignores the "in-between". It should not be inferred that the "in-between" is of no interest to the engineer. Indeed the designer is often as much concerned with the *rate* at which a process advances as with its end-result.

It must therefore be emphasised that thermodynamics has no time scale; to determine the rate of a process, on which often depends the size of the apparatus, the engineer must turn to neighbouring subjects. The one bulking largest in engineering curricula is *heat transfer*, which is concerned with conduction, insulation, radiation and convection. Allied to it is *mass transfer*, which deals with mixing processes, for example between air and fuel in a furnace. Finally there is the subject of *chemical kinetics*, which is the study of how rapidly chemical reactions proceed. Engineers need some knowledge of all three processes in their work on power production; only the purely thermodynamic aspects of the subjects are dealt with in the present book.

The microscopic structure of matter. Another body of knowledge excluded from thermodynamics is that concerned with the ultimate constitution of matter, its construction from atoms and molecules and from the still smaller elementary particles now known to physics. Although understanding of the *microscopic* properties of matter is helpful in interpreting some of the *macroscopic** properties which thermodynamics deals with, the thermodynamicist treats matter as a continuum.

This is not the result merely of a lack of interest in small-scale phenomena, but of the fact that the laws of thermodynamics do not apply when only a few particles are in question; for example the distinction between heat and work then becomes blurred. Although we shall have no occasion to discuss the matter below, the laws of thermodynamics are essentially *statistical* in nature, and only have meaning when large numbers of particles are considered at once.

* Large-scale.

THE SCOPE OF THE BOOK

Aim

The intention of the book is to provide the knowledge of thermodynamics required by every engineer, whether his career is to be spent in mechanical, chemical, civil, electrical or aeronautical engineering. The emphasis is on the fundamental theory, and applications are primarily dealt with as illustrations. The reader must look elsewhere for detailed discussion of how particular plants are designed and operated. The coverage of the fundamentals is fairly complete, although chemical engineers will need knowledge of the theory of chemical equilibrium, which we have had no space for.

Content

The subject matter falls into four main parts.

Chapters 2 to 5 are devoted to treating, with the extra care which thermodynamics demands, concepts which will already be familiar to the reader from his study of mechanics and physics. The main new concept introduced is the *system*, which assumes great importance throughout the book.

The second part (Chapters 6 to 9) begins with Joule's discovery: the First Law of Thermodynamics. Here *energy* is introduced. The field of attention is then narrowed to the sort of materials with which the power engineer is chiefly concerned, namely the *pure substance*, and its properties. In this part we discuss a particular form of the First Law, the *Steady Flow Energy Equation*, with the aid of which a wide variety of engineering processes can be analysed.

Chapters 10 to 13 discuss engines and their *efficiency*. Here we introduce Carnot's Principle: the Second Law of Thermodynamics. The subsequent deductions constitute a body of theory which is both elegant and of the highest practical importance. In order to bring the theory to bear on engineering analysis, Clausius' concept of *entropy* is defined and studied. This completes the main theoretical apparatus which the thermodynamicist needs.

In the final part we turn once more to the properties of materials. In Chapter 14, Ideal Gases are discussed; the reader will already have some knowledge of these. Then in Chapter 15 we deal with gaseous mixtures, concentrating particular attention on mixtures of air and water vapour because of their familiarity and importance, although the principles are of wider application. Finally, in Chapter 16, fuels and combustion are treated.

Final remarks

At the end of each chapter problems are provided. The reader is strongly advised to solve at least some of these before proceeding; for each chapter pre-supposes a knowledge of what has gone before, and it is only by practice that the significance of the text, packed as it will sometimes seem to be with pedantic hedgings and qualifications, can truly be appreciated. The only justification for this book is that it may help engineers to solve practical problems of design and analysis with certainty and ease; we hope it does so.

BIBLIOGRAPHY

Dickinson, H. W., *A Short History of the Steam Engine.* Cambridge University Press, 1938.
Classified Lists of Historical Events: Mechanical and Electrical Engineering. Science Museum: H.M.S.O., 1955.
Lenard, P., *Great Men of Science.* G. Bell & Sons, 1933.

CHAPTER 1—PROBLEMS

1.1 The mechanical unit of power, the horse-power, is equivalent to a rate of working of 550 foot pounds per second; in electrical units it is equivalent to 746 watts.

Express the following work quantities in foot pounds:—

(a) One horse-power hour.

(b) One kilowatt hour.

1.2 The performance of a power plant is often expressed in terms of its specific fuel consumption, namely in pounds of fuel consumed per horse-power hour.

Evaluate and compare the specific fuel consumptions of the following historical methods of power production:—

(a) A man working a treadmill can produce an average of 10·5 metre kilograms of work per second for 8 hours out of 24. His daily food intake is 2 kilogrammes. (One pound $\equiv$ 453·6 grammes; one inch $\equiv$ 2·54 centimetres.)

(b) The average performance of fifteen Newcomen steam engines in England in 1769 was to raise 5·59 million pounds of water one foot in height while consuming one bushel (84 pounds) of coal.

(c) The guaranteed performance of Watt steam engines in 1800 was to raise 35 million pounds of water one foot in height while consuming one bushel of coal.

(d) A Worthington steam-driven pumping plant (early 20th century) pumped 13,400 gallons of water per minute through a vertical height of 54 feet while consuming coal at the rate of 456 pounds per hour. (One gallon of water has a mass of 10 pounds.)

1.3 Evaluate the specific fuel consumption of each of the following modern power-producing installations:—

(a) An oil engine for a submarine develops 1600 h.p. Its rate of fuel consumption is 11 pounds per minute.

(b) A gas engine drives a dynamo which delivers 120 amperes DC at 110 volts. The gas is obtained from a gas-producing plant which is fed with coke at the rate of 3 cwt in 8 hours. (One cwt $\equiv$ 112 pounds.)

(c) A petrol engine drives a motor car at an average speed of 40 mph against a total resisting force of 275 pounds. Its petrol consumption is 20 miles per gallon. The specific gravity of the petrol is 0·73. (1 gallon of water has a mass of 10 pounds.)

(d) A base-load power-station incorporates a steam turbine plant driving AC generators. The hourly coal consumption of the boilers is 181·3 tons and the electrical power delivered is 500,000 kilowatts.

(e) A gas-turbine engine is used as a standby for base-load power production in a generating station. The shaft power delivered by the engine is 63 h.p. per pound of air flowing through the engine per second. The rate of air flow through the engine is 140 pounds per second and the ratio air flow: oil-fuel flow rates is 80 : 1.

(f) Each of the two reactors of the nuclear central generating station at Berkeley, Gloucestershire (under construction 1958) is expected to consume 0·051 tonnes per day of Uranium 235. The gross power produced by each of the 4 generators is 85 megawatts. The power required to recirculate the coolant (CO_2 gas) through the reactors and the heat exchangers and to drive auxiliaries is 17 megawatts per reactor. (1 tonne $\equiv$ 1,000 kilogrammes.)

1.4 The performance of aircraft propulsion devices is often expressed in terms of the number of pounds of fuel consumed per hour per pound of thrust developed. Compare the following on this basis:—

(a) A rocket carries a total fuel load of 60 tons. The rocket engine operates steadily for 2·5 minutes and develops a thrust of 150 tons.

(b) An aircraft powered by four gas-turbine jet engines consumes 30,000 gallons of kerosene on a flight of 3,500 miles when flying at a steady speed of 550 mph. Each engine develops a thrust of 10,000 pounds. The specific gravity of kerosine is 0·81.

(c) An aircraft is powered by a gas-turbine propeller engine (turbo-prop). In level flight at constant speed the engine consumes 16 pounds of kerosine per minute and the drag of the aircraft is 1,770 pounds.

1.5 An electricity supply for use in isolated districts incorporates a lead–acid secondary cell which may be charged periodically by means of a DC generator driven by a petrol engine.

The average load on the accumulator during discharge at 100 volts is 40 amperes for 6 hours per day.

During charging the generator output is 33 amperes at 115 volts. The charging period is 8 hours per day and the weekly petrol consumption of the engine is 22 gallons. The specific gravity of the petrol is 0·73.

Determine (a) the power delivered by the accumulator during discharge, in horse-power;

(b) the power delivered to the accumulator during charging, in horse-power;

(c) the specific fuel consumption of the accumulator plus charging plant in pounds of fuel per horse-power hour.

CHAPTER 2

MECHANICAL UNITS

INTRODUCTION

Chapter 1 shows that the engineer is concerned with the production of power; he seeks new methods of producing power and of improving existing ones. Thermodynamics enables him to determine the work done by power-producing devices and to compare it with what might reasonably be expected of them.

All measurements are made in terms of *units*, which are defined quantities of standard size. Those relevant to the measurement of work, are familiar from Mechanics. In this Chapter we review mechanical units; combinations of these units are discussed and special reference is made to pressure and its measurement.

Symbols

a	Acceleration.	p_{atm}	Atmospheric pressure.
F	Force.	V	Volume.
g	Gravitational acceleration.	v	Specific volume.
g_0	Constant in Newton's Second Law.	w	Weight.
		z	Difference in liquid level.
m	Mass.	ρ	Density.
p	Pressure.		

BASIC MECHANICAL QUANTITIES

Length, time, mass and force are taken as the primary defined quantities; given below are the units which are used for their measurement by engineers in English-speaking countries and which will be adopted in this book.

Length, time and mass

Length. The unit is the foot (ft), which is measured by reference to a standard platinum bar, the Imperial Standard Yard. [1 yard = 3 feet].

Time. The unit is the second (s), which is measured by reference to a standard clock, the solar system.

Mass. The unit is the pound mass (lb_m), which is measured by reference to a standard block of platinum, the Imperial Standard Pound.

Force and the constant g_0

Instead of following the above pattern by setting up an independent standard of force, the unit of force is *defined* in terms of the units of length, time and mass through *Newton's Second Law of Motion*. This difference of procedure is of no importance here.*

* End note 1.

The unit of force is the pound force (lb_f) defined as follows—**One pound force is the force necessary to give one pound mass an acceleration of 32.174 feet per second per second.**

Newton's Second Law of Motion states that force F is proportional to the product of mass m and acceleration a. Thus

$$F \propto ma \qquad \ldots \quad (2.1)$$

Introducing a constant of proportionality, eq. (2.1) becomes

$$F = \frac{ma}{g_0} \qquad \ldots \quad (2.2)$$

where $g_0 = $ a constant.*

It follows from eq. (2.2) that the magnitude and units of g_0 depend upon the units in which force, mass and acceleration are expressed. Using ft, s, lb_m, lb_f units and applying the definition of the lb_f to eq. (2.2), we have

$$1\ \text{lb}_f = \frac{1\ \text{lb}_m \times 32 \cdot 174\ \text{ft/s}^2}{g_0}$$

$$\therefore \qquad g_0 = 32 \cdot 174\ \frac{\text{lb}_m\,\text{ft}}{\text{lb}_f\,\text{s}^2} \qquad \ldots \quad (2.3)$$

This is the value of g_0 which we shall use below.

Other sets of units

Other sets of units can be used. For example two sets based on the metric system are:

centimetre, second, gramme mass, gramme force

and   *metre, second, kilogramme mass, kilogramme force.*

Each set has its corresponding value of g_0. Some sets are chosen to give $g_0 = $ unity; g_0 can then be omitted from equations, so abbreviating the algebra. Examples of sets of units having $g_0 = 1$ are:

foot, second, pound mass, poundal;
foot, second, slug, pound force;
centimetre, second, gramme mass, dyne;
metre, second, kilogramme mass, newton.

The *poundal* (pdl) is a unit of force defined as the force necessary to accelerate one pound mass at 1 ft/s². Hence $1\ \text{pdl} = \dfrac{1}{32 \cdot 174}\ \text{lb}_f$.

The *slug* is a unit of mass equal to $32 \cdot 174\ \text{lb}_m$. Hence 1 slug, when acted upon by 1 lb_f, will accelerate at 1 ft/s².

The *dyne* is a unit of force defined as the force necessary to accelerate one gramme mass at 1 cm/s².

The *newton* (N) is a unit of force defined as the force necessary to accelerate one kilogramme mass at 1 metre/s².

Each of these definitions when combined with eq. (2.2) makes g_0 equal to unity. This is shown in Table 2.1 which also gives the values of g_0 for other commonly used sets of units.

* Sometimes written g_c.

Weight and gravity

In defining the lb_f a standard acceleration of $32 \cdot 174 \, ft/s^2$ is taken. Why is this value chosen when, in fact, *any* value could have been selected? We now discuss the reason for its choice by considering a particular sort of force, namely that due to the earth's gravitational field.

TABLE 2.1.

Units used				Value and units of g_0
Length	Time	Mass	Force	
ft	s	lb_m	lb_f	$32 \cdot 174 \, \dfrac{lb_m \, ft}{lb_f \, s^2}$
ft	h	lb_m	lb_f	$4 \cdot 17 \times 10^8 \, \dfrac{lb_m \, ft}{lb_f \, h^2}$
ft	s	lb_m	pdl	$1 \cdot 0 \, \dfrac{lb_m \, ft}{pdl \, s^2}$
ft	s	slug	lb_f	$1 \cdot 0 \, \dfrac{slug \, ft}{lb_f \, s^2}$
cm	s	g_m	dyne	$1 \cdot 0 \, \dfrac{g_m \, cm}{dyne \, s^2}$
m	s	kg_m	N	$1 \cdot 0 \, \dfrac{kg_m \, m}{N \, s^2}$
m	s	kg_m	kg_f	$9 \cdot 81 \, \dfrac{kg_m \, m}{kg_f \, s^2}$
cm	s	g_m	g_f	$981 \, \dfrac{g_m \, cm}{g_f \, s^2}$

Definition and measurement of weight. Any body in the earth's gravitational field experiences a force of attraction towards the earth's centre. The magnitude of this force is the *weight* of the body.

The weight of a body is the force exerted on it by the earth's gravitational field.

Weight is measured in force units, but sometimes the unit is given a special name in this case. For example a body on which the gravitational force is one pound force is said to weigh one pound weight (lb wt); lb_f and lb wt are identical units of force and differ in name only. The use of lb wt may, however, lead to confusion (it has sometimes been mistakenly used as a unit of mass); in this book, therefore, we use the pound force exclusively.

Variations in weight: the gravitational acceleration g. At any instant the *gravitational force* on a body is proportional to the mass of the body but independent of the motion of the body. The motion of the body is determined by the *net* force acting on it, to which, of course the gravitational force contributes. For example when the body is supported, i.e. stationary, in the earth's gravitational field, the net force on the body is zero; the gravitational force is balanced by an equal and opposite force exerted by the support on the body. However, if the body is unsupported, the net force acting on it is the weight* which causes it to accelerate at the rate *g*. The value of *g* is the same for *all* bodies in that locality just because of the proportionality of the weight to the mass of the body. Therefore the gravitational force on the body, i.e. its weight, may be related to the mass of the body and the local gravitational acceleration through Newton's Second Law. For if *w* is the weight (in force units), of a body of mass *m* (in mass units), and *g* is the local gravitational acceleration, eq. (2.2) gives

$$w = m \ \frac{g}{g_0} \qquad \qquad \ldots \ (2.4)$$

where g_0 has the value appropriate to the units used for length, time, mass and force.

Variations in g. An important point arising from eq. (2.4) is that although the mass of a body is invariable, its weight can vary from place to place, depending on the value of *g*, the *local* gravitational acceleration.

For example, using the lb_f, lb_m, ft, s, set of units, for which $g_0 = 32 \cdot 174 \ (lb_m \ \text{ft})/(lb_f \ \text{s}^2)$, we have from eq. (2.4)

$$w = \frac{m(lb_m) \times g(\text{ft/s}^2)}{32 \cdot 174(lb_m \ . \ \text{ft}/lb_f \ . \ \text{s}^2)} = \frac{mg}{32 \cdot 174} \ lb_f. \qquad \ldots \ (2.5)$$

Relation between g and g_0. The value of *g* at any point in the earth's gravitational field varies with the distance of the point from the earth's centre. Therefore, *g* varies over the earth's surface and with height above the earth's surface. As a matter of fact, however, *g* is approximately equal to $32 \cdot 174 \ \text{ft/s}^2$ everywhere on the earth's surface and is exactly equal to it at one place (Sèvres). Hence, in the lb_m, lb_f, ft, s, unit system, the value of *g* at the earth's surface is approximately equal *numerically* to g_0. It follows from eq. (2.5) that at the earth's surface, the weight and mass of a body are also approximately equal *numerically*. Confusion between numerical equality and identity of concept should be avoided, however; *g* and g_0 are not the same thing; nor are weight and mass, since the units in which they are measured are different. In the case considered *g* is in ft/s^2 and g_0 is in $(lb_m \ \text{ft})/(lb_f \ \text{s}^2)$; weight is in lb_f and mass is in lb_m. In other unit systems neither *g* and g_0 nor weight and mass are even approximately equal numerically.†

---

* It is assumed that external influences such as air resistance, local magnetic fields, etc., are absent.

† End note 2.

Standard gravitational acceleration. The fact that the gravitational acceleration g has almost the same value everywhere on the earth's surface has led to the adoption, by international agreement, of a standard value for g of 32·174 ft/s². This is the figure used in the definition of pound force (p. 20), which leads to the approximate numerical equality between g and g_0 and weight and mass discussed above.

The motion of the observer

The foregoing analysis has been concerned with motion, i.e. the movement of bodies relative to an observer. For convenience it has been assumed above that the observer is stationary on the earth's surface or, stated more formally, that the co-ordinate axes are fixed with respect to the earth. This procedure is frequently the simplest one to adopt. If, however, the observer is moving, his motion must be included in the analysis; indeed the solution of many problems is simplified by considering the observer to be in motion instead of stationary. In such cases it should be noted that the magnitudes of velocities, accelerations and forces will be different from those seen by the stationary observer. Later we shall see that the magnitude of work also depends upon the motion of the observer (p. 35).

COMBINATION OF UNITS

Volume, specific volume, density, pressure

Often the basic quantities are found in combination, as in the units of acceleration (ft/s²) above; other important examples now follow. The units given are those corresponding to the lb_m, lb_f, ft, s, system which we use throughout this book.

Volume. The space occupied by a substance is its volume, V; the unit of volume is the cubic foot (ft³).

Specific volume. The specific volume, v, is the volume of unit mass of a substance*; it is measured in cubic feet per pound mass (ft³/lb_m). It follows that

$$v = \frac{V}{m} \qquad \dots \quad (2.6)$$

Density. The density, ρ, is the mass of unit volume of a substance; it is measured in pounds mass per cubic foot, (lb_m/ft³). We have therefore

$$\rho = \frac{m}{V} = \frac{1}{v}$$

Pressure. The pressure, p, is the force per unit area exerted by a body on its surface, in a direction normal to the surface.

---

* Where relevant and possible lower case type will be used for the value per lb_m of any quantity signified by capital type. Shortage of letters precludes complete consistency with this convention.

In some cases the pressure may vary over the surface; to specify it at any point, an infinitesimal area must be taken over which the pressure can be assumed constant. The pressure may be expressed in several units. The pressure unit corresponding to the units introduced above is the pound force per square foot (lb_f/ft^2); it is used for *all* calculations. This unit is, however, inconveniently small for specifying most pressures met in practice; therefore two larger units are commonly used. These are the pound force per square inch (psi or lb_f/in^2), and the atmosphere ($= 14\cdot7$ psi); therefore

$$1\ lb_f/ft^2 = \frac{1}{144}\ \text{psi} = \frac{1}{144 \times 14\cdot7}\ \text{atm.}$$

Often pressure is specified in the units in which it is measured. To illustrate this we now consider some common methods of measurement.

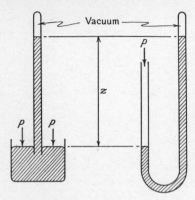

Fig. 2.1   Barometer.

The measurement of pressure

The barometer. Fig. 2.1 shows two instruments; the essential part of each is a tube, closed at one end, containing mercury, water, or other liquid. The space above the liquid surface in the closed end is evacuated, i.e. at zero pressure,* and the pressure, p, acting on the "free" liquid surface causes the liquid to rise to height z in the closed limb. Since the pressure in the closed end is zero, z will be a direct measure of the pressure p.

From hydrostatics $$p = z \cdot \frac{\rho g}{g_0} \qquad \qquad \dots \quad (2.7)$$

where $\rho =$ density of liquid in the tube.

If the atmospheric pressure (p_{atm}) is being measured the device is a *barometer*.

EXAMPLE

Problem. For mercury (Hg) $\rho = 850\ lb_m/ft^3$ at a temperature of 60°F. What is the pressure in psi corresponding to $z = 1$ inch of mercury at a place where $g = 32\cdot2\ ft/s^2$?

Solution. From eq. (2.7) we have

$$1\ \text{in. Hg} \equiv \frac{1}{12} \times \frac{850 \times 32\cdot2}{g_0}\ lb_f/ft^2$$

---

* In practice complete evacuation is not possible due to evaporation from the liquid surface. However, the pressure exerted by the vapour is usually small and can be allowed for.

and $g_0 = 32 \cdot 17$ in the lb_m, lb_f, ft, s, unit system.

$$\therefore \qquad 1 \text{ in. Hg} \equiv \frac{850}{12} \times \frac{32 \cdot 2}{32 \cdot 17} \ lb_f/ft^2$$

$$\equiv 0 \cdot 491 \text{ psi} \qquad \qquad \dots \textit{Answer}$$

Note, however, that the value obtained depends upon the density of the mercury, which varies slightly with temperature, and on the local value of g, the gravitational acceleration, which varies slightly with position.

The manometer. This consists of an open-ended U-tube (Fig. 2.2) containing a liquid. The pressure, p, to be measured is communicated to one limb of the tube, while the other limb is open to atmosphere. As before, the difference in the liquid levels, z, measures the difference between the pressures acting on the two limbs. Hence in this case we have

$$z \cdot \frac{\rho g}{g_0} = p - p_{atm}$$

Gauge pressure and absolute pressure. The manometer is one form of pressure *gauge;* another type, the Bourdon gauge, is discussed below. Pressure gauges register directly the pressure difference $p - p_{atm}$; the gauge reading, $p - p_{atm}$, is therefore given a special name: the *gauge pressure.*

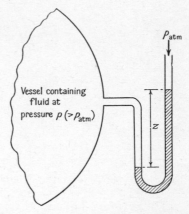

Fig. 2.2   Manometer.

Values of gauge pressure are expressed in the units of pressure introduced above (p. 24), but to emphasise that it is the gauge pressure in question we add the word 'gauge' or the letter 'g' to the unit. For instance if a water manometer registers a difference in level $z = 1 \cdot 3$ feet we state the pressure as $1 \cdot 3$ feet of water gauge (ft H_2O gauge). Similarly if the psi unit is used, the pressure is expressed in pounds per square inch gauge (psig).

To emphasise further the distinction between p and $p - p_{atm}$, we describe p as the *absolute pressure* and add the letter 'a' to the unit in which p is expressed; for example an absolute pressure p of 100 pounds per square inch is written as 100 psia. It follows that the absolute pressure and the gauge pressure are related by:

Absolute pressure = gauge pressure + atmospheric pressure   ...   (2.8)

From now on we qualify the term 'pressure' by the words 'absolute' or 'gauge' and distinguish the units as appropriate; when in later chapters 'pressure' is discussed, absolute pressure is meant unless otherwise stated. In all calculations the absolute pressure *must* be used.

3

"*Vacuum*". Gauge pressures less than atmospheric are often referred to as *vacuum*.

$$\text{vacuum} = \text{atmospheric pressure} - \text{absolute pressure}$$

$$= p_{atm} - p \qquad \qquad \ldots \quad (2.9)$$

It is usually expressed in inches of mercury; for instance, the height z

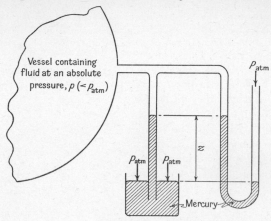

Fig. 2.3 Manometers.

inches of the mercury in the manometers in Fig. 2.3 indicates the "inches mercury vacuum" (in. Hg vac) corresponding to absolute pressure p. Since the atmospheric pressure varies, a barometer reading is always required to convert the gauge pressure or vacuum reading of a manometer to absolute pressure via eq. (2.8) or eq. (2.9).

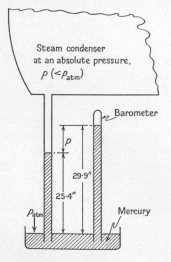

Fig. 2.4

EXAMPLE

Problem. A mercury manometer measuring the vacuum in a steam engine condenser reads 25·4 inches. The barometer in the engine room reads 29·9 inches of mercury. What is the absolute pressure in the condenser in psia?

Solution. Referring to Fig. 2.4 we have from eq. (2.9)

$$p_{atm} - p = 25\cdot4 \text{ in. Hg vac}$$

$$\therefore \qquad p = (29\cdot9 - 25\cdot4) \text{ in. Hg abs}$$

$$= 4\cdot5 \times 0\cdot491 \text{ psia}$$

$$= 2\cdot21 \text{ psia.} \qquad \ldots \quad Answer$$

The Bourdon gauge. This is a device which measures gauge pressure and vacuum. It consists essentially of an oval-sectioned metal tube shaped as shown in Fig. 2.5. The inside of the tube is subjected to the absolute pressure, p, to be measured, and the outside to atmospheric pressure. An increase in p tends to make the section become circular and so to unbend the tube. A pointer, connected via a gear-and-lever mechanism to the end of the bent tube, moves against a scale and registers the pressure difference imposed on the tube.

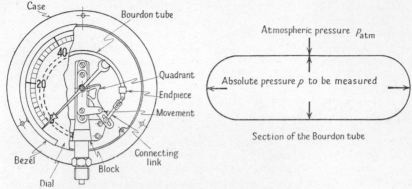

Fig. 2.5   Bourdon pressure gauge.

Such gauges have to be calibrated against manometers or dead-weight testers: they are graduated in any of the above mentioned pressure units as required.

As with the manometer, a barometer reading is necessary to convert the Bourdon gauge readings to absolute pressures via eq. (2.8) or eq. (2.9) as appropriate.

BIBLIOGRAPHY

British Standard: Pressure Gauges. BS 1780. British Standards Institution, 1951.

Ower, E., *The Measurement of Air Flow.* Chapman and Hall, 3rd edition, 1949.

CHAPTER 2—PROBLEMS

2.1 (*a*) By using the definitions given on page 20 determine the value and units of g_0 for each of the following sets of units:—

(i)   pdl, lb_m, ft, s;

(ii) dyne, g_m, cm, s;

(iii) newton, kg_m, m, s;

(iv) lb_f, slug, ft, s;

(v) lb_f, lb_m, ft, h;

(vi) pdl, ton_m, mile, year.

(*b*) Express one pound force in poundals and one newton in dynes.

2.2 The mass of one of the pistons of a petrol engine is 0·8 lb_m. At a particular point in its motion the piston has an acceleration of 20,000 ft/s^2. Calculate the net force on the piston in lb_f.

2.3 A force of 2 lb_f acts on a mass of (*a*) 100 g_m (*b*) 0·3 slug. Find the acceleration of each mass in cm/s^2. (1 $\text{lb}_m \equiv 453\cdot6\ g_m$).

2.4 A new unit of force is to be set up. This unit force, the *cant* (c), is specified as that force which, when acting on the end of a standard cantilever beam, will cause the end of the beam to deflect 0·100 inches.

It is found that 1 c when acting on 1 lb_m causes it to accelerate at 100 ft/s².

(a) Evaluate g_0 for the c, lb_m, ft, s, set of units.

(b) Determine the relation between the lb_f and the c.

(c) Compare the numerical values of the mass and the weight of a body in the c, lb_m, ft, s, unit system at a point where the gravitational acceleration is 32 ft/s².

2.5 (a) The first artificial earth satellite is reported to have encircled the earth at a speed of 18,000 mph and its maximum height above the earth's surface was stated to be 560 miles. Taking the mean diameter of the earth to be 7920 miles, and assuming the orbit to be circular, evaluate the value of the gravitational acceleration at this height. (The acceleration of a body moving with velocity V in a circular path of radius r is V^2/r towards the centre of rotation.)

(b) The weight of the satellite is reported to have been 86 kg_f at sea-level ($g = 32 \cdot 2$ ft/s²). Estimate its weight in lb_f at the operational altitude.

2.6 A mercury barometer reads 30·1 in. Express the reading in psia. (Take $g = 32 \cdot 2$ ft/s² and the density of mercury = 850 lb_m/ft³).

2.7 The air supply to an internal combustion engine is metered by observing the pressure drop across an orifice in the air supply line to the engine. The pressure drop is measured by means of a manometer containing paraffin having a specific gravity of 0·81.

Express a difference of level of 10 inches in the manometer in (a) psi and (b) feet of air. (Take the density of water = 62·4 lb_m/ft³ and of air = 0·077 lb_m/ft³).

2.8 A turbine is supplied with steam at a pressure of 210 psig. After expansion in the turbine the steam passes to a condenser which is maintained at a vacuum of 28 in. Hg by means of pumps (the wet and dry air pumps). The barometric pressure is 30·5 in. Hg. Express the inlet and exhaust steam pressures in psia.

2.9 A British manufacturer of internal combustion engines is to supply a supercharged petrol engine to a customer in Johannesburg.

The engine specification calls for a guaranteed absolute boost pressure (i.e. the pressure at which the petrol-air mixture enters the engine cylinders) of 18 psia.

What reading should the customer obtain on a mercury manometer used to measure the boost pressure and by how much (per cent) will it differ from that obtained during the manufacturer's test in Britain?

Use the following data:

	Altitude, feet	Atmospheric pressure, psia	Atmospheric temperature, °F	g ft/s²
Britain	180	14·6	60	32·2
Johannesburg	5740	12·0	79	32·1

The variation of the density of mercury, ρ lb_m/ft³, with temperature, t°F, is given by $\rho = 850[1 - 1 \cdot 01 \times 10^{-4}(t - 60)]$.

CHAPTER 3

WORK

INTRODUCTION

In Chapter 1 it was stated that a main pre-occupation of the mechanical engineer is the production of *work*, whether for pumping water, for driving machine tools or for transportation. In the present chapter therefore a precise definition of work is given, in order that its amount can be measured in the various circumstances arising in engineering.

It will be assumed that the reader is familiar with the concept of work used in mechanics; however this concept is too restricted to suffice for the more complex problems of thermodynamics. A new definition therefore has to be introduced which covers mechanical work but includes other forms also. As a preliminary, one of the central ideas of thermodynamics, the *system*, has to be defined.

The remainder of the chapter will be taken up by a discussion of the various forms which work can assume and of the ways in which it can be evaluated.

Symbols

A	Area of piston face; Area of part of a system boundary	$\mathcal{Q}$	Quantity of electrical charge
		r	Radius
		S	Indicator spring number
a	Area of indicator diagram	T	Torque
F	Force	V	System volume
I	Current		Velocity
k	Constant in $pV = k$ and $pV^n = k$	V_c	Clearance volume in engine cylinder
L	Distance; Displacement; Length of piston stroke	V_{sw}	Volume swept by part of a system boundary; Swept volume of an engine cylinder
l	Length of indicator diagram		
m	Mass of a system	$\mathscr{V}$	Potential difference
N	Rotational speed	v	Specific volume of a fluid system
n	Exponent in $pV^n = k$		
P	Power	W	Work done by a system
p	System pressure	W_d	Displacement work; '$p\,dV$' work
p_{atm}	Atmospheric pressure		
p_b	Pressure at a system boundary	W_s	Shear work
		θ	Angular displacement
p_l	Pressure on lower surface eq. (3.7)	σ	Shear stress
		τ	Time
p_m	Mean effective pressure		
p_u	Pressure on upper surface, eq. (3.7)		

DEFINITION AND MEASUREMENT OF WORK

Work as defined in mechanics

Most readers will be familiar with the following definition:—

Work is done when the point of application of a force moves in the direction of the force. The amount of the work is equal to the product of the force and the distance moved in the direction of the force.

This definition is expressed symbolically by the equation

$$W = F \times L \qquad \qquad \ldots \ (3.1)$$

where W is the work, F is the force, and L is the distance (See Fig. 3.1).

Units of work. In the British engineering system, the unit of work is the ft lb_f, corresponding to the units used for F and L. Other units can of course also be used, e.g. the kg_f m (kilogramme force metre); in some cases, special names are used: thus 1 dyne cm is called an *erg*, while 10^7 ergs is called 1 *joule*.

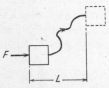

$F \longrightarrow$

$\longmapsto L \longrightarrow$

Fig. 3.1 Illustrating the definition of work used in mechanics.

Although in thermodynamics a different definition of work is used, the units are the same. Table 3.1 contains some conversion factors for changing from one unit system to another.

Power is the rate at which work is done. It may be measured, for example, in ft lb_f/s. Often a larger unit is used, the *horse-power*, introduced by Watt in 1783. 1 horse-power (h.p.) $\equiv$ 550 ft lb_f/s $\equiv$ 33,000 ft lb_f/min.

TABLE 3.1. *Conversion factors for work quantities*

	kg_f m	erg	joule	ft lb_f
1 ft lb_f =	0·13825	1·356 × 10⁷	1·356	1
1 kg_f m =	1	981 × 10⁷	981	7·233
1 joule =	0·1019	10⁷	1	0·7375

Positive and negative work quantities. The length L in eq. (3.1) is measured in the direction of F. In Fig. 3.1, L is a positive quantity so the product $F \times L$ is positive: *positive work* has therefore been done.

However, the point of application of the force might have been "pushed backwards", making L, and the product $F \times L$, negative quantities: in this case *negative work* would have been done by F.

A similar distinction of *sign* is made in the thermodynamic definition.

The system

Before proceeding further we introduce an idea which, despite its simple appearance, is of profound importance in thermodynamics: the *system*. Its definition is as follows:—

A system is any prescribed and identifiable collection of matter.

Nearly all the statements and laws of thermodynamics relate to a system. Fig. 3.2 shows the usual representation of one. The important part of this amoeba-like sketch is the *boundary*, which completely encloses the system and separates it from the *surroundings*. Of course the surroundings can also be regarded as a system.

The boundary will usually not be a material envelope but an imaginary closed surface which contains (prescribes and identifies) the collection of material we are talking about. Consequently no material crosses the boundary of a system, by definition. Often the system will change position and shape while we are watching it, but the boundary then moves so as *always* to hold the same collection of matter. This means that a system has *constant mass*.

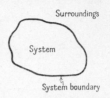

Fig. 3.2
Conventional
representation
of a system.

Thermodynamics is concerned with *interactions* between systems, i.e. the "influences" of a system on its surroundings and vice versa. These interactions are of only two kinds: the first is work, the subject of the present chapter; the second is heat, which is discussed in Chapter 5. Thereafter we shall be concerned with the changes within the system brought about by these interactions across its boundaries.

The thermodynamic definition of work

We are now in a position to give the definition of work which will be used throughout this book. It is

Positive work is done by a system, during a given operation, when the *sole* effect *external* to the system *could be reduced to* the rise of a weight.

This definition may appear arbitrary, yet its form is actually forced on us by the need to make a distinction between work and heat which the Second Law of Thermodynamics states as existing in the physical world. This necessity will not be fully apparent until Chapter 10 is reached. Below, each of the italicised phrases will be discussed. First however, we hasten to show that the definition covers the restricted kind of work treated in mechanics.

Relation between "mechanical" and "thermodynamic" work. Fig. 3.3a shows a system S exerting a force, *F*, on its surroundings at one point of its boundary. The surroundings comprise a block on a rough surface, which is pushed along as the system changes shape. Work is therefore done, according to the "mechanics" definition.

Now in this process no weights have been raised in the surroundings. Yet by carrying out the *same operation* in *changed surroundings*, a weight *could* have been raised, as is shown by Fig. 3.3b; and this could have been the *sole external effect*. Therefore the system does positive work in the operation according to the thermodynamic definition.

Measurement of work. The magnitude of the positive work done by the system is accomplished by counting the standard weights which could have been raised through a standard vertical height in a standard gravitational field. In the British system of units, the weights are taken to comprise 1 lb$_m$ of material each, the standard height is 1 ft, and the gravitational acceleration has the standard value of 32·174 ft/s². The gravitational force on each weight is therefore 1 lb$_f$, and the work unit is the ft lb$_f$ as already stated.

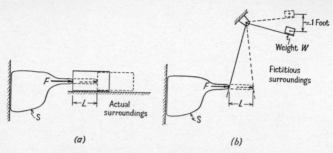

Fig. 3.3   Illustrating the relation between "mechanical" and "thermodynamic" work.

Application of the principle of the lever to the operation in the fictitious surroundings of Fig. 3.3b shows that the number of standard weights raised through 1 ft would be $F \times L$. The work done by the system is therefore $F \times L$ ft lb$_f$, which is in accordance with the "mechanics" definition.

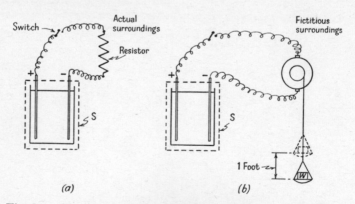

Fig. 3.4   Illustrating the application of the thermodynamic definition of work to an electric storage battery discharging through a resistor.

Width of application of the thermodynamic definition of work. The example just considered does not explain why we are not content with the "mechanics" definition. An example will now be given to show that the thermodynamic definition covers a wider field.

Consider the system S shown in Fig. 3.4a comprising an electrical storage battery. External to the system boundary the terminals are connected to an electrical resistance coil through a switch. We suppose that the switch is closed for a period, during which current flows through the battery and the resistance, which becomes warmer as a result. The system has therefore interacted with its surroundings. Can this interaction be classified as work?

According to the mechanics definition the answer is "No", for no force has moved its point of application. Yet, according to the thermodynamic definition, the answer is "Yes", as will now be demonstrated.

Imagine the surroundings of the system to be altered by the replacement of the resistance by an electric motor which winds up a string on which a weight is suspended (Fig. 3.4b). This can be arranged so that, when the switch is closed, exactly the same current flows as when the resistance was there; as far as events within the battery (system) are concerned there has been no change. Yet this time, provided care has been taken to eliminate friction from the motor bearings and to use wire of heavy gauge so that the motor does not become warmer, the sole effect external to the system has been the rise of a weight.

Therefore according to the thermodynamic definition the system does positive work in the operation, whether its surroundings comprise the resistance or the motor.

Remarks on the thermodynamic definition of work. We now consider the reasons for the wording used in the definition.

(a) *"Sole effect"*. The qualification "sole" is necessary because there is another kind of interaction between a system and its surroundings which can have the rise of a weight as *part* of its effect: this we shall later learn to call *heat*. Thus a hot body (system) placed in contact with water can cause it to boil; the steam can then drive an engine which raises weights. It will be found however that there are always other effects; either the water does not return to its original state after passing through the engine, or the surroundings became warmer. The weight-raising cannot be the sole effect.

(b) *"External"*. This word emphasises that work is defined only with reference to a system boundary, separating the system from its surroundings. Work is an interaction across the boundary. If the boundary is drawn differently, i.e. if a different system is chosen, the work quantity will be different. Thus, if in Fig. 3.3a the boundary were to enclose the block and rough surface as well, the work would be zero; for there are *no* effects external to this new boundary.

(c) *"Could be reduced to"*. The examples already given show that, for work to be done by the system, it is not required that weights actually *are* raised. It suffices for us to imagine a means by which this could be the sole effect. Imagination must be kept within the bounds of what is physically possible however. It is permissible to imagine the friction in the imagined mechanism to be zero, because we know that, by taking sufficient trouble, friction can always be made negligibly small. On the other hand, merely to postulate a "black box", which will convert *any* interaction completely into weight-raising, is not imagination but fantasy; it is not permissible.

The imaginary reconstruction of the surroundings must not involve any alteration to the operation performed by the system. If it does, we find ourselves evaluating the work in a different operation; there is no point in that.

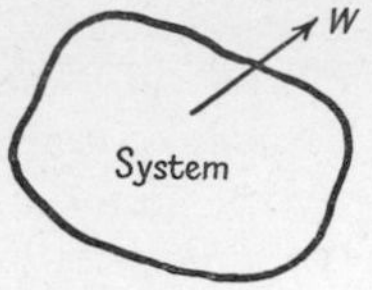

(*d*) It will have been noted that the definition is restricted to *positive* work only. Negative work will now be discussed.

Fig. 3.5
Conventional
representation
of a system
doing work.

Thermodynamic definition of negative work

When a system does positive work, its surroundings do an equal quantity of negative work. Conversely, when the surroundings do positive work, the system does an equal quantity of negative work.

This definition enables us to evaluate the work when, for example, the system of Fig. 3.3 is compressed rather than extended, or when the battery of Fig. 3.4 is charged instead of discharged. We do it by turning our attention to the surroundings, treating *them* as the system, and applying the definition of positive work to the operation performed by them.

It may be thought that negative work could have been defined more simply as occurring when the sole external effect could be the *fall* of a weight. This is not so. Once again the apparent circumlocution results from the need to distinguish work from heat in accordance with the Second Law; for there exist interactions *not* involving negative work according to the above definition which, as far as the system is concerned, could be caused solely by the fall of an external weight. (See for example p. 77.)

Sign convention. When positive work appears in equations it is given the symbol W. If, on evaluation, W turns out to stand for a negative number, the work done by the system is negative. This is the usual algebraic sign convention used for other physical quantities such as length.

A diagram of the system is an essential part of every thermodynamic calculation. Work is indicated on the diagram by an outwardly directed arrow as shown in Fig. 3.5.

In speech, it is often convenient to describe the direction of work by emphatic use of the prepositions "*by*" and "*on*". We say, "work is done *by* the system", when W stands for a positive number, and "work is done *on* the system", when W stands for a negative number. It follows that if work is done *by* the system it is done *on* the surroundings, and vice versa.

Concluding remarks on the definition of work

Three points should be noted before leaving this subject. The first is that the measurement procedure for work involves the arbitrary specification of a standard surroundings for the system (the standard weights) and a standard effect in the surroundings (the increase of height in a standard gravitational field). This pattern will be repeated when we come to define heat in Chapter 5.

Secondly, the measurement procedure implies an observer; for an increase of elevation means motion relative to some point taken as fixed. Usually we think of the observer as standing on the earth counting the weights rising past his head, but this is not necessary or even always convenient. For example, the observer *could* sit on the weight in Fig. 3.3b, in which case he would say that no weight had been raised past *him*, and so would assert that the system had done no work. From his point of view he would be right. That no inconsistency is involved will not be apparent until energy is discussed in Chapter 6.

Thirdly, work is *transient*. It is present during the interaction but does not exist either before or after the interaction. It is something which happens to a system but it is not a characteristic of the system. It therefore differs from, for example, pressure or force, which can have finite values in a system at rest.

DISPLACEMENT WORK

The remainder of the chapter will be taken up by derivation of the relations between the work done by a system and measurements made at the system boundary. To derive these relations we have to consider various ways in which work can be done. Since in engineering thermodynamics the system often comprises a fluid, rather than a rigid structure, special attention is given to this case in the present section.

It will be observed that, in the examples dealt with first, the "mechanics" definition of work is just as good as the thermodynamic one. In the later examples the greater scope and power of the thermodynamic definition will become evident.

Stresses at the boundary of a system

The force exerted by a system on its surroundings across an element of area of the system boundary can be split into two components: one normal to the area element; the other in the plane of the element. Since the magnitudes of these components vary, in general, with position, it is useful to consider the magnitudes of the forces *per unit area;* these are known as the *stresses*.

The stress acting normal to the area in the direction away from the system is known as the *pressure*, p_b. The component in the plane of the area element is known as the *shear stress*, σ. Both these stresses can result in work being done when the system boundary moves. The normal stress is usually the more important in thermodynamics; we consider it first. The mode of work associated with the normal stresses is known as *displacement work*, or, for reasons which will appear, '$p\,dV$' *work*.

Displacement work done by part of a system boundary

Work done on a piston. Fig. 3.6 illustrates a mechanism comprising a piston and a cylinder, for example for a steam engine. The cylinder is filled by a working fluid, for example steam, which enters and leaves through valves at the end remote from the piston.

The mass of working fluid enclosed in the system boundary S will be considered. Initially this is in the position marked S_1 in Fig. 3.6, and finally in that marked S_2. Attention will be restricted to that part of S which is in contact with the face of the piston.

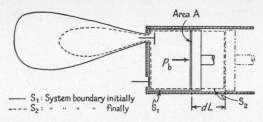

Fig. 3.6   Piston-cylinder mechanism used in the derivation of eq. (3.6).

The pressure at all points of the piston face will be taken as having the uniform value, p_b. If the piston face area is A, the force, F, on it is given by

$$F = p_b A \qquad \qquad \text{... (3.3)}$$

Suppose that the piston moves an infinitesimal distance, dL, to the right. Then the displacement work done by the system as a result of this movement, dW_d, is given by eq. (3.1) as

$$dW_d = p_b A \, dL \qquad \qquad \text{... (3.4)}$$

An alternative expression is derived by noting that $A \, dL$ represents the infinitesimal volume *swept out* by the part of the system boundary in question. Calling this volume increment dV_{sw} we can write

$$dW_d = p_b \, dV_{sw} \qquad \qquad \text{... (3.5)}$$

whence the name "$p \, dV$ work" for displacement work.

Eq. (3.5) is a differential equation. If the piston moves through a finite distance, the work done on the piston force must be evaluated by integrating eq. (3.5). If 1 and 2 denote the initial and final piston positions, and W_d is the displacement work done in the process, we have

$$W_d = \int_1^2 p_b \, dV_{sw} \qquad \qquad \text{... (3.6)}$$

If this is to be evaluated, the value of the boundary pressure at each increment of volume must be given; for in general p_b varies with piston position.

The interpretations of p_b and dV_{sw} in the integral are important. Particularly to be noted is that dV_{sw} is *not* in general the differential of the system volume. For example when a rigid mass is suddenly placed on a spring-supported platform (Fig. 3.7), it does displacement work in its subsequent motion; for although the volume of the mass does not change, the pressure on the lower surface exceeds that on the upper surface. Let these two surface pressures be p_l and p_u respectively. As the lower surface sweeps out a small volume δV_{sw}, say, the upper one sweeps out the volume $-\delta V_{sw}$. The net displacement work is therefore

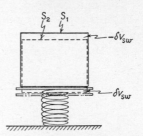

$$\delta W_d = p_l \delta V_{sw} + p_u(-\delta V_{sw})$$
$$= (p_l - p_u)\delta V_{sw} \qquad \dots \quad (3.7)$$

which is positive.

It should also be noted that in general the total work done by a system is not equal to $\int p_b \, dV_{sw}$ because other sorts of work, e.g. electrical, may be done simultaneously.

Fig. 3.7 Illustrating that swept volume is not the same as the change in system volume.

Resisted expansion; engine indicators

Engineers need to measure the work done on the piston of an engine for comparison with the work which is actually delivered at the output shaft (these quantities usually differ because of bearing friction). Eq. (3.4) shows that this may be done by measuring the pressure exerted by the fluid on the piston face throughout its movement. However this is not easy to do experimentally because of the rapid movement and the inaccessibility to observation of the piston.

Fortunately most piston-cylinder machines operate at a sufficiently low speed for the fluid pressure at any instant to be very nearly *uniform* throughout the cylinder. This situation is known as *fully-resisted expansion* (or compression) of the fluid and arises when all the effort of the fluid goes into moving the piston and none into moving itself. More precisely it occurs when the speed of piston motion is much less than the velocity of sound in the fluid. The latter is usually some thousands of feet per second; the former rarely exceeds 60 ft/s even in the engines of racing cars.

A consequence of the uniformity of pressure in the cylinder is that the piston-face pressure, p_b, can be inferred from a measurement of the pressure at a part of the cylinder wall where a pressure gauge can be more easily fixed.

The engine indicator. In order to evaluate the work done on the piston, the piston-face pressure needs to be recorded at each piston position. This is accomplished for slow-speed engines by a device known as the engine indicator, first invented by J. Southern in 1796.

Figs. 3.8 and 3.9 show the essential features. The cylinder pressure is measured by the motion of a small piston, P, moving in a small cylinder communicating with the main one. The motion of this piston is opposed by a spring, the compression of which is directly proportional to the pressure in the cylinder. The motion of the indicator piston is transmitted through a mechanical linkage B to a stylus C which may be pressed against a piece of paper. A rise of cylinder pressure causes the stylus to move vertically over the paper.

The cylinder pressure has to be plotted against piston displacement. Instead of making the stylus move horizontally in response to piston position, it is found easier to transmit this second motion to the paper, which is therefore mounted on a drum D rotating about a vertical axis. The rotation is made proportional to engine piston movement by a system of strings and levers (E, F).

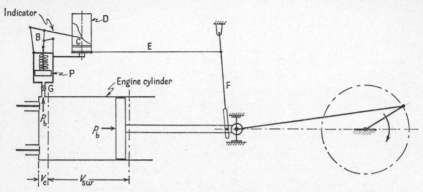

Fig. 3.8   Showing the essential features and the general arrangement of an engine indicator.

The indicator diagram. When the engine is running steadily, the stylus is pressed against the paper for a revolution or two. Since events in the cylinder repeat themselves, the stylus traces out a closed curve on the paper; this curve is called the *indicator diagram* or *indicator card*. Fig. 3.10*a* shows such a diagram typical of a steam engine. It discloses the following events:—

When the piston is in its extreme left-hand position the cylinder pressure has its highest value (at point a). The cylinder is now in communication with the steam supply main through the inlet valve. The pressure remains high at first as the piston moves to the right, but begins to fall when the inlet-valve is closed (the *cut-off* point, b). The stylus then traces out a roughly hyperbolic path which steepens as the piston approaches the extreme right-hand position due to the opening of the exhaust valve (at the *release* point, c), which causes the cylinder to communicate with the condenser which is at a low pressure. The cylinder pressure remains low throughout almost the whole of the return path of the piston, but rises again towards the end of the piston travel due to the closure of the exhaust valve (at the *compression* point, d). Thus the steam pressure is already high when the inlet valve opens once more (at the *admission* point, e).

In addition to the closed curve, an *atmospheric line*, fg, is recorded. This is usually achieved by setting the indicator cock, G, (Fig. 3.8) so that the indicator is isolated from the engine cylinder and is placed in communication with the atmosphere. The atmospheric line is required if the absolute pressure of the fluid in the cylinder has to be measured.

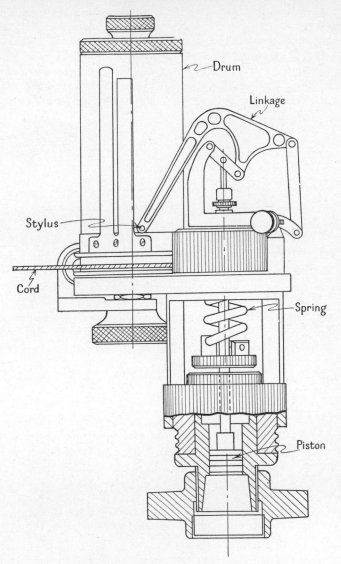

Fig. 3.9   Spring and piston type indicator.

Evaluation of the work done per revolution: indicated work. We have seen that the displacement work done at a piston face may be determined from eq. (3.6),

$$W_{\mathrm{d}} = \int p_{\mathrm{b}} \, \mathrm{d}V_{\mathrm{sw}} \qquad \qquad \dots \quad (3.8)$$

provided that the pressure at the piston face, p_{b}, and the corresponding volume swept by the piston, $\mathrm{d}V_{\mathrm{sw}}$, are known. The indicator diagram provides this information since it is a plot, to scale, of the pressure on the piston face for each position (displacement) of the piston. The area of the diagram, therefore, represents, to scale, the displacement work done at the piston face, for its measurement corresponds to the integration of eq. (3.6), carried out around the closed curve of the diagram.

The evaluation of the work done on the piston face usually proceeds in the following manner. It is necessary to know the *spring number*, S, i.e. the increase in steam pressure in psi, which causes the stylus to rise 1 inch on the paper, and the total volume swept out by the piston (*swept volume*).

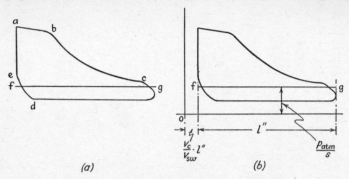

Fig. 3.10   Steam engine indicator diagrams.

First the area enclosed by the stylus trace is measured by means of a *planimeter*. Let this be a in². This is divided by l in., the horizontal length of the diagram. The quotient multiplied by the spring constant is known as the mean effective pressure, p_m. Thus,

$$p_m = \frac{aS}{l} \text{ psi} \qquad \dots \quad (3.9)$$

Now a/l represents the average height of the diagram, so p_m is the average difference between the cylinder pressure on the out-stroke and that on the in-stroke. If the swept volume is V_{sw} ft³, the *indicated work* per revolution is then, given by

$$\text{Indicated work} = p_m V_{sw} \times 144 \text{ ft lb}_f/\text{rev} \qquad \dots \quad (3.10)$$

It is often convenient to express this work on a time basis. If the number of revolutions per minute is N, the power exerted on the piston face, usually called the indicated power, is

$$P = N p_m V_{sw} \times 144 \text{ ft lb}_f/\text{min} \qquad \dots \quad (3.11)$$

Expressed in horse-power, and with V_{sw} replaced by the product of the length of piston stroke L and the piston area A, this becomes the *indicated horse-power* (i.h.p.), given by

$$\text{i.h.p.} = \frac{p_m LAN \times 144}{33000}$$

$$= \frac{p_m LAN}{229} \text{ h.p.} \qquad \dots \quad (3.12)$$

a form which some engineers find easy to remember.

EXAMPLE

  Problem. A single-cylinder steam engine has a cylinder diameter of 10 inches and a stroke of 14 inches. The area of the indicator diagram is $1·4$ in^2 and its mean length is $2·7$ in; the indicator spring number is 50 psi/in. Calculate (a) the indicated work per revolution, and (b) the indicated horse power, given that the engine speed is 140 rpm.

  Solution.

(a) Swept volume, $V_{sw} = \dfrac{\pi}{4} \times \left(\dfrac{10}{12}\right)^2 \times \dfrac{14}{12} = 0·636$ ft^3

Mean effective pressure, $p_m = \dfrac{1·4}{2·7} \times 50 = 25·9$ psi

$\therefore$ From eq. (3.10) we have

      Indicated work per revolution =

$$25·9 \times 0·636 \times 144 = 2370 \text{ ft lb}_f/\text{rev} \quad \dots \quad Answer \ (a)$$

(b) I.h.p. = Indicated work $\times \dfrac{N}{33000}$ from eq. (3.12)

$$= 2370 \times \frac{140}{33000} = 10·1 \text{ h.p.} \qquad \dots \quad Answer \ (b)$$

  Remark: Note that p_{atm} does not affect the work done on the piston; since the atmosphere does work $= p_{atm} V_{sw}$ as the piston moves into the cylinder and $-p_{atm} V_{sw}$ as it moves out, its net effect is zero.

  Two-stroke and four-stroke engines. The above analysis applies to engines in which the sequence of events occurring in the engine cylinder repeats itself once for every revolution of the crankshaft. Such engines are referred to as *two-stroke* engines. A *four-stroke* engine on the other hand completes the sequence of events in *two* revolutions of the crankshaft. In this case the indicated work, given by eq. (3.10), is the work done per two revolutions, and to obtain the indicated power, the indicated work has to be multiplied by $N/2$; correspondingly the indicated horse-power will be *one half* that given by eq. (3.12). Reciprocating internal combustion engines operate on either the two-stroke or the four-stroke cycle whereas steam engines invariably use the two-stroke cycle.*

  Single-acting and double-acting engines. A feature of the engine considered above is that only one face of the piston is exposed to the working fluid; for this reason it is termed a *single-acting* engine. In *double-acting* engines, however, the working fluid is admitted to both ends of the cylinder with the result that work is done on each face of the piston. In this case there is an indicator diagram for each end of the cylinder and consequently the indicated horse-power will be approximately double† that of the

---

* The use of the term 'cycle' to describe the complete sequence of events occurring in the engine cylinder is common practice. Later, however, we use the term to describe a special sort of thermodynamic process.

† It is only approximately double for two reasons: (i) the indicator diagrams for each end of the cylinder are not exactly similar and, (ii) the piston rod reduces the effective area of the piston on one side and hence the swept volumes will not be equal for both ends of the cylinder.

4

corresponding single-acting engine. Most reciprocating steam engines are double-acting. Internal combustion engines for road transport are always single-acting; marine diesel engines are often double-acting.

The scale of the indicator diagram. The spring number, S, fixes the pressure scale of the diagram since 1 inch vertical movement of the stylus corresponds to S psi pressure change in the engine cylinder. It follows that the line of zero pressure is p_{atm}/S inches below the atmospheric line (Fig. 3.10b). The swept volume, V_{sw}, fixes the horizontal scale of the diagram, since l inches corresponds to V_{sw}, Fig. 3.10b, and correspondingly the line of zero volume is $(V_c l/V_{sw})$ inches from the left hand end of the diagram; V_c is the *clearance volume*, i.e. the "dead" space at the end of the cylinder which is not traversed by the piston (Fig. 3.8).

With the axes of the indicator diagram so fixed, the absolute pressure and the volume of the *fluid in the cylinder* may be determined for any piston position.

Although an indicator diagram has pressure as ordinate and volume as abscissa, it must not be confused with the pressure-volume relation of a system, discussed below (p. 43). Even during one revolution, the quantity of material within the cylinder changes as a result of the valve openings and piston motion.

Displacement work done by the whole system boundary

Having discussed the displacement work done at *part* of a system boundary, we now consider the system *as a whole*. To evaluate the displacement work for the whole system boundary we take the summation of the values of displacement work for each part of the boundary.

The case most frequently met in practice is that of a system the boundary of which may be divided into sections which have uniform, but different, pressures acting on them. For such a system we may, from eq. (3.6) write the summation as

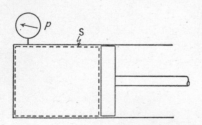

$$W_d = \int_A p_b \, dV_{sw} + \int_B p_b \, dV_{sw} + \cdots \tag{3.13}$$

in which the terms on the right-hand side represent the displacement work done at sections A, B, ... of the boundary on each of which there is a different uniform pressure.

Fig. 3.11 Cylinder and piston enclosing a fluid system.

To illustrate this procedure we consider two cases. The first is the especially simple case in which the pressure is uniform throughout the system; in the second the system can be sub-divided into uniform pressure regions.

Displacement work when the system pressure is uniform. Consider, for simplicity, the case in which a fluid system S is enclosed within a cylinder by a leakproof piston (Fig. 3.11). The cylinder has no valves, so the same

collection of matter is present at all times. If only slow motions of the
piston occur, the expansions and compressions can be regarded as "fully-
resisted", so the pressure is uniform at all points, as has been seen*; a
single pressure gauge will therefore indicate the system pressure p.

Since both pressure and volume have definite values at any instant we
can trace out the history of the system on a pressure-volume diagram.
Fig. 3.12 illustrates this, the system
volume, V, being employed as
abscissa. Such a plot is called a *state
diagram*.

At this point it is convenient to
introduce some definitions for the
sake of precision. Some of the terms
have already been used.

**A property is any (macroscopic)
observable characteristic of a system.**
For example, pressure, volume and
density are properties.

The state of a system is the totality
of the properties of the system, i.e. it
is the complete description of the
system.

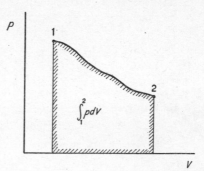

Fig. 3.12   State diagram for a fluid
system which undergoes a fully
resisted expansion, showing the
system pressure, p, plotted against
the system volume, V.

A state-point is a point on a diagram representing the properties of a
system at any moment.

A process is that which brings about a change of state of the system. It is
partially described in terms of the succession of states passed through.
This succession is known as the path of the process.

On Fig. 3.12 the points marked 1 and 2 are state-points representing
two states of the system. The line joining them represents a possible path
of a process in which the system changes from state 1 to state 2; it shows
how the system pressure and system volume change during the process.

On p. 36 it was stated that, in the $\int p_b \, dV_{sw}$ expression for displacement
work, dV_{sw} cannot be interpreted in general as the change in system volume.
In the present case however the pressure at the boundary, p_b, is the same
at all points and is equal to the system pressure, p; this interpretation
therefore *is* permissible. For if $p_b = p$ we have from eq. (3.13)

$$W_d = \int_A p_b \, dV_{sw} + \int_B p_b \, dV_{sw} + \dots$$

$$= \int p[(dV_{sw})_A + (dV_{sw})_B + \dots]$$

Now $[(dV_{sw})_A + (dV_{sw})_B + \dots] = dV$, the elemental change in the system

* Differences due to gravity (hydrostatic pressure) will be neglected.

volume, V. We can therefore write our expression for the displacement work done by a system changing from state 1 to state 2, as

$$W_d = \int_1^2 p\,dV$$

The integral has an obvious geometrical interpretation: it is proportional to the area beneath the curve of Fig. 3.12, shown shaded. Inspection of the diagram shows that merely specifying the points 1 and 2 does not determine the area: the run of the connecting curve needs to be known also; it may be arched upwards or it may sag downwards, and the area will vary accordingly. The mathematical significance of this is that we need to know p as a function of V if we are to evaluate the integral $\int_1^2 p\,dV$. Some examples are dealt with below. Before discussing these however we note that if the system has mass m, the expression for the displacement work becomes

$$W_d = \int_1^2 p\,dV$$

$$= m \int_1^2 p\,dv \qquad \qquad \text{... (3.14)}$$

since the system volume, V, is mv from the definition of v, and m is constant.

In most cases of fully-resisted expansion, the displacement work is the whole work done by the system; other forms are usually absent.

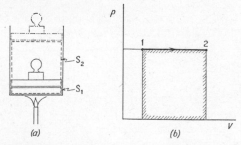

Fig. 3.13   Illustrating a constant-pressure process.

Displacement work in processes undergone by systems of uniform pressure

(a) *The constant-pressure process.* Fig. 3.13a shows a vertical cylinder fitted with a frictionless leakproof piston enclosing a fluid system S_1. A weight rests on the piston, and adjusts its position to keep the system pressure constant in accordance with principles of hydrostatics. If the system is heated, for example by an external flame, it will expand, causing the piston to rise; S_1 becomes S_2.

The corresponding $p - V$ diagram is shown in Fig. 3.13b: the path of the process is a horizontal line, because p is constant.

In this case the evaluation of the displacement work done by the system is easy. It is, from eq. (3.14), simply

$$W_d = p_1 \int_1^2 dV$$
$$= p_1(V_2 - V_1)$$
$$= mp_1(v_2 - v_1) \qquad \dots (3.15)$$

Although seldom occurring in cylinders, constant-pressure processes are common in engineering thermodynamics. For example they occur in boilers and condensers.

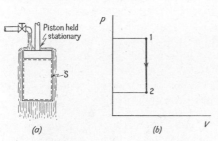

Fig. 3.14 Illustrating a constant-volume process.

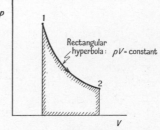

Fig. 3.15 State diagram for a system which undergoes the process $pV = constant$

(b) *The constant-volume process.* A process permitting a still simpler evaluation of W_d is that in which the piston is prevented from moving, so that the system volume remains unchanged. An example is found in primitive steam engines in which condensation occurred by a sudden chilling of the steam by cold water before the piston had time to move from its uppermost position.

Fig. 3.14a illustrates the arrangement schematically. Fig. 3.14b is the corresponding state diagram. The path of the process is a vertical straight line. In this case

$$W_d = \int_1^2 p \, dV$$
$$= 0 \qquad \dots (3.16)$$

for the volume does not change.

(c) *The process: $pV = constant$.* We now consider a process represented by a simple algebraic formula. Later (Chapter 14) it will be shown that many (but not most) substances carry out such processes when expanding in a fully resisted manner at constant temperature. The algebraic relation is

$$pV = constant$$
$$= k, \text{ say} \qquad \dots (3.17)$$

which represents a rectangular hyperbola on the state diagram (Fig. 3.15).

To evaluate the work we write

$$W_d = \int_1^2 p \, dV$$

$$= k \int_1^2 \frac{dV}{V}$$

$$= k \ln \left(\frac{V_2}{V_1} \right)$$

$$= p_1 V_1 \ln \left(\frac{V_2}{V_1} \right) = m p_1 v_1 \ln \left(\frac{v_2}{v_1} \right) \quad \dots \quad (3.18)$$

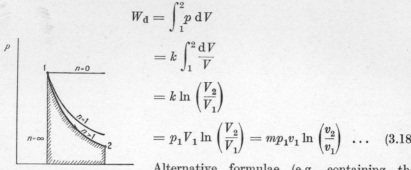

Fig. 3.16   State diagram for a system undergoing processes characterized by $pV^n = constant$.

Alternative formulae (e.g. containing the logarithm of p_1/p_2) can also be derived. We see, as is to be expected, that, starting from a given initial state, the work increases as the volume increases; not proportionately however, for the pressure is falling.

(d) *The process:* $pV^n = constant$. Finally, a family of processes will be discussed which often form useful approximations to real processes. This family is characterised by the formula

$$pV^n = constant$$

$$= k, \text{ say} \qquad \dots \quad (3.19)$$

where n is some number. Fig. 3.16 contains sketches of some members of the family. Such processes assume some importance in Chapter 14.

Evaluation of the displacement work is carried out as follows:—

$$W_d = \int_1^2 p \, dV$$

$$= k \int_1^2 \frac{dV}{V^n}$$

$$= \frac{k}{1-n} (V_2^{1-n} - V_1^{1-n})$$

$$= \frac{p_2 V_2^n \cdot V_2^{1-n} - p_1 V_1^n \cdot V_1^{1-n}}{1-n}$$

$$= \frac{p_2 V_2 - p_1 V_1}{1-n} = m \left(\frac{p_2 v_2 - p_1 v_1}{1-n} \right) \qquad \dots \quad (3.19)$$

together with alternative formulae.

It will be noted that, although the process $pV = constant$ is a member of the family, having $n = 1$, formula (3.19) fails in this case, becoming indeterminate ($= 0/0$). This is why it was treated separately above.

Displacement work when the system pressure is not uniform. We now evaluate the displacement work in three important special cases of systems of non-uniform pressure. In the first two, the dV_{sw} in $\int p_b \, dV_{sw}$ can again, as it happens, be interpreted as the differential of system volume dV because the *moving* part of the system boundary has uniform pressure. In the third example, two parts of the boundary move and the pressures acting on them differ; dV_{sw} can no longer be regarded as the change in system volume.

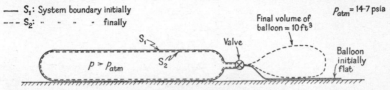

Fig. 3.17   Filling a balloon from a bottle.   Example (i).

EXAMPLE (i). Filling a balloon from a bottle.

Problem. A balloon of flexible material is to be filled with air from a storage bottle until it has a volume of 10 ft³. The atmospheric pressure is 14·7 psia. Determine the work done by the system comprising the air initially in the bottle, if the balloon is light and requires no stretching.

Solution. The first step in any thermodynamic analysis is to sketch the apparatus, indicating the system boundary. Fig. 3.17 shows this. Initially the system boundary coincides with the inner surface of the storage bottle: boundary S_1 in the sketch. At the end of the process the boundary also encloses the 10 ft³ content of the balloon: S_2 in the sketch.

The displacement work, the only work in the process, is obtained by taking the summation of the values of $\int p_b \, dV_{sw}$ for each part of the boundary, according to eq. (3.13). dV_{sw} is zero for the part of the boundary in contact with the bottle surface, for the bottle can be taken as rigid; we therefore do not need to know the pressure of the air in the bottle.

The moving part of the boundary sweeps out a volume of 10 ft³. The pressure on this part is uniform and constant at 14·7 psia (since the balloon is light and requires no stretching, the pressures on both sides of the fabric are equal). From eq. (3.13) the displacement work is therefore

$$W_d = \int_{\text{Balloon}} p_b \, dV_{sw} + \int_{\text{Bottle}} p_b \, dV_{sw}$$

$$= p_{\text{atm}} \int dV_{sw} + 0$$

$$= 14{\cdot}7 \times 144 \times 10$$

$$= 21{,}200 \text{ ft lb}_f \qquad\qquad \textit{Answer} \quad \ldots \quad (3.20)$$

Remarks.

1. From the definition of negative work it follows that the work done by the atmosphere is $-21{,}200$ ft lb$_f$.

2. The solution of the problem rests on the assumption that the pressure in the balloon is equal to p_{atm} at all times. It is valid if the balloon fabric is light,

inelastic and unstressed. If, however, the fabric were elastic, and stretched during the filling process, the pressure within the balloon could exceed p_{atm} and vary with time; the pressure on the outside surface of the balloon is, of course, equal to p_{atm} at all times. It follows, therefore, that while the displacement work done by the atmosphere would be —21,200 ft lb$_f$., as before, the W_d for the gas system would be greater than 21,200 ft lb$_f$ by an amount equal to the work done in stretching the balloon. However, for the system comprising the gas *and* the balloon, the displacement work would be 21,200 ft lb$_f$ as calculated above.

3. It should be noted that the balloon forms a convenient way of marking part of the system boundary. In examples (ii) and (iii) which follow, this material system boundary is absent.

EXAMPLE (ii). Filling an evacuated bottle from the atmosphere.

Problem. Determine the work done by the air which enters an evacuated bottle from the atmosphere when the cock is opened. The atmospheric pressure is 14·7 psia and 2 ft^3 of air (measured at atmospheric conditions) enter.

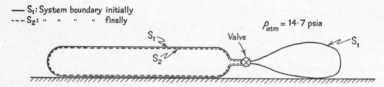

Fig. 3.18 Filling a bottle from the atmosphere. Example (ii).

Fig. 3.18 shows a sketch with initial and final system boundaries. Once again no work is done by the part of the boundary in contact with the bottle; only the moving part external to the bottle need be observed. Over this part the pressure is uniform at 14·7 psia. The displacement work done by the system is therefore evaluated from eq. (3.13) as follows:—

$$W_d = \int p_b \, dV_{sw} + \int p_b \, dV_{sw}$$

Free air   Bottle
boundary

$$= p_{atm} \int dV_{sw} + 0$$

$$= 14{\cdot}7 \times 144 \times (-2)$$

$$= -4{,}230 \text{ ft lb}_f \qquad\qquad Answer \quad ... \quad (3.21)$$

It should be noted that this time the work is *negative*; $\int dV_{sw}$ for the free air boundary is negative because the boundary is contracting.

EXAMPLE (iii). The induction process of an internal combustion engine.

The piston of an oil engine, of area 7 in^2, moves downwards 3 in., drawing in 18 in^3 of fresh air from the atmosphere. The pressure in the cylinder is uniform during the process at 11 psia, while the atmospheric pressure is 14·7 psia, the difference being accounted for by flow resistance in the induction pipe and inlet valve. Determine the displacement work done by the air finally in the cylinder.

Fig. 3.19 sketches the apparatus with the initial and final system boundaries S_1 and S_2. Two parts of the system boundary do work, which is evaluated from eq. (3.13) as

$$= \int p_b \, dV_{sw} + \int p_b \, dV_{sw} + \int p_b \, dV_{sw}$$

$$\text{Piston} \qquad \text{Free air} \qquad \text{Stationary}$$
$$\text{boundary} \qquad \text{boundaries}$$

$$= 11 \times 144 \times \frac{7 \times 3}{12^3} - 14.7 \times 144 \times \frac{18}{12^3} + 0$$

$$= 19.3 - 22.1$$

$$= -2.8 \text{ ft lb}_f \qquad\qquad\qquad Answer \quad \dots \quad (3.22)$$

In this case the first two terms have opposite signs since the piston moves in the direction of the pressure on it while the free air boundary moves against

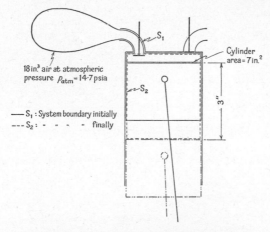

Fig. 3.19 Induction process of an internal
combustion engine. Example (iii).

the pressure exerted on it by the system. The negative work term happens to be the larger. Such calculations have to be made as part of the determination of the state, and so for example of the temperature, of the air finally drawn into the cylinder.

It should be noted that *within* the system very complicated events are occurring and individual parts of the system do work on other parts. All these however can be ignored in the above calculation; we need only consider the system boundary.

General case: displacement work done by the whole system when the pressure varies continuously along the boundary

In the above examples, the moving parts of the system boundary have different uniform pressures acting on them. We now consider the general case in which the pressure varies from point to point along the system boundary. To do this we refer once more to eq. (3.5) which, although it was developed for the piston-cylinder mechanism of Fig. 3.6, is of general application; for it also expresses the displacement work done by an element of the system boundary which sweeps out the local volume element dV_{sw} where the local pressure is p_b. In general p_b varies with position *on* the boundary and with position *of* the boundary and so to obtain the displacement work for the whole boundary, eq. (3.5) has to be integrated. Thus

$$W_d = \int_S p_b \, dV_{sw}$$

in which the symbol $\int_S$ is used to emphasise that the summation has to be carried out over the whole boundary *and* its movement.

In practice, for example in fluid systems where the hydrostatic pressure at the boundary varies from point to point, it may be convenient to give W_d the form of a double integral.

Displacement work in unresisted expansion

In the final example of the present section, a fluid expands in an unresisted manner, i.e. the relative velocities of the parts of the system boundary are not small compared with the velocity of propagation of a sound wave through the system. This example demonstrates the power of the thermodynamic technique of referring work to a system boundary.

Collapse of a diaphragm. Consider the rigid vessel shown in Fig. 3.20, separated by a light diaphragm. Initially the left-hand half of the vessel is filled with gas, while the right-hand half is evacuated. The problem is to evaluate the work done by the gas when the diaphragm gives way under the pressure on it and the gas expands to fill the whole vessel. For definiteness, each half of the vessel will be supposed to have a volume of 1 ft³, and the gas in the left-hand half will be supposed to have the pressure 100 psia initially. The initial pressure in the right-hand half is of course zero.

The problem will be solved in two ways. The first follows the treatment given earlier, but requires some physical insight into the nature of the expansion process. The second is simpler and shows what can be done by judicious choice of the system boundary.

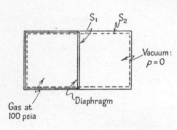

Fig. 3.20 An example of unresisted expansion.

First method. Consider a system boundary S_1 enclosing the left-hand half of the vessel. As a result of the process, this boundary finally takes up the position S_2 in Fig. 3.20. From eq. (3.13) we have to evaluate

$$W_d = \underbrace{\int p_b \, dV_{sw}}_{\substack{\text{Moving part} \\ \text{of S}}} + \underbrace{\int p_b \, dV_{sw}}_{\substack{\text{Stationary part} \\ \text{of S}}} \qquad \dots \quad (3.23)$$

Clearly the volume swept out by the boundary is finite. However reflection reveals that the pressure on the moving part of the boundary, i.e. the face of the diaphragm exposed to the vacuum, is always zero; for there is no material to the right of the moving boundary to exert a pressure. We conclude

$$W_d = \int_1^2 0 \, dV_{sw} + 0 = 0 \qquad \ldots \quad (3.24)$$

There is *no* displacement work done by the gas in expanding.

Second method. The same result can be achieved more directly by considering the system boundary to occupy position S_2 initially as well as finally. The system is still the same because the boundary still encloses nothing but the gas and the diaphragm.

When we now come to evaluate the displacement work we see that $dV_{sw} = 0$ at *all* points of the boundary. This leads to $W_d = 0$ immediately.

Examples of unresisted expansion occur in practice, though seldom in quite the simple form just discussed; for instance, the discharge of gas from a petrol-engine cylinder when the exhaust valve is opened is such a process. Unresisted expansion will be discussed again later in this book (Chapter 11, page 192).

WORK DONE AS A RESULT OF SHEAR FORCES

We now turn to *shear work*, which is associated with the force exerted by a system on its surroundings, in a direction lying in the plane of the local system boundary. It is necessary to distinguish several cases. The first is that in which the system boundary is an imaginary one cutting a rigid solid; the most important example in engineering thermodynamics is *shaft work*. Then two sorts of friction will be discussed: *fluid friction* and *solid friction*. Finally we deal with *stirring work*.

Shear work across a system boundary in a solid

Consider the block being pushed slowly along a rough horizontal surface in Fig. 3.21. We suppose that it is desired to determine the work done by the upper half of the block on the lower; accordingly we consider a system boundary S around the upper half. A shear stress exists along the lower part of the system boundary *tending* (of course in vain) to make the system slide relative to the lower half of the block. If this shear stress has the uniform value σ, the area over which it operates is A, and the force applied to the block is F, the principles of statics lead to the relation

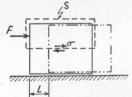

Fig. 3.21 Illustrating shear work at a system boundary in a solid.

$$F = \sigma A \qquad \ldots \quad (3.25)$$

Using the "mechanics" definition of work, which suffices here, it is easily seen that, when the block, and with it the system boundary, has moved a distance L in the direction of the shear stresses, the shear work by the system W_s is

$$W_s = \sigma A L \qquad \ldots \quad (3.26)$$

Generalising this result to the case in which the shear stress is not uniform or constant, we write

$$W_s = \int\int \sigma \, dA \, dL \qquad \ldots \quad (3.27)$$

which simply means that we must consider each element, dA, separately, and multiply it by the value of σ prevailing there at the moment in question

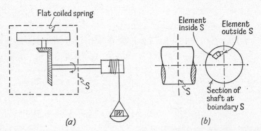

Fig. 3.22   Illustrating a system doing shaft work.

and by the elementary distance, dL, which the material on both sides of the system boundary moves in the direction of the stress. The total shear work is evaluated by adding up all these elementary contributions. A particular example of this integration now follows.

Shaft work. Consider a shaft penetrating the system boundary shown in Fig. 3.22a. The system comprises a flat-coiled circular spring which is unwinding and so raising weights by means of a winch. Fig. 3.22b shows a section through the shaft at the system boundary. At each element of area, dA, there is a shear stress σ, in a tangential direction, tending to cause relative rotation of the two parts of the shaft on either side of S.

The shear stress depends on the radius, r, at which the element is situated, and is related, according to the principles of statics, to the torque T exerted by the shaft across the boundary by

$$dT = (\sigma \, dA)r$$

or

$$T = \int \sigma r \, dA \qquad \ldots \quad (3.28)$$

in which the integral represents a summation over all the elements of area.

When the shaft turns through a small angle $d\theta$, each element (on both sides of S) moves a distance $r \, d\theta$ in the direction of the stress. The shear work done by the element dA on its surroundings during the elementary rotation is given, according to eq. (3.26) by

$$dW_s = (\sigma \, dA)(r \, d\theta) \qquad \ldots \quad (3.29)$$

It follows from eq. (3.29) that the shear work done by the system on its surroundings is given by

$$W_s = \int \int \sigma r \, dA \, d\theta \qquad \ldots \quad (3.30)$$

and hence, from eq. (3.28) we obtain

$$W_s = \int T \, d\theta \qquad \ldots \quad (3.31)$$

This form of shear work is known as *shaft work*. Its engineering importance lies in the fact that most power plants deliver their output in the form of a shaft rotation at some stage, because of the mechanical ease with which it can be transmitted in this form.

Eq. (3.31) enables the shaft work to be evaluated when T varies with θ. Often, however, steady conditions exist, in which case T is constant and independent of θ. Eq. (3.31) then becomes

$$W_s = T \times \theta$$

Expressing θ in terms of the speed of rotation of the shaft, N rev/min, and T in lb_f ft, we obtain the rate at which shaft work is done, i.e. the shaft-power, P, as

$$P = T \times \frac{2\pi N}{60} \text{ ft } lb_f/s$$

wherein the factor $\frac{2\pi}{60}$ converts the shaft speed to radians/s.

It follows that

$$\text{Shaft horse-power} = \frac{T \times 2\pi N}{550 \times 60} \text{ h.p.}$$

Fluid friction

When a fluid flows relative to a solid surface, for example in a pipe, its velocity is never uniform. Fig. 3.23 illustrates the distribution of longitudinal velocity which is found in practice. Its most striking feature is that discontinuities of velocity are absent, even at the interface between fluid and pipe wall.* Thus although there is relative motion between the fluid, treated as a whole, and a solid pipe, it is not possible to find any surface for which a finite difference of velocity exists between the materials *immediately* on either side of it.

In this respect therefore the situation is similar to that of a solid body. An important consequence is that the shear work across a system boundary in a fluid exerting shear stresses can be evaluated by means of the same formula, namely eq. (3.27). Two cases will be considered.

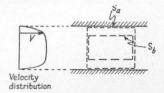

Velocity distribution

Fig. 3.23 Fluid flow in a pipe.

---

* This only ceases to be true for very rarefied gases, which will not be dealt with in this book.

Shear work done by a fluid system on a solid surface at rest. Consider the system with the boundary S_a in Fig. 3.23. If the shear work done by the fluid on the wall across the boundary is evaluated, we find, from eq. (3.27)

$$W_s = \int\int \sigma \, dA \, . \, dL$$
$$= 0, \text{ because } dL = 0 \qquad \qquad \dots \quad (3.32)$$

for the material at the part of the boundary in question does not move. We conclude that a fluid system does no shear work on a surface at rest, even though a shear stress is exerted.

Shear work done by a fluid system on adjacent fluid. To illustrate the next point a smaller system is chosen, S_b, in Fig. 3.23. A glance at the velocity diagram shows that a finite velocity exists at the upper and lower system boundaries. Suppose that these velocities both have the value V. Then the boundaries across which the shear stress σ is exerted move a distance, dL, in an element of time, $d\tau$, given by

$$dL = V \, d\tau \qquad \qquad \dots \quad (3.32)$$

Taking for simplicity the case in which the stress σ is uniform over the relevant system boundary area A, the shear work done by the system is given by

$$W_s = \int \sigma A V \, d\tau \qquad \qquad \dots \quad (3.33)$$

Correspondingly the *rate* of doing work i.e. the power P is given by

$$P = \frac{dW_s}{d\tau} = \sigma A V \qquad \qquad \dots \quad (3.34)$$

Such calculations are important in the theory of lubrication, where the shear work causes the oil to become hot, and in supersonic aerodynamics, where very large temperature rises result from the high shear work adjacent to surfaces.

Stirring work

Allied both to shaft work and to fluid friction is *stirring work*. This occurs when a fluid is stirred in a more or less random manner, usually by a paddle wheel on the end of the shaft. Fig. 3.24 illustrates the apparatus. If the system boundary S_a is considered, enclosing the fluid but excluding the wheel and shaft, it is found that both normal and shear forces are exerted on the wheel surface. In principle the work associated with these forces can be evaluated in the manner indicated above.

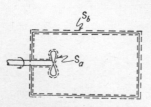

Fig. 3.24   Stirring work.

Usually however the force distribution over the wheel surface is not known with sufficient precision. It is therefore simpler to re-draw the system boundary in the position S_b. Now we merely have shaft work crossing the boundary, which can be determined by means of the eq. (3.31).

It should be noted that stirring work is *negative*, for the surroundings do work on the system.

Solid friction

The case of solid friction has been left to the end because it exhibits a special difficulty. Suppose that we wish to determine the shear work done by the whole block of Fig. 3.21 on the plane beneath. An attempt to use the formulae already given eq. (3.26) leads to the question: What is the value of L? For though the material above the system boundary moves, that below does not. There does not seem to be any reason to give either the priority.

The answer to the question cannot be given here, for, surprisingly enough, the value of the shear work depends on the relative *thermal conductivities* of the two materials. This will be dealt with, after thermal quantities have been precisely introduced, on p. 86; although of minor practical importance, this matter throws further light on the thermodynamic definition of work.

ELECTRICAL WORK

There are as many sorts of work as there are forces to cause change—capillary, magnetic, electric, electromagnetic, and so on. Here, however, we shall merely discuss electrical work.

Already on page 32 it was shown that the thermodynamic definition of work covers electrical effects. It remains to relate the units of electrical work to those used for the mechanical variety. The important statement is:—

When $\mathcal{Q}$ coulombs of positive electricity cross a system boundary at a point 'A' and re-enter the system at a point 'B', the electric potential of 'A' being $\mathscr{V}$ volts above the potential of 'B', the system does positive work on its surroundings equal to $\mathcal{Q}\mathscr{V}$ joules.

This statement is the definition of the volt in a form acceptable to thermodynamicists. The coulomb is a unit of electric charge, which is defined in texts on electricity. The joule has already been introduced on p. 30.

We conclude with a miscellany of electrical units and their relations to the units used in the remainder of the book.

1 coulomb flowing per second is called a current of 1 ampere.

Consequently when a steady current of I amperes flows between the points A and B of the above definition the system does work at the rate of IV joules per second.

1 joule per second is called 1 watt. The watt is a unit of power.

A power of 1,000 joule per second is called 1 kilowatt.

1 watt is equivalent to 0·7375 ft lb_f/s.

1 kilowatt is equivalent to 1·34 h.p.

NET WORK DONE BY A SYSTEM

In the present chapter we have considered the various ways in which work may be done by a system. Often many of these various sorts of work occur simultaneously during a process executed by the system. When all the sorts of work done by a system have been evaluated, the *total* or *net* work done by the system, W, can be computed by simple *algebraic* addition of the separate work terms. Note that the algebraic sum must be taken and therefore due attention must be paid to the sign of each work term.

BIBLIOGRAPHY

Keenan, J. H., *Thermodynamics*. John Wiley & Sons and Chapman & Hall, 1941.

CHAPTER 3—PROBLEMS

3.1 A rigid body of mass 10 lb$_m$ rests on a rough horizontal table. An agent applies a horizontal force of 3 lb$_f$ to the body and so slowly pulls the latter across the table. How much work is done by the agent in moving the body a distance of 5 feet?

3.2 A rigid body rests on a rough horizontal plane. A coiled compression spring is attached to the body with its axis horizontal; the spring is such that a force of 2 lb$_f$ causes it to compress 1 inch.

An agent applies a horizontal force to the free end of the spring causing the block to move slowly along the table. When the block has moved a distance of 6 inches it comes into contact with a rigid stop fixed to the surface of the table. During its motion the resisting force on the block is 4 lb$_f$.

(*a*) How much work is done by the agent?

(*b*) If after the block has contacted the stop, the agent slowly relaxes the applied force, how much work will it have done altogether?

(*c*) How much work is done by the spring in (*a*) and (*b*)?

3.3 A steel structure is to be tested by measuring the deflections caused by slowly-applied external loads.

In a particular test a weight of 10 ton$_f$ causes a deflection of 0·008 inches at its point of application. What is the work done (in ft lb$_f$) by the applied load? (1 ton$_f$ = 2240 lb$_f$.) (Assume that the deflection increases in direct proportion to the force.)

3.4 Evaluate the work done in the following processes. The systems to be considered are printed in italics.

(*a*) An *agent* slowly raises a *body* of mass 5 lb$_m$ a distance of 10 ft in a gravitational field. The gravitational acceleration is standard. Neglect air resistance.

(*b*) A *body* of mass 30 lb$_m$ is lowered by a *crane* slowly through a vertical distance of 100 ft in a gravitational field for which $g = 20$ ft/s^2. Neglect air resistance.

(*c*) A *body* of mass 30 lb$_m$ falls freely through a vertical distance of 100 ft in a gravitational field for which $g = 20$ ft/s^2. The drag force of the *atmosphere* on the body is 1 lb$_f$.

(*d*) A *body* of mass 30 lb$_m$ falls freely (in a vacuum) through a vertical distance of 100 ft. The gravitational acceleration is 20 ft/s^2.

(*e*) A *rat*, weight 1 lb$_f$, climbs a stair 1 ft in height.

3.5 The *electric motor* of a crane is supplied with a current of 12·5 amperes from a 200 volt DC supply for a period of 15 seconds while the crane lifts a *machine* of weight 2 ton$_f$ through a vertical distance of 6 ft. The weight of the inextensible *cable* and the resistance of the *pulleys* over which the cable passes are negligible.

Evaluate the work done by the systems printed in italics.

3.6 In the figure A is a frictionless leakproof piston of area 1 ft^2. The pressure of the fluid in the container is 8·3 in. water gauge and the atmospheric pressure is 14·7 psia. After a body of weight 1 lb$_f$ is suddenly placed upon the piston it oscillates and eventually comes to rest, due to damping within the vessel, in a new position 9 in. lower. Assuming that the pressure, exerted by the atmosphere on the top of the piston and the weight, remains constant at 14·7 psia, calculate the work done by each of the following systems:—

(a) the weight, (b) the piston, (c) the atmosphere, (d) the fluid in the container.

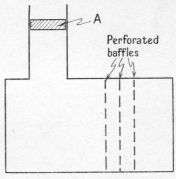

Problem 3.6

3.7 A cylinder closed by a frictionless leakproof piston contains a gas at a pressure of 20 psia. The cylinder area is 36 in^2. As the piston is pushed inwards, some of the gas is forced out of the cylinder through a spring-loaded valve in the cylinder cover. An indicator connected to the cylinder shows that during this process the pressure of the gas in the cylinder increases linearly with the piston position to 40 psia.

Evaluate the work done at the piston face as the piston is pushed inwards a distance of 8 in. if the shape of the piston crown (i.e. the surface exposed to the gas in the cylinder) is (a) flat and (b) hemispherical.

3.8 A single-cylinder, double-acting, 2-stroke oil engine has a cylinder diameter ('bore') of 8 in. and a stroke of 10 in. When the engine is run at a speed of 300 rev/min, the mean effective pressure is 130 psi. Evaluate the work done per 'cycle' and the indicated horse-power.

3.9 An indicator spring is found to require an axial force of 30 lb$_f$ to shorten it by 0·1 in. The spring is used in an indicator having a piston area of 0·5 in.^{2} and a pencil mechanism which magnifies the motion of the indicator piston six-fold.

(a) Calculate the spring number in psi/in.

(b) A single-cylinder, single-acting, 4-stroke gas engine of bore 6 in. develops an indicated power of 6 h.p. when running at 220 rev/min. Calculate the area of the indicator diagram that would be obtained using the above indicator, given that the length of the diagram is 0·1 times the length of the stroke of the engine.

3.10 A six-cylinder, 4-stroke petrol engine is run at a speed of 2500 rev/min. The area of the indicator card of one cylinder is 3·61 in.^{2} and its length is 2·42 in. The spring number is 80 psi/in. The bore of the cylinders is 6 in. and the piston stroke is 6·5 in.

Evaluate the indicated horse-power, assuming that all cylinders contribute equal powers.

3.11 The following description is an idealization of the sequence of events which occur in the cylinder of a reciprocating air compressor:—

(a) Initially, with the piston at its innermost position (inner dead-centre) and with the inlet and delivery valves shut, the clearance volume contains air at the delivery pressure p_2.

(b) The piston moves slowly outwards causing the clearance air to expand to the inlet pressure p_1 according to $pV^n = constant$; p and V are respectively the pressure and volume of the clearance air at any instant during this process.

(c) When the pressure of the clearance air has fallen to p_1 the inlet valve opens and as the piston completes its outward stroke atmospheric air is drawn into the cylinder. The pressure on the piston face is p_1 throughout this induction process.

(d) With the piston in its outermost position (outer dead-centre) the inlet valve closes. The piston now commences its inward stroke and compresses the air in the cylinder (i.e. the clearance air plus the induced air) according to $pV^n = constant$ until its pressure rises to p_2; p and V are respectively the pressure and volume of the air in the cylinder during the compression process.

(e) When the pressure has risen to p_2, the delivery valve opens and air is discharged at pressure p_2 as the piston completes its inward stroke.

(f) Finally with the piston at the inner dead-centre the delivery valve closes leaving the clearance volume filled with air at pressure p_2. The sequence is then repeated.

All motions of the piston are assumed to be fully resisted. The clearance volume is c per cent of the swept volume V_{sw}.

(i) Sketch the indicator diagram.

(ii) Derive an expression for the net work done at the piston face per 'cycle' in terms of p_1, p_2, V_{sw}, c and n.

(iii) Evaluate the net work when $p_2 = 90$ psia, $p_1 = 15$ psia, $V_{sw} = 144$ in³. $c = 5$ per cent and $n = 1 \cdot 2$.

(iv) Evaluate the indicated horse-power when the compressor speed is 400 rev/min assuming single-acting operation. (Note that one complete sequence of events occurs during one revolution of the crankshaft.)

3.12 The figure shows a piston-cylinder mechanism employed to pump a corrosive fluid. The 10 in. diameter cylinder is closed by a light flexible diaphragm attached to the 6 in. diameter piston. The stroke of the piston is

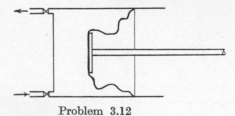

Problem 3.12

10 in. and the length of the cylinder is 5 in. The shape of the diaphragm in its extreme positions is the frustum of a cone.

During the delivery stroke an agent pushes the thin piston rod slowly inwards against the constant fluid pressure of 25 psig. The atmospheric pressure acts on the outer side of the diaphragm and piston.

Evaluate the work done by the agent.

3.13 The following description is an idealization of the sequence of events which occur in the cylinder of a reciprocating steam engine.

(a) Initially, with the piston at its innermost position (inner dead-centre) and with the inlet and exhaust valves shut, the clearance volume contains steam at the exhaust pressure p_e.

(b) The inlet valve now opens causing the steam pressure to rise rapidly to the supply pressure p_1.

(c) The piston commences its outward stroke so admitting steam to the cylinder. When the piston has moved a per cent of the swept volume the inlet valve closes ('cut-off'). The pressure on the piston face is p_1 throughout the admission process.

(d) As the piston continues its outward stroke, the steam in the cylinder (i.e. clearance steam plus admitted steam) expands according to $pV = constant$ ('hyperbolic expansion') where p and V are respectively the pressure and volume of the steam in the cylinder during this process.

(e) When the piston has reached the end of its stroke (outer dead-centre) the exhaust valve opens, so causing the steam pressure to fall rapidly to the exhaust pressure p_e ('the back-pressure').

(f) The piston now performs its return stroke so discharging the steam from the cylinder at the exhaust pressure p_e.

(g) Finally with the piston at the inner dead-centre the exhaust valve closes leaving the clearance volume filled with steam at the exhaust pressure p_e. The sequence is then repeated.

All motions of the piston are assumed to be fully-resisted. The clearance volume is c per cent of the swept volume V_{sw}.

(i) Sketch the indicator diagram.

(ii) Derive expressions for the net work done at the piston face per 'cycle' and for the mean effective pressure in terms of p_1, p_e, V_{sw}, a and c.

(iii) Evaluate the mean effective pressure when $p_1 = 80$ psia, $p_e = 15$ psia, $a = 30$ per cent, $c = 5$ per cent. Hence evaluate the net work done per 'cycle', given that the bore and stroke of the engine are 9 in. and 11 in. respectively.

(iv) Evaluate the indicated horse-power when the engine speed is 130 rev/min, assuming double-acting operation. Neglect the *area* of the piston rod.

3.14 A fluid system at a pressure of 60 psia occupies a volume of 0·5 ft³. The system undergoes a fully-resisted process to a final pressure of 20 psia, and during the process the system pressure and volume are related as follows:—

p	psia	60	50	40	30	20
V	ft³	0·50	0·88	1·13	1·34	1·50

Sketch the process on a pressure-volume state diagram and evaluate the work done by the fluid.

3.15 A horizontal cylinder, area 24 in², is fitted with a freely-floating, frictionless leakproof piston, i.e. there is no piston rod.

The left-hand end of the cylinder, which contains 0·15 ft³ of air at atmospheric pressure (15 psia), is connected to a light inextensible balloon; the balloon is flat initially. The right-hand end of the cylinder is connected, via a valve, to a rigid vessel containing nitrogen at high pressure.

The balloon is inflated by slowly admitting nitrogen to the right-hand end of the cylinder. During the inflating process the piston moves a distance of 9 in. and when fully inflated the volume of the balloon is 0·1 ft³. Any changes in the air pressure p are related to the air volume V by $pV = constant$.

(a) Sketch the trace that would be obtained on an indicator connected to the left-hand end of the cylinder.

(b) Evaluate the work done by each of the following systems:—

(i) the atmosphere, (ii) the balloon, (iii) the air, (iv) the piston, (v) the nitrogen.

3.16 A steam main carries steam at a pressure of 200 psia and a temperature of 400°F A rigid vessel containing steam at a pressure of 50 psia is connected, via a valve, to the main. Over a period of time $0 \cdot 1$ lb$_m$ of steam from the main leaks into the vessel thereby raising the pressure of the contents of the vessel to 60 psia.

For the system comprising the steam finally in the vessel, find the magnitude and sign of the work. (The specific volume of steam at a pressure of 200 psia and a temperature of 400°F is $2 \cdot 361$ ft³/lb$_m$.)

3.17 An open tank is filled to the brim with a liquid of density 70 lb$_m$/ft³. A flexible spherical balloon 1 ft in diameter is immersed in the liquid with its centre 5 ft below the free liquid surface. Gas from a storage vessel is used to inflate the balloon thereby causing the tank to overflow.

Assuming that the centre of the balloon remains fixed and neglecting the work done in stretching the balloon fabric, evaluate the work done by the gas in the balloon and the bottle as the balloon diameter increases to 2 ft. (The gravitational acceleration is standard.)

3.18 A motor car petrol engine running at a speed of 3000 rev/min develops a torque of 190 lb$_f$ ft. Calculate the shaft power of the engine in horse-power.

3.19 A ship's propeller is driven by a steam turbine through an 8 : 1 reduction gear. The mean resisting torque imposed by the water on the propeller is 260 ton$_f$ ft and the shaft power delivered by the turbine to the reduction gear is 20,000 h.p.; the turbine speed is 1400 rev/min.

Evaluate (a) the torque developed by the turbine;

        (b) the power delivered to the propeller shaft;

        (c) the net rate of working of the reduction gear in ft lb$_f$/min.

3.20 A fluid, contained in a horizontal cylinder fitted with a frictionless leakproof piston, is continuously agitated by means of a stirrer passing through the cylinder cover. The cylinder diameter is 16 in.

During a stirring process occupying 10 minutes the piston moves slowly outwards a distance of $19 \cdot 5$ inches against the atmosphere ($p_{atm} = 14 \cdot 7$ psia). The net work done by the fluid during the process is 1500 ft lb$_f$.

Given that the speed of the electric motor driving the stirrer is 800 rev/min estimate the torque in the driving shaft and the shaft power output of the motor.

3.21 The electric motor in example 3.20 is supplied with current from a 24-volt accumulator. The current taken is $0 \cdot 35$ amperes. Evaluate the net work done by (a) the accumulator and (b) the motor.

CHAPTER 4

TEMPERATURE

INTRODUCTION

In Chapter 3 work was discussed. In Thermodynamics the only other type of interaction between systems which has to be considered is heat. Heat will be defined in terms of temperature difference and we need to know, therefore, what we mean by temperature.

The sensations of relative hotness and coldness are familiar. Temperature is defined in such a way as to make these sensations quantitative. This is important because, as will be seen later, without temperature differences many types of engine would not run. Usually they run "better" the bigger is the temperature difference available; we need to know what "bigger" means.

We begin by discussing temperature equality and the Zero'th Law of Thermodynamics. Inequality of temperature, temperature measurement and temperature scales are then considered, and the dependence of temperature scales on the nature of the thermometric substance used is emphasised. We then introduce the International Scale of Temperature and make preliminary mention of the absolute thermodynamic temperature scale. Finally the gas thermometer and the Ideal Gas temperature scale are discussed.

Symbols

p Pressure.

p_i Pressure at the ice-point in a gas thermometer.

p_s Pressure at the steam-point in a gas thermometer.

x "Error" in alcohol-in-glass thermometer reading.

y "Error" in mercury-in-glass thermometer reading.

t Temperature.

t_C Centigrade temperature.

t_F Fahrenheit temperature.

t_a Alcohol-in-glass temperature (Fahr.).

t_m Mercury-in-glass temperature (Fahr.).

α A constant.

EQUALITY OF TEMPERATURE

Definition of temperature equality

If two bodies, one hot and one cold, are placed in contact, then after a time the one feels less hot and the other less cold. In addition, changes in their physical properties (e.g. length, electrical resistance) occur. After contact for a long time, however, no further change takes place: equilibrium is established. The bodies are then said to have the *same temperature*.

Definition. Two systems are equal in temperature when no change in any property occurs when they are brought into communication.

The definition must not be reversed; it does *not* imply that "when two systems are equal in temperature, no changes result from their communication". For example, water and sulphuric acid, initially at the same temperature, will rise in temperature when mixed; the change is often violent.

Zero'th* Law of Thermodynamics

If we apply the concept of temperature equality in an experiment involving three systems, S_1, S_2, and S_3 (Fig. 4.1), an experimental law regarding temperature can be established.

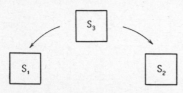

Fig. 4.1   Systems which can be brought into contact.

Suppose that systems S_1 and S_3 are equal in temperature, so that no change occurs in the physical properties of either when they are brought into contact. Similarly let S_2 and S_3 be equal in temperature so that no change occurs when they are brought into contact. Systems S_1 and S_2 are supposed not to react with each other chemically or electrically. If now S_1 and S_2 are placed in contact, it is an *observed fact* that no change occurs in their physical properties. Therefore S_1 and S_2 must be equal in temperature.

This experimental fact is embodied in the *Zero'th Law of Thermodynamics* which may be stated as follows: **Two systems which are equal in temperature to a third system are equal in temperature to each other.**

This law provides the basis for temperature measurement.

INEQUALITY OF TEMPERATURE

We now consider a different case. Suppose that, when system S_3 has contacted S_1 and reached equilibrium with it, and then is subsequently removed and brought into contact with system S_2, observable changes *do* take place in S_3. Then the temperatures of S_1 and S_2 are said to be *unequal*.

To facilitate the recognition of temperature inequality, it is usual to select system S_3 so that changes in its physical characteristics are easily observed. A common choice for S_3 is mercury in a glass capillary tube; changes in the volume of the mercury relative to the glass are readily seen.

In the above experiment therefore, a change in the length of the mercury column, when S_3 contacts S_1 and S_2 in turn, means that S_1 and S_2 have unequal temperatures. Correspondingly an absence of change in the length means that S_1 and S_2 have equal temperatures.

MEASUREMENT OF TEMPERATURE

Temperature scales

Thermometers and fixed points. In order to measure the magnitude of the inequality, a *thermometer* is constructed. For example, the glass tube

---

* i.e. The Law preceding the First Law of Thermodynamics.

containing mercury, which was selected for S_3 above, becomes a mercury-in-glass thermometer if the glass tube is marked so that the position of the mercury meniscus can be noted. To do this the following procedure may be adopted:—

Two standard systems are established, being so chosen that their conditions are easily reproducible. The first, S_{ice}, consists of a mixture of ice and water at a pressure of one atmosphere; the second, S_{steam}, consists of water boiling at a pressure of one atmosphere. The position of the mercury meniscus of S_3 when in contact with S_{ice} is marked by a scratch on the glass and is called the *ice-point;* the position when S_{steam} is contacted is marked and is termed the *steam-point*. The length of glass tube between these two marks, which are usually called the *fixed points*, is then divided into a number of *equal* intervals marked by further scratches.

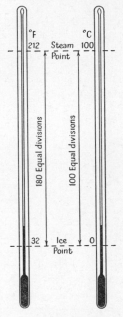

Fig. 4.2 Mercury-in-glass Fahrenheit and Centigrade temperature scales.

Fahrenheit and Centigrade temperature scales. Temperature scales are defined by assigning numbers to the ice-point, the steam-point and to the equal divisions between those points. A mercury-in-glass Fahrenheit temperature scale has the ice-point marked 32 and the steam-point marked 212 with 180 equal sub-divisions. Then if the thermometer (S_3), graduated in this way, is brought into communication with system S_1, whereupon the mercury rises to the sub-division marked 122, we say that the system S_1 has a temperature of 122 degrees Fahrenheit, written 122°F. Another common procedure is to mark the ice-point and the steam-point 0 and 100 respectively, with 100 equal intermediate intervals; this procedure defines the mercury-in-glass Celsius (or Centigrade) scale of temperature.

The two sets of graduations could be marked on the same thermometer. Examination of Fig. 4.2 shows that there is a simple relation between the Centigrade and Fahrenheit temperatures of a given body, t_C and t_F, namely

$$t_C = \tfrac{5}{9}(t_F - 32) \qquad \ldots \quad (4.1)$$

$$t_F = \tfrac{9}{5}t_C + 32 \qquad \ldots \quad (4.2)$$

The fraction $\tfrac{5}{9}$ of course is 100/180.

Thus if S_1 is at 122°F, its temperature on the Centigrade scale is $\tfrac{5}{9}(122 - 32)$ degrees, i.e. $t_C = 50$°C.

Extrapolation beyond the fixed points. So far only temperatures between those of ice and boiling water have been defined. However the uniform graduation of the glass tube can obviously be continued above and below the fixed points: if the mercury rises 50 divisions above the steam-point mark of a Fahrenheit thermometer, its temperature is then defined as 262°F.

This extrapolation is limited in practice by the fact that if the temperature falls too low the mercury freezes (−38°F), while at high temperatures

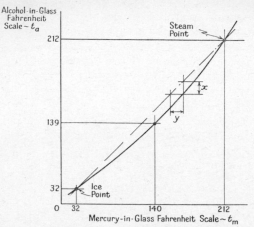

Fig. 4.3   Comparison of temperature scales (not to scale).

glass becomes an unsuitable casing material. This difficulty is met by adopting different fluids and casing materials, or by using an altogether different property from thermal expansion. Thus ethyl alcohol in glass can be used down to temperatures of −166°F, while the electrical resistance of platinum wire can be used as a temperature indicator up to 1800°F. Other examples of properties used to indicate temperature are the potential difference between the junctions of dissimilar metals (the thermocouple) and the change in the colour of materials.

However, the change to new thermometric substances brings with it a difficulty: if an alcohol-in-glass thermometer and a mercury-in-glass thermometer measure the temperature of the same system, they give, in general, different readings, even though they were graduated with reference to the same standard systems. Fig. 4.3 illustrates this by a plot of alcohol-in-glass temperature t_a versus mercury-in-glass temperature t_m (not to scale).

The alcohol-in-glass Fahrenheit scale and the mercury-in-glass Fahrenheit scale must agree at the fixed points by definition, i.e. each has the numbers 32 and 212 assigned to the ice- and steam-points respectively; in general these are the only points at which the two scales agree. We see, for example, in Fig. 4.3 that when t_m is 140°F, t_a is only 139°F.* Which thermometer is correct?

Arbitrariness of temperature scales. All temperature scales are arbitrary. Each step, from the selection of the thermometric substance and the casing

* These are not the true figures.

material to the choice of the number of equal sub-divisions between the fixed points, is unrelated. The answer to the question "Which thermometer is correct?" therefore is that which we shall call right and which wrong is up to us. All that is necessary is that we should make a decision and stick to it. For example, in Fig. 4.3, if the mercury-in-glass thermometer is taken as standard, then x is the "error" in the alcohol-in-glass reading. Similarly y is the "error" in the mercury-in-glass reading if the alcohol-in-glass thermometer is taken as standard. While in principle, therefore, any thermometer may be selected as a standard, it is desirable for everyone to use the same standard. International agreement has been obtained for the following arbitrary scale.

The International Scale of Temperature

The International Temperature Scale is an agreed practical standard scale. It is defined by specifying a number of fixed points (standard systems) together with a method of interpolating between them (standard thermometers). Table 4.1 gives the fixed points* which have been adopted.

TABLE 4.1.

Fixed points	Standard system at 1 atm. pressure	Temperature	
		°C	°F
Ice-point	Ice melting	0·000	32·000
Steam-point	Water boiling	100·000	212·000
Oxygen-point	Oxygen boiling	−182·97	−297·35
Sulphur-point	Sulphur boiling	444·60	832·28
Antimony-point	Antimony melting	630·50	1166·90
Silver-point	Silver melting	960·8	1761·4
Gold-point	Gold melting	1063·0	1945·4

Interpolation between the fixed points is achieved by using prescribed thermometers. Different thermometers are prescribed for different ranges of temperature. For example from the ice-point to 660°C a platinum-resistance thermometer is used. Full details of the International Scale are given in the standard references on temperature measurement at the end of this chapter.

Absolute Scale of Temperature

The numbers assigned to the various fixed points of the International Scale have not been chosen without reason, but in order that this scale should approximate closely to another temperature scale which is discussed in Chapter 12, subsequent to the introduction of the Second Law of Thermodynamics. This, the Absolute Scale of Temperature, has the great merit that it is independent of the properties of particular substances or

* There are secondary fixed points in addition.

systems. This will be discussed in the appropriate place, but it is convenient here to mention a class of thermometers which give readings which are very close to the absolute scale.

The gas thermometer

We have seen that temperature scales are arbitrary, depending on the properties of the substances from which the thermometer is constructed. However, one group of substances, the so-called "permanent gases" (e.g. oxygen, nitrogen, hydrogen) may be used to define temperature scales which are almost identical, irrespective of the gas used; in addition, these scales agree closely with the absolute scale of temperature.

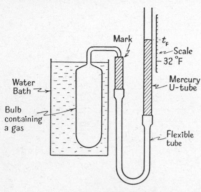

Fig. 4.4 Constant-volume gas thermometer.

A gas thermometer, Fig. 4.4, consists essentially of a vessel (a glass bulb for example) connected to a U-tube containing a liquid, say mercury. A permanent gas is enclosed within the bulb and the connecting tube by the mercury, the other limb of the U-tube being open to the atmosphere. During use, with the bulb in contact with systems at different temperatures, the level of the mercury can be adjusted to keep either the volume or the pressure of the gas constant.

Let us consider its use as a constant-volume gas thermometer. Following the above procedure for setting up a temperature scale we note the difference in the right-hand meniscus level (i.e. the gas pressure) at the two fixed points, keeping the mercury level in the left-hand limb, and so the gas volume, the same in each case. Assigning 32 and 212 to the ice- and steam-points respectively, with 180 equal sub-divisions between them, a gas-thermometer Fahrenheit scale is defined. This scale, linear in gas pressure p, can be expressed as

$$p = p_i[1 + \alpha(t - 32)]$$

where p_i = the gas pressure at the ice-point, 32°F

t = the "gas thermometer" Fahrenheit temperature

α = a constant, equal to $(p_s - p_i)/180p_i$

p_s = the gas pressure at the steam-point, 212°F.

Repeating this procedure, using equal volumes of the *same gas* at progressively lower gas pressures (i.e. smaller masses of gas), a series of values of α is obtained. Plotting these values of α against the pressure at the ice-point p_i in each determination, and extrapolating the curve to zero pressure, a value of α corresponding to zero pressure is determined.

Similarly, using a number of *different gases*, a value of α corresponding to zero pressure is obtained for each gas; the important experimental result is that these values of α are the same *irrespective of the gas used*.

The Ideal Gas Temperature Scale. The behaviour of gases at very low pressures corresponds to that of an Ideal Gas* and the value of α, so obtained by extrapolation, defines the Ideal Gas temperature scale.

Two Ideal Gas Scales are commonly used, namely:

The Ideal Gas Fahrenheit Scale, $t°F$, is given by

$$p = p_i[1 + \tfrac{1}{492}(t_F - 32)] \qquad \ldots \quad (4.3)$$

The Ideal Gas Centigrade Scale, $t°C$, is given by

$$p = p_i[1 + \tfrac{1}{273} t_C] \qquad \ldots \quad (4.4)$$

Corresponding equations, with the same values of α but with volumes replacing pressures, would be obtained using the constant-pressure gas thermometer.

It will be seen in eq. (4.3) and (4.4) that when the pressure p is zero, $t = -460°F$ on the Ideal Gas Fahrenheit scale and $t = -273°C$ on the Ideal Gas Centigrade scale. These temperatures will assume particular significance in Chapter 12.

BIBLIOGRAPHY

British Standard Code: Temperature Measurement. B.S. 1041. British Standards Institution, 1943.

Zemansky, M. W., *Heat and Thermodynamics.* McGraw-Hill, 1943.

CHAPTER 4—PROBLEMS

4.1 (a) The temperature of the coolant (CO_2 gas) at exit from a gas-cooled nuclear reactor is $336°C$. Express the temperature in degrees Fahrenheit.

(b) The temperature of the atmosphere at a height of 20,000 ft above the earth's surface is $5°F$. Express the temperature in degrees Centigrade.

(c) The correct temperature for the storage of apples during overseas shipment is $-1°C$. Express the temperature in degrees Fahrenheit.

(d) The temperature of the steam at entry to the turbines in a generating station is $1050°F$. Express the temperature in degrees Centigrade.

(e) A high-performance gas-turbine jet engine incorporates an axial-flow compressor. During the test-bed running of the engine, atmospheric air enters the compressor at a temperature of $68°F$ and a pressure of 15 psia. After compression the air is delivered to the combustion chambers at a temperature of $554°F$ and a pressure of 115 psia. Express the increase in temperature of the air in degrees Centigrade.

4.2 The temperature t on a thermometric scale is defined in terms of a property P by the relation

$$t = a \ln P + b$$

where a and b are constants.

* Defined in Chapter 14.

The temperatures of the ice-point and the steam-point are assigned the numbers 32 and 212 respectively. Experiment gives values of P of 1·86 and 6·81 at the ice-point and steam-point respectively.

Evaluate the temperature corresponding to a reading of $P = 2·50$ on the thermometer.

4.3 The readings, t_A and t_B, of two Centigrade thermometers, A and B, agree at the ice-point (0°C) and the steam-point (100°C), but elsewhere are related by the equation

$$t_A = l + mt_B + nt_B^2$$

where l, m and n are constants.

When both thermometers are immersed in a well-stirred oil bath, A registers 51°C while B registers 50°C.

(a) Determine the reading on B when A reads 25°C.

(b) Discuss the question: "Which thermometer is correct?".

4.4 A constant-volume gas thermometer containing helium gives readings of gas pressure, p, of 1000 and 1366 mm of mercury at the ice-point and the steam-point respectively.

(a) Express the gas-thermometer Fahrenheit temperature, t_F in terms of the gas pressure p.

(b) The thermometer, when left standing in the atmosphere, registers 1073 mm. Determine the atmospheric temperature.

CHAPTER 5

HEAT

INTRODUCTION

Equality of temperatures has been defined as the relation between two systems which exists when no change results from their communication. This implies that when the temperatures are unequal some change does result. Examples are the change in state of the contents of a kettle when a flame plays on the outside, or of molten iron poured into a cold casting mould.

In this chapter we shall be concerned with the interaction which invariably results from temperature differences. The interaction is given a name, *heat;* a method of measurement is defined; and some space will be devoted to showing what heat is *not*. Distinctions will be made which at first sight appear pedantic but which are, in fact, essential if the later chapters are to be understood, particularly those concerned with the Second Law of Thermodynamics.

Symbols
Q Heat, heat transfer.

DEFINITION AND MEASUREMENT OF HEAT

Definition of heat. Heat is the interaction between systems which occurs by virtue of their temperature difference when they communicate.

Comments. To be useful, the definition must be combined with a statement about how heat is to be recognised and measured. The latter is particularly important because the effect of heat on, say, an engine which it is driving, or on a structure in which it is causing undesirable stresses, is directly dependent on the magnitude of the heat involved.

In defining a measurement procedure for work, it was necessary to define a standard system (1 lb_m of any substance) and a standard process which the system was caused to undergo by the work (change of elevation of 1 ft in a standard gravitational field). The quantity of work causing this process was then given a name, one foot pound, and established as the unit of work.

The same steps are needed in defining a measurement procedure for heat.

The measurement procedure for heat

Standard System:
1 lb_m of water at a temperature of 60°F and a pressure of 1 atm.
Standard process:
The standard system communicates with a second system at a different temperature. A heat interaction takes place which causes the temperature of the standard system to rise to 61°F.

Definition of the heat unit:

The magnitude of the heat interaction in the above experiment is defined as one British Thermal Unit (1 Btu).

Remarks on the measurement of heat

1. It is found experimentally that the second system mentioned above has to be at a temperature higher than 61°F. This is an instance of the general rule that a heat interaction tends to reduce the temperature difference which causes the interaction. Exceptions to this rule exist however, (see p. 73).

2. The magnitude of the heat when a system S_a at high temperature communicates with a system S_b at a lower temperature can be determined as follows. Imagine S_b to be replaced by a number of standard pound masses of water which rise in temperature from 60°F to 61°F as S_a performs the same process as when communicating with S_b. The number of pound masses is the required magnitude in Btu.

Of course it is not necessary actually to carry out this process (often it would be impossible to perform), any more than we fetch the standard metre bar from Paris when we want to measure the pitch of a screw thread. Physicists have devised numerous more practical devices, in effect *sub-standards*, to serve every-day needs; but these are all referred to, i.e. calibrated in terms of, the standard systems and process described.

3. Even this is not the whole story. Firstly there are other standard systems and processes in use. (i) If lb_m of water is used, but is required to undergo a temperature rise of 1°C, a unit of larger size is obtained, namely the Centigrade Heat Unit*, or Chu (1 Chu = $\frac{9}{5}$ Btu). (ii) Use of 1 gramme of water and 1°C leads to the gramme-calorie, or cal (1 cal = $\frac{1}{252}$ Btu). (iii) The initial temperature of the standard system may also be varied, e.g. 59·5°F or 14·5°C. These variations of practice between English-speaking and European engineers, and between engineers and physicists, are tiresome but not difficult to comprehend.

4. As a second complication it has been discovered that there is a quantitative relation between heat and work. This will be discussed fully in Chapter 6 on the First Law of Thermodynamics. The relation makes it possible to do away with the heat standard altogether and refer everything to that of work (see p. 80).

5. Since the first four significant figures of a heat quantity in Btu are not affected by which standard is being used, the engineer seldom has to inquire about how the particular Btu he is working with is defined. The reader is advised merely to note the above remarks and pass on.

THE DIRECTION OF HEAT: "HEAT TRANSFER"

In defining the unit of heat a standard process involving a temperature rise of 1 lb_m of water was described. It is found experimentally that when, as a result of a heat interaction, the temperature of 1 lb_m of water *falls*

* Sometimes called the Pound Calorie (lb cal).

from 61°F to 60°F, the magnitude of the heat interaction is again 1 Btu.*
In order to distinguish these two cases, a directional language is used with
a corresponding algebraic sign convention.

Directional language. If in a heat interaction between two systems, S_a
and S_b, system S_a is at the higher temperature, we say that a "heat
transfer" has taken place *from* S_a *to* S_b. Thus the
standard process, in which 1 lb_m of water rises in temperature from 60°F to 61°F, may be described as a
transfer of 1 Btu of heat *to* the water and *from* the
second system which communicates with it; the
process in which the 1 lb_m of water falls from 61°F to
60°F on the other hand is described as a heat transfer
from the water *to* the second system.

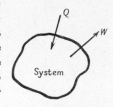

Fig. 5.1. Sign con-
vention for heat
and work.

The words "transfer", "to", and "from" are metaphorical. They are universally used because of their
convenience, but it should be clearly understood
that there is not really any substance, "hotness", which is being transferred in the sense in which water can be poured from a jug into a glass.
The "transfer" metaphor derives historically from the long-discredited
caloric theory (see p. 73 below).

Algebraic sign convention. When a heat interaction appears in an equation,
it is given the symbol Q and is associated with one of the two systems
taking part in the interaction. Usually the specified system is called "*the*
system" while the other system is called "the surroundings". By convention Q is positive when the surroundings have the higher temperature, and
negative when the system temperature is the higher. This means that
heat transfer to the system is positive while heat transfer from the system
is negative.

It will be noted that this convention is opposite to that for work, as is
shown in Fig. 5.1 where the arrows express symbolically the "transfer"
metaphor.

A consequence of the convention is that if, in a given interaction, the
heat for *the* system is positive, that for the surroundings is negative.

Finally it may be mentioned that the directional language and the sign
convention may appear simultaneously in phrases such as "the heat transfer
to the system was negative", signifying that the system temperature
exceeded that of its surroundings and so that the direction of heat transfer
was from the system to its surroundings.

HOW HEAT TRANSFER OCCURS

It has been stated above that two systems of different temperature
must "communicate" if a heat interaction is to occur. We now briefly
consider ways in which the communication may be effected.

Conduction. The simplest form of communication is by contact between
the systems, either directly or across a separating layer. Then heat

* End note 3.

conduction occurs at a rate (in Btu/ft^2 h) that is proportional to the existing temperature gradient (in °F/ft). The proportionality constant is known as the *thermal conductivity;* it depends on the material, being large for metals, smaller for non-metallic solids, and smallest of all for gases.

Thermal insulation. In practice two systems are nearly always in communication by conduction through the intervening material, so that heat transfer occurs constantly. However, the rate of transfer can be reduced to negligible proportions by separating the systems by relatively thick layers of poorly-conducting materials: the so-called *thermal insulators* or lagging materials. These are usually non-metallic solids containing pores filled with air, e.g. glass wool.

Convection. If the conducting medium is a fluid in motion, the mode of heat transfer is called *convection.*

The mechanism is as follows: heat transfer from a hot body to the particles of fluid in contact with it occurs by *conduction* causing the fluid temperature to rise. The warmed fluid, being in motion, subsequently comes into contact with a body at a temperature lower than that of the fluid and heat transfer occurs by conduction from the fluid to the cold body.

Radiation. Even when all intervening matter between systems is removed, the systems are still in thermal communication, for electromagnetic radiation occurs between their surfaces. Radiative heat transfer from the sun to the earth is a familiar example. The rate of radiative heat transfer increases rapidly with the temperature of the surfaces. It is often negligibly small at room temperature.

Adiabatic processes. It is clear from the above that systems are always in communication and that no process is entirely without heat. Nevertheless the magnitude of the heat transfer may be negligibly small if the systems are separated by insulators, if the separation distance is large, or if the period of time under consideration is small. Idealising this situation, we therefore find it useful to imagine processes in which the heat is zero. These processes are termed *adiabatic.* Similarly, a system which is isolated from its surroundings as regards heat transfer is called an *adiabatic system.*

"Adiabatic" is sometimes used to denote a type of zero-heat process which we shall later learn to call "reversible adiabatic" (Chapter 11). This restriction of meaning is undesirable: in the present book "adiabatic" means neither more nor less than "$Q = 0$".

"Heat Transfer" as a branch of Engineering Science. The design of equipment for the power-producing, process and other industries is often dominated by the necessities of effecting heat interactions. The design procedures form a separate subject known as "heat transfer", textbooks on which are mentioned at the end of this Chapter. "Heat transfer" differs from thermodynamics in being concerned with the *rate* at which things happen.

WHAT HEAT IS NOT

By defining heat as above, a number of meanings attaching to its use in common speech and elsewhere are excluded. Some of these will now be brought to light to avoid later confusion.

1. It used to be thought that heat was a fluid which passed from hot bodies to cold. This fluid was given the name "caloric" and attempts were made to weigh and isolate it. Such phenomena as the temperature rise which occurs in metal-turning were explained as the escape of the caloric as the material became sub-divided. The caloric theory was disproved by Rumford in 1798 in a famous experiment: by boring a cannon with a blunt cutting-tool, he showed that the effects of heat, namely the rise in the temperature of the water

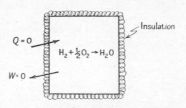

Fig. 5.2 Adiabatic, constant-volume combustion.

used to cool the tool, could be produced indefinitely without cutting (subdividing) any metal at all. Many an apprentice mechanic must wonder why it was so long before this fact was observed.

Heat, therefore, is not a conserved fluid and it is consequently inconsistent with thermodynamic usage to speak of "the heat in the steam", "the heat contained in the exhaust gases", etc. More precisely, *heat is not a property* of a system.

All that remains of the caloric theory is its metaphorical use in the terms "heat transfer to" and "heat transfer from", denoting the sign of a heat interaction.

2. Heat is not "that which inevitably causes a temperature rise". To demonstrate this it suffices to consider a system comprising ice and water. If a heat transfer to the system occurs, for example, from a container at higher temperature, it is well known that the temperature of the system does not rise, at least until all the ice has melted. In exceptional circumstances, heat transfer to a system causes a fall in temperature, for example if the system is a gas flowing in a straight pipe at a velocity just below that of sound.

3. Heat is not "that which is always present when a temperature rise occurs". To demonstrate this it may be noted that work can cause a temperature rise, as in the cannon-boring experiment just mentioned. Since the boring tool and the cannon will, in general, have the same temperature, the definition of heat makes it clear that heat is absent from this process.

As another example, consider a well-lagged rigid vessel containing hydrogen and oxygen, Fig. 5.2. Ignition of the contents of the vessel results in the formation of H_2O accompanied by a temperature rise. However, since the vessel is lagged, there can be no heat transfer from it, even though the temperature of the H_2O exceeds that of the surroundings; so $Q = 0$. A similar process occurs in the cylinder of a petrol engine. Ignition of the petrol-air mixture in the cylinder initiates a reaction in

6

which the fuel and air combine chemically to produce gases of higher temperature. As this occurs very quickly, whereas heat transfer takes time, heat transfer cannot be held responsible for the temperature rise. Indeed if heat transfer did occur, it would be *from* the system comprising the high temperature gases and *to* the water-cooled combustion-chamber walls. As another example of the lack of inevitable connection between a temperature change and a heat interaction, the adiabatic solution of common salt in water may be evidenced; this causes a fall in temperature.

Final remarks about heat. The most important point about heat, as defined above, is that it only has meaning when referred to the boundary of a system. In this it is similar to work. Heat is also similar to work in that it is transient: it exists during the interaction only. Heat is a happening, not a substance. It may be likened in this respect to speech between two persons: though the effects may remain for ever, the communication comes to an end with the last word.

BIBLIOGRAPHY

Eckert, E. R. G., *Introduction to the Transfer of Heat and Mass.* McGraw-Hill, 1950.

Jakob, M. and Hawkins, G. A., *Elements of Heat Transfer.* Wiley & Sons and Chapman & Hall, 3rd Edition, 1957.

McAdams, W. H., *Heat Transmission.* McGraw-Hill, 3rd Edition, 1954.

Fishenden, M. and Saunders, O. A., *Introduction to Heat Transfer.* Clarendon Press, Oxford, 1950.

CHAPTER 5—PROBLEMS

5.1 (*a*) Express one Centigrade heat unit (Chu) in British thermal units (Btu).

(*b*) Express one British thermal unit in calories.

5.2 2 lb_m of water at a temperature of 64°F are poured into an insulated copper vessel which initially is at a temperature of 60°F. When the temperatures have equalised, the water is at a temperature of 63·2°F. Determine the magnitude and sign of the heat transfer for each of the following systems:—

(i) the vessel; (ii) the water; (iii) the vessel plus the water.

5.3 The insulated copper vessel of problem 5.2 contains 10 lb_m of water at a temperature of 60°F. A steel bar, of mass 0·2 lb_m, at a temperature of 1500°F, is suddenly dropped into the water. When the temperatures have equalised, the temperature of the water is 63·2°F. Determine the magnitude and sign of the heat transfer for each of the following systems:

(i) the water; (ii) the vessel; (iii) the steel bar; (iv) the vessel and its contents.

5.4 The insulated copper vessel of problem 5.2 contains a quantity of oil at a temperature of 60°F. A steel bar, of mass 0·2 lb_m, at a temperature of 1500°F is suddenly dropped into the oil. When the temperatures have equalised the temperature of the oil is 63·2°F. Determine the magnitude and sign of the heat transfer for each of the following systems:—

(i) the vessel; (ii) the steel bar; (iii) the oil; (iv) the vessel and its contents.

5.5 A copper block, with its top and sides insulated, slides slowly down a rough, non-conducting inclined plane. The weight of the block is 1 lb_f and it falls a vertical distance of 1 ft. Evaluate the heat transfer for the system comprising the block.

5.6 State whether the heat transfer, Q, and the work, W, are $+$, $-$, or 0 in each of the following processes. The systems to be considered are printed in italics.

(a) A rigid steel vessel containing *steam* at a temperature of 300°F is left standing in the atmosphere which is at a temperature of 80°F.

(b) 0·1 lb$_m$ of *gas* contained in an insulated cylinder expands as the piston moves slowly outwards.

(c) A *mixture of ice and water* is contained in a vertical cylinder closed at the top by a piston; the upper surface of the piston is exposed to the atmosphere. The piston is held stationary while a flame, applied to the base of the cylinder, causes some of the ice to melt.

(d) As under (c), but the piston is allowed to move so as to keep the mixture pressure constant.

(e) A *mixture of ice and water* is contained in an insulated vertical cylinder closed at the top by a non-conducting piston; the upper surface is exposed to the atmosphere. The piston is held stationary while the mixture is stirred by means of a paddle-wheel protruding through the cylinder wall. As a result some of the ice melts.

(f) As under (e), but the piston is allowed to move so as to keep the mixture pressure constant.

(g) A rigid vessel containing *ammonia gas* is connected through a valve to an evacuated rigid vessel. The vessels, the valve and the connecting pipe are well insulated. The valve is opened and after a time, conditions through the two vessels become uniform.

(h) *One pound of air* flows adiabatically from the atmosphere into a previously evacuated bottle.

5.7 Evaluate the magnitudes and signs of the heat transfer and of the work in the following processes. The system to be considered is printed in italics.

(a) A well-insulated, sealed vessel contains one gramme of fuel-oil and some oxygen gas. The oil ignites, causing a rise in the temperature of the *vessel and its contents*.

(b) A *sealed calorimeter* containing powdered coal and oxygen gas is immersed in a tank containing 2 lb$_m$ of water. In the first half-minute after ignition of the coal, the water rises in temperature 0·05°F.

5.8 A rigid insulated vessel is divided into two parts by a diaphragm. One part of the vessel contains sulphuric acid at a temperature of 60°F and the other part contains water at a temperature of 60°F. The diaphragm is removed so allowing the two fluids to mix; the pressure and temperature of the contents rise and after a time conditions are uniform throughout the vessel.

(a) Considering the contents of the vessel as the system, state whether the heat transfer Q and the work W are $+$, $-$, or 0.

(b) The insulation is subsequently removed, allowing the temperature of the contents to fall to that of the atmosphere, 60°F. State whether Q and W are $+$, $-$, or 0 for this process.

(c) State whether Q and W are $+$, $-$, or 0 for the combined processes (a) and (b).

CHAPTER 6

THE FIRST LAW OF THERMODYNAMICS

INTRODUCTION

Now that heat has been defined, it is useful to recall that heat interactions between systems are essential processes in many forms of prime mover. To take the steam power plant as an example, unless the boiler feed-water is brought into communication with a hotter substance, usually the reaction products of some fuel, no steam will be formed and the plant will not run: the production of *work* is conditional on the transfer of *heat* to the steam.

This example has great economic importance, for fuel is often expensive and in short supply, while man's appetite for power is almost insatiable. We must therefore establish what quantitative connexions exist between the "raw material" and the "end-product" of the power-plant engineer, i.e. between heat and work. One connexion is suggested by Rumford's cannon-boring experiment, in which, it will be recalled, work is transferred continuously to the (system comprising) boring-tool and cannon, while heat is transferred continuously to the cooling water; meanwhile the cannon and boring tool remain unchanged. This is a case of work being "converted into" heat.

In the present chapter the "rate of exchange" between heat and work will be shown to be a constant and universal one, a fact that is embodied in the First Law of Thermodynamics. In formulating and discussing this law the concepts of *cyclic process* and *energy* will be introduced, while new light will be thrown on what is meant by a property.

Symbols

E Energy of a system.

e Specific energy of a system.

J Mechanical Equivalent of Heat.

Q Heat transfer to a system.

W Work done by a system.

Δ Increase in (= Final value − Initial value).

$\sum_{\text{cycle}}$ Algebraic summation around a cycle.

$\oint$ Integral around a cycle, cyclic integral.

Subscripts

1,2 Initial, final state of a system.

THE RATE OF EXCHANGE BETWEEN HEAT AND WORK

There is no *logical* relation between heat and work, so that if a relation does exist it must be found in an *experimental* investigation. Such a study was carried out between 1840 and 1849 by J. P. Joule, to whom credit for discovering the First Law of Thermodynamics is due.* His experiments were of two types, which will now be described.

* R. Mayer is stated to have formulated the Law in 1840.

Experimental evidence on the equivalence of heat and work

Experiments using heat and work to obtain equal effects

We have already seen that a heat transfer can bring about a temperature rise in one of the participating systems. For example, 1 Btu of heat will cause 1 lb_m of water to rise from 60°F to 61°F. (Fig. 6.1a).

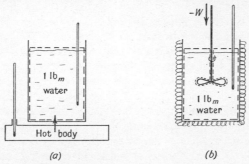

(a)   *(b)*

Fig. 6.1   Heat and work transfer to systems to produce equal effects within them.

But a precisely similar change in the water can be brought about without any heat transfer at all: for example a shaft carrying a paddle-wheel can project into the water; its continued rotation causes the water temperature to rise steadily even though the container is thermally insulated. Fig. 6.1b illustrates this case. The shaft may be supposed uniform in temperature so that no heat interaction occurs. The change in the state of the system (the water) has therefore been brought about by the stirring work.

Since heat and work can bring about equal effects, measurements of the heat and work quantities which separately cause a given change in a system should provide interesting information. Joule carried out many experiments of this type with various systems and various sorts of work. He established that, within the limits of accuracy of his experiments, the number of work units required to accomplish a given effect, divided by the number of heat units required to bring about the same effect, was equal to a constant.

Symbolically we write this experimental result as

$$\frac{W}{Q} = a \ constant \qquad \qquad \ldots \ (6.1)$$

where W and Q are respectively the work and the heat transfer which cause the same change of state in identical systems.

The constant in eq. (6.1), which is known as "The Mechanical Equivalent of Heat" and is given the symbol J, has the value 778, if the work is measured in ft lb_f and the heat in Btu.* We write this as

$$J = 778 \ ft \ lb_f/Btu \qquad \qquad \ldots \ (6.1)$$

---

* This is the value we shall use in the present book. A more accurate one is 778·16. Joule, in his early experiments, decided that 773·4 was the right value.

Experiments involving cyclic processes. In experiments of the type just mentioned, the initial and final states of the system are different. These experiments, together with what we know about heat and work, suffice as a basis for the First Law. The modern formulation of this law can be introduced more smoothly however by considering a second type of experiment, also carried out by Joule, in which heat and work are caused to *undo* each other's effects rather than to emulate them. To make this idea precise, a new definition is required:—

A process is cyclic if the initial and final states of the system executing the process are identical, i.e. if all system properties have the same values at the end of the process as at the beginning.

As an example simultaneously of a cyclic process and of Joule's second type of experiment, consider Fig. 6.1 once more. Let the stirring process of Fig. 6.1b be carried out first, resulting in a rise in water temperature. Then let the stirring be stopped, and the water container be brought into contact with another body as shown in Fig. 6.1a. This time the body is chosen to be at lower temperature than the water, so that the heat transfer is *from* the water, not *to* it; as a result the water temperature falls.

Suppose that, as soon as the water temperature has fallen to the value obtaining before stirring began, the communication between the container and the cold body is broken. Then the water is in exactly the same state at the end as at the beginning of the process; this may be established by measuring all conceivable properties of the water in the two cases. The stirring and cooling of the water have combined to form a cyclic process.

Many such cyclic experiments have been carried out, by Joule and later workers. Both the nature of the system and the nature of the process have been varied. Thus the system may comprise a different fluid; chemical reaction may occur; a mechanism may be incorporated; the heat and work transfers may take place in several stages of unequal amount and direction; shear work, displacement work and electrical work may all take part. Yet in each cyclic experiment, when all the work transfers and all the heat transfers are separately added, it is found that the first sum is equal to a constant times the second, this constant being J, the Mechanical Equivalent of Heat.

J has the same value, as might be expected, in these experiments as in those of the first type, namely 778 ft lb$_f$/Btu. J does vary, however, with the units used. Thus J is 1400 in ft lb$_f$/Chu, and 4·2 in joules/cal.

The First Law of Thermodynamics

Although the number of systems and processes which have been investigated in the way described has obviously not exhausted all possibilities, the uniformity of the outcome of the experiments which have been performed has led to eq. (6.2) being regarded as universally true. We use it as our statement of the *First Law of Thermodynamics* which, for formality's sake, will also be stated in words, as:—

When a system executes a cyclic process, the algebraic sum of the work transfers is proportional to the algebraic sum of the heat transfers.

Symbolically, this experimental result is written

$$\oint dW = J \oint dQ$$

or
$$J \oint dQ - \oint dW = 0 \qquad \dots \quad (6.2)$$

Here dQ and dW represent infinitesimal elements of heat and work transfer respectively, with the conventional signs, while $\oint$ stands for adding up all the elements occurring in the cyclic process. $\oint$ is known as the "cyclic integral" or "integral around the cycle".

EXAMPLE

Problem. In a cyclic process the heat transfers are $+10$ Btu, -24 Btu, -3 Btu and $+31$ Btu. What is the net work for this cyclic process?

Solution. When, as in this case, the heat and the work transfers occur in finite steps, the integral signs are replaced by summations. So eq. (6.2) becomes

$$\sum_{\text{cycle}} W = J \sum_{\text{cycle}} Q$$

In this example $\sum_{\text{cycle}} Q$ stands for the sum $(10 - 24 - 3 + 31)$ Btu.

$\therefore$
$$\sum_{\text{cycle}} Q = 14 \text{ Btu.}$$

Hence
$$\sum_{\text{cycle}} W = J \times 14 \text{ Btu}$$
$$= 778 \text{ ft lb}_f/\text{Btu} \times 14 \text{ Btu}$$
$$= 10,880 \text{ ft lb}_f$$

$\therefore$ Net work $= 10,880$ ft lb$_f$ $\qquad \dots$ *Answer*

Discussion of the First Law

Engineering implication. An immediate consequence of the First Law is that a power plant relying on heat transfer, from fuel reaction products for example, cannot produce more than 778 ft lb$_f$ of work for every Btu of heat transferred. As will be seen below, the combustion of a given mass of fuel under specified conditions allows a definite amount of heat to be transferred to its surroundings. With this quantity known, the lowest fuel consumption per bhp-h can be calculated.

That no more than 778 ft lb$_f$ of work can be obtained for each Btu of heat may be disappointing, but the First Law also suggests that at least this amount of work should be forthcoming. In Chapter 12 it will be shown that, for a reason unconnected with the First Law, often no more than 200 to 300 ft lb$_f$ of work are obtainable for each Btu of heat *transferred from the fuel reaction products.*

The ft lb$_f$ of heat and the Btu of work. The fixed rate of exchange between heat and work enables heat quantities to be expressed in work units, e.g. ft lb$_f$ or ergs, while work quantities can be expressed in, for example, Btu or Chu, just as the price of an article can be expressed in dollars or pounds sterling regardless of whether it is a product of the United Kingdom or the United States. This does not mean of course that heat and work are the same thing, any more than the dollar is the same, in all its capabilities, as its nominal equivalent in sterling.

When both heat and work quantities occur in the same calculation, it is convenient to use the same unit for both. This means that J can be dropped from the equation. The First Law of Thermodynamics, for example, now becomes

$$\oint dQ - \oint dW = 0$$

or
$$\oint (dQ - dW) = 0 \qquad \ldots \quad (6.3)$$

in which it is understood that *both* Q and W are expressed in ft lb$_f$, or Btu or other appropriate unit.

Abandoning the "heat standard". In Chapters 3 and 5, independent procedures for measuring work and heat quantities were described. The determination of J was then shown to be an experimental matter. As experiments of increasing accuracy have been performed, the actual value ascribed to J has altered continually, the changes in recent years being of course only to the last one or two significant figures. In this situation it is natural to suggest that the constant re-adjustment of J, and of calculations involving it, should be stopped once and for all by abandoning either the heat or the work standard and *defining J* to have a definite value.

This has in fact been done. Since work measurements are easier to make than those of heat, the definition of the Btu in terms of 1 lb$_m$ of water raised from 60°F to 61°F has been abandoned. Instead we define 1 Btu as the equivalent in heat of 778·16 ft lb$_f$ of work, where the latter unit is defined in terms of the "mechanical" standards.

This change in standardisation procedure, which is a common device of metrologists, should not be regarded as diminishing the status of the heat unit in any way. For most engineering purposes it suffices to imagine the Btu as still defined in terms of water.

Concluding remark on equation (6.2). The First Law of Thermodynamics, as expressed by eq. (6.2), relates the boundary interactions occurring when a system executes a cycle. It applies whatever the nature of the system or its interactions with its surroundings, but one restriction remains: the process must be cyclic. Most processes that the thermodynamicist must deal with are not cyclic; a way must therefore be found of re-formulating the First Law so that it can be brought to bear on non-cyclic processes also. This is done in the next section by the introduction of a new concept: energy. The re-formulation has the effect of relating the interactions *at* the boundary to changes *within* the system.

ENERGY

Properties of properties

The concept "property" was defined on p. 43 as "any observable characteristic of a system". It is now desirable to point out three logical consequences of this definition, namely:—

(i) The change in the value of a property of a system depends only on the end-states of the process and not on the path of the process.

(ii) If a magnitude related to a system changes during a process by an amount that depends only on the end-states and not on the path of a process, that magnitude is a property of the system.

(iii) In a cyclic process the net change in each property of a system is zero.

Explanatory examples. The truth of these statements is best perceived by way of examples:—

The *latitude* and *longitude* of a ship on the ocean are *properties*, for they may be ascribed definite values as a result of observations of the ship at a given moment. When the ship moves to a new position, the changes in the latitude and longitude can be calculated from knowledge of the new and the old positions alone: there is no need to know where the ship went to in between. In particular, if the ship leaves port for a voyage *and then returns* to that port, the changes in latitude and longitude are zero: *properties suffer no net change in a cyclic process.*

The *distance travelled* by the ship is *not a property*. It can not be determined from mere observation of the ship's position at any one time, nor can it be calculated given only the initial and final position. The distance travelled is not zero merely because the ship returns from a round trip to the same berth from which it set out.

The *balance* in a bank account is a *property* because it has a definite value at any one time. Knowing the values of the balance at the beginning and end of a year, the net effect of the deposits and withdrawals can be calculated. What can not be determined from the two end-states however, is whether a decrease in the balance took place as a result of a single large withdrawal, as a result of many small withdrawals, or as a result of larger withdrawals inadequately compensated by a few deposits of money into the account. The *deposits* and *withdrawals* therefore are *not properties*. It is the balance, which is the sum of the deposits minus the sum of the withdrawals, which is the property. If, by careful budgetting, the balance at the end of the year is identical with that at the beginning, this does not mean that no deposits or withdrawals have taken place, but merely that the difference between them is zero: a cyclic process has been performed.

Definition of energy

The "properties of properties" have been discussed at some length as an introduction to the demonstration that the First Law implies the existence of a property which will be called *energy*. Although students of mechanics will already have some notion of energy, thermodynamicists require an extended definition. Moreover the pattern of argument proving the existence of a property from a statement about cyclic processes will be repeated in Chapter 13 in connexion with entropy.

First energy will be defined:—

The increase of energy of a system during a change of state is numerically equal to the heat transfer during the process minus the work transfer during the process.

In symbols this is written as

$$E_2 - E_1 \equiv Q - W \qquad \ldots \quad (6.4)$$

where E_2 and E_1 are the energies of the system in the final state 2 and the initial state 1 respectively.

Remarks on the definition of energy

1. Only *changes* of energy have been defined. This merely means that, like longitude for example, energy has to be measured with respect to some arbitrary base.

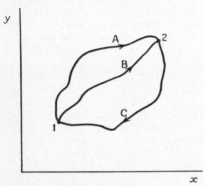

2. In order that the numerical difference between the heat and the work should be physically meaningful, Q and W must both be measured in the same units, e.g. ft lb$_f$ or Btu. These same units must correspondingly be attributed to E.

3. Often the increase in a magnitude is symbolised by a delta, Δ. In this notation, eq. (6.4) is written

$$\Delta E \equiv Q - W \quad \ldots \quad (6.5)$$

Fig. 6.2 Paths of cyclic processes passing through two common state-points.

4. The energy of a system of unit mass, sometimes called the *specific energy*, will be given the lower-case symbol e.

5. So far we have supposed the whole process between states 1 and 2 to be specified. We now show by reference to the First Law that only the end-states 1 and 2 need be specified, and so that E is a property.

Proof that energy is a property

Fig. 6.2 is a diagram with arbitrary properties of a system, x and y, as abscissa and ordinate. (For definiteness, x and y might be thought of as volume and pressure respectively.) The points marked 1 and 2 represent two states of the system.

Consider a cyclic process executed by the system, starting from state 1, proceeding to state 2 along the path marked A on Fig. 6.2, and returning to state 1 along the path C. From the First Law we can write

$$\oint (dQ - dW) = \int_{1 \atop A}^{2} (dQ - dW) + \int_{2 \atop C}^{1} (dQ - dW) = 0 \ \ldots \quad (6.6)$$

wherein the summation around the cyclic process has been split into its component parts. The two integrals on the right hand side of eq. (6.6) represent, respectively, the summation of the heat and work transfers during the change of state from 1 to 2 along path A and the summation from 2 to 1 along path C.

Now consider a second cyclic process differing from the first only in that the outward path is the different one marked B on Fig. 6.2. Applying the First Law to this cyclic process, we obtain

$$\int_{1 \atop B}^{2} (dQ - dW) + \int_{2 \atop C}^{1} (dQ - dW) = 0 \qquad \ldots \quad (6.7)$$

Combining eq. (6.6) and eq. (6.7) we obtain

$$\int_{1 \atop A}^{2} (dQ - dW) = \int_{1 \atop B}^{2} (dQ - dW) \qquad \ldots \quad (6.8)$$

signifying that the integral of $(dQ - dW)$ from state 1 to state 2 is the same for path A as for path B.

But all that has been specified about paths A and B is that they are different. It follows that

$$\int_{1}^{2} (dQ - dW) \text{ has the same value for } \textit{any} \text{ path between 1 and 2} \ldots \quad (6.9)$$

If we now write

$$\int_{1}^{2} dQ = Q, \text{ the net heat in a change from state 1 to state 2} \quad \ldots \quad (6.10)$$

and

$$\int_{1}^{2} dW = W, \text{ the net work in the same change} \qquad \ldots \quad (6.11)$$

statement (6.9) becomes:

$Q - W$ has the same value for *any* path between 1 and 2.

But from the definition of energy, eq. (6.4),

$$Q - W \equiv E_2 - E_1$$

Therefore

$E_2 - E_1$ has the same value for *any* path between 1 and 2 $\ldots$ (6.12)

This means that the value of $E_2 - E_1$ depends only on the end-states. From what has been said above of the "properties of properties" (consequence (ii) p. 81), it follows that *energy E is a property.*

Remarks about energy, E

Relation to the "energy" concept of mechanics. In mechanics, energy is defined as "the capacity for doing work" of a system. This "mechanical energy", as we may call it, is not the same thing as the energy of thermodynamics, although the two concepts have features in common. An example will illustrate similarities and differences.

The ball in the bowl: Fig. 6.3 shows a system comprising a hemispherical bowl and a steel ball. Suppose that initially the ball is at rest at the lowest point of the bowl, and that then it is raised by an external force (for example a hand) until it is at rest near the rim. The work done by the system is negative in this process; heat transfer being absent, it follows from eq. (6.4) that $E_2 - E_1$ is positive, i.e. the energy of the system increases. The "mechanical energy" has also increased, and indeed by the same amount, for the ball is higher than it was.

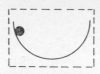

Fig. 6.3 Bowl containing a steel ball.

Now suppose that the ball is released so that it rolls backwards and forwards within the bowl. Since neither heat nor work crosses the boundary of the system during the oscillations it is seen from eq. (6.4) that there can be no change of energy. If friction may be ignored, this is true also of the "mechanical energy"; for, regarding only the ball (the bowl does not change), the loss of gravitational potential energy which the ball suffers in reaching the bottom of the bowl is exactly counteracted by its increase in kinetic energy: the sum of the two energy terms remains constant.

If friction is present on the other hand, the height reached by the ball in each successive oscillation is reduced; the maximum velocity attained is also lower at each oscillation. Finally the ball comes to rest again in the bottom of the bowl. Since still no heat or work have crossed the system boundary, the energy of the system has the same value as immediately after the ball was first raised. The "mechanical energy" however has *decreased* to the value prevailing *before* the ball was first raised. In mechanics it is said that "the energy has been dissipated".

An alternative phrase used in mechanics to describe the events of the last paragraph is: "the energy has been converted into heat". This phrase is not in accordance with thermodynamic usage of the word "heat"; for although the ball and the bowl no doubt have a higher temperature than in the beginning, this has not been accomplished by heat transfer between the system and its surroundings.

A legitimate form of the above phrase is: "the mechanical energy has been transformed into that mode of energy which can be directly altered by heat transfer". This latter mode of energy is termed internal energy* (see p. 97).

Summarising, energy is seen to include the energy which is defined in mechanics, but to be more general than it. For example, it covers internal energy also. Processes may occur in which the energy of the system remains constant, but transformations occur from one form of mechanical energy to another and from mechanical to internal energy.

---

* Many students find it helpful to retain a "mechanical" picture of this mode of energy by associating it with the energies of translation, rotation, and intermolecular attraction of the microscopic structure of the system. This interpretation is substantially correct, but it is not necessary. Eq. (6.4) tells the thermodynamicist all he needs to know about energy.

It may be mentioned that the "capacity-for-doing-work" idea plays an important part in more advanced thermodynamic texts than the present. It forms the core of the concept of "availability".

The Law of Conservation of Energy. Eq. (6.4) and eq. (6.5) may be regarded as alternative statements of the First Law of Thermodynamics, if coupled with the statement that E is a property. A particular case of some interest is that of a system for which both heat and work interactions are zero. We obtain

$$Q = 0, \quad W = 0: \quad \Delta E = 0 \qquad \ldots \quad (6.13)$$

This equation represents a corollary of the First Law which is known as the *Law of Conservation of Energy.* In words, this is:—

The energy of a system remains constant if the system is isolated from its surroundings as regards heat and work.

This statement is of course less general than the First Law, since it does not state how the energy changes when Q and W are not zero.

Other modes of energy. Gravitational potential energy, kinetic energy, and internal energy have all been mentioned above (p. 84) as modes of energy. The first two will be dealt with quantitatively in Chapter 8, while the third, internal energy, which can be altered by heat transfer alone, will be given a special symbol and treated in Chapter 7, page 97. In this section we mention qualitatively some of the other modes of energy.

A system may change its chemical state, as for example when petrol and air react so as to form carbon dioxide, water vapour and other combustion products. Often, if the system is isolated from its surroundings as regards heat and work, the temperature of the system changes greatly as a result of such a chemical reaction process. In the petrol-air case the temperature increases. It is sometimes helpful to regard such processes, which are at constant energy (see eq. (6.13)), as involving a transformation of "chemical energy" into energy.

A compressed spring or elastic structure may be regarded as having part of its energy in the form of "strain energy". A related form of energy is that associated with the phenomenon of capillarity, or surface tension; systems exhibiting this phenomenon have part of their energy in the form of "surface energy".

A system comprising electrically charged elements may be considered, by reason of the attractions and repulsions existing between these elements, to have part of its energy in the form of "electrical energy". "Magnetic energy" correspondingly is present if the system comprises magnetic poles. If both magnetic and electric effects are simultaneously present, their interactions also produce a contribution to the energy of the system.

The above remarks are of interpretative value only. When any one of the above modes of energy is to be used in a calculation, strict definition and derivation in terms of the First Law are necessary (see page 329 for example). The important point is that the First Law and the energy concept are entirely general, and cover any sort of process that may be met with.

SOME EXAMPLES INVOLVING ENERGY

Block-and-plane problems

Although somewhat academic, the following two problems bring out important features of heat, work and energy.

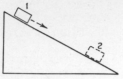

Fig. 6.4 Blocksliding down a rough inclined plane.

1. *Non-conducting block; conducting plane.*

Fig. 6.4 shows a rough inclined plane on the sloping face of which stands a rectangular block. The block is a poor conductor of heat while the plane is a good one; for example the block might be of wood and the plane of copper.

Problem. The block slides slowly down the plane, which rises in temperature as a result. State whether the heat, work and increase in energy are positive, negative, or zero, for each of the following systems: (*a*) the block, (*b*) the plane, (*c*) the block and the plane.

Answer. The solution is contained in the following table:—

System	Q	W	ΔE
(*a*) Block	0	+ve	−ve
(*b*) Plane	0	−ve	+ve
(*c*) Block + plane	0	0	0

Comments. System (a). $Q = 0$ because the system is a non-conductor of heat; the block acts as a thermal insulator to the surface of the plane with which it is in contact. $W = +$ve because, although the actual external effect is the rise in temperature of the plane, the block could have carried out the *same process* and had as its sole effect the raising of a weight (for example if the plane had been lubricated and the block connected to a suitable pulley mechanism).

Since $Q - W$ is thus negative, $\Delta E = -$ve follows by definition, eq. (6.5). The mode of energy which has suffered a decrease is clearly the gravitational potential energy, for only the position of the block has changed.

System (b). $Q = 0$ for the same reason as before. $W = -$ve for the plane because it is $+$ve for the block. So $Q - W$ is $+$ve, and therefore ΔE is $+$ve by definition. It is the internal energy of the plane which has increased.

System (c). The combined system block + plane does not interact with its surroundings in any way. Therefore $Q = 0$ and $W = 0$ for this system. By definition therefore $\Delta E = 0$ also. The decrease in the gravitational potential energy of one part of the system (the block) has been exactly counteracted by the increased internal energy of another part of the system (the plane).

2. Conducting block; non-conducting plane

Suppose this time that the block is made of some good conductor such as copper, while the inclined plane is made of such a poor conductor of heat that its conductivity may be taken as zero.

Problem. As before, except that this time it is the block which becomes warmer.

Answer.

System	Q	W	ΔE
(a) Block	0	0	0
(b) Plane	0	0	0
(c) Block + plane	0	0	0

Comments. System (a). $Q = 0$ because a heat interaction requires two systems in communication, and in the present case one of them (the plane) is non-conducting. $W = 0$ because the system has no effect external to itself whatever*. Consequently $\Delta E = 0$ also, the decrease in gravitational potential energy of the block being exactly compensated by the increase in its own internal energy.

System (b). $Q = 0$ and $W = 0$ for the plane because they are zero for the block. ΔE is consequently zero, which is easily understood since the plane suffers no change whatsoever.

System (c) $Q = W = \Delta E = 0$ because the combined system has no interaction with its surroundings.

Final remark: It may be thought puzzling that in the two cases the work done, by the block for example, differs, even though the mechanical aspects of the process are apparently the same. There is not much to be said about this other than to confirm that it is a logical consequence of the definitions of heat and work, which are themselves not arbitrary but merely express the distinction which will be needed to formulate the Second Law of Thermodynamics below. It will be remembered that the "force-moving-through-a-distance" definition of work leads to difficulties in the case of solid friction, since the "distance" is different for the two sides of the boundary*† (see p. 55).

Problems involving chemical reaction

We conclude by applying the First Law to systems which undergo chemical reaction. As well as illustrating the generality of the energy concept, the examples have engineering importance and are also relevant to Chapter 16 on Combustion.

The constant-volume calorimeter (bomb calorimeter)

Fig. 6.5 illustrates a rigid sealed bomb immersed in a bath of water which is kept at a uniform temperature by stirring. The bomb contains a crucible holding $0 \cdot 002$ lb_m of fuel oil, and an atmosphere of oxygen at a pressure of 20 atm. The oil can be ignited electrically from outside.

Problem. The oil is ignited. For $\frac{1}{2}$ minute after ignition no detectable temperature rise occurs in the water bath. Thereafter the water temperature begins to rise and after some time becomes steady at 5°F above its original

* End note 4.

† Someone is sure to ask, "What happens when both block and plane are non-conducting?" The simplest answer is that the question has no meaning, since "non-conducting" means "a very poor conductor relative to the other system." The question partakes of the nature of that involving an irresistible force and an immovable object.

value. If the mass of water is $7 \cdot 2 \, lb_m$, by how much has the energy of the system comprising bomb and contents increased, (a) $\frac{1}{2}$ minute after ignition, (b) when the temperatures have become steady?

Neglect the work transfers associated with the igniting current and with the stirring, and heat transfer from the water to its surrounding container and to the atmosphere.

Solution (a). $\frac{1}{2}$ minute after ignition the system comprising bomb and contents has had no external effects whatever. Specifically therefore $Q = 0$ and $W = 0$, so that from eq. (6.4),

$$\Delta E = 0. \qquad \qquad \text{... } Answer \text{ (a)}$$

Solution (b). In the whole process, the heat transfer in Btu from the bomb to the water bath is equal to the mass of water in lb_m times the number of degrees F temperature rise, i.e.

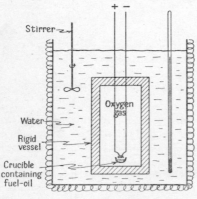

Stirrer
Water
Rigid vessel
Crucible containing fuel-oil
Oxygen gas

Fig. 6.5 Bomb calorimeter.

$$Q = -7 \cdot 2 \times 5$$

$$= -36 \, \text{Btu}$$

Since the bomb is rigid, $W = 0$, so that

$$\Delta E = Q - W$$

$$= -36 - 0$$

$$= -36 \, \text{Btu} \qquad \text{... } Answer \text{ (b)}$$

or

$$\Delta E = \frac{36}{0 \cdot 002} = 18,000 \, \text{Btu/lb}_m \text{ fuel.}$$

Comments: (a) It is noteworthy that during the initial period the energy change is zero even though the bomb contents will have a very high temperature as a result of the combustion. This may be interpreted as an increase in internal energy being exactly compensated by a decrease in "chemical energy".

(b) Note that finally the energy of the system is lower than initially, even though the final system temperature is slightly above the initial temperature.

An estimate can be made of the value that ΔE would have if the final system temperature had been exactly equal to the initial temperature, as would occur if the water bath were very large. The *negative* of this new ΔE, when expressed on a basis of unit mass of fuel, in known* as the *constant-volume heating value* of the fuel. For hydrocarbon fuels its value is around 19,000 Btu/lb, fuel. This is discussed in greater detail in Chapter 16, p. 340.

The internal-combustion engine

Petrol and oil engines burn hydrocarbon oil fuels with air under approximately constant-volume conditions. If we suppose that the ΔE for the combustion process is a constant of the fuel, when the final combustion product temperature equals the initial fuel and air temperature, a calculation can be made of the specific fuel consumption of a hypothetical engine which effects such energy changes with work transfer only.

* Among other names.

EXAMPLE

Problem. An oil of constant-volume heating value 19,000 Btu/lb$_m$ is burnt with air in a hypothetical engine in such a way that (i) the oil-air mixture reacts adiabatically at constant volume, (ii) the final temperature of the combustion products equals the initial temperature of the oil-air mixture. What is the specific fuel consumption of the engine in lb$_m$ fuel/h.p. h?

Solution. Since $Q = 0$ by hypothesis, we have for a system comprising 1 lb$_m$ of oil with associated air, from eq. (6.5)

$$0 - W = -19,000 \text{ Btu/lb}_m \text{ fuel}$$

i.e.
$$W = 19,000 \times 778 \text{ ft lb}_f/\text{lb}_m \text{ fuel}$$

$$= \frac{19,000 \times 778}{550 \times 3,600} \text{ h.p. h/lb}_m \text{ fuel.}$$

Therefore the specific fuel consumption

$$= \frac{550 \times 3,600}{19,000 \times 778} \text{ lb}_m \text{ fuel/h.p. h}$$

$$= 0.134 \text{ lb}_m \text{ fuel/h.p. h} \qquad \dots \quad Answer$$

Comment. Actual petrol and oil engines have specific fuel consumptions three or four times as large as this figure. The reasons for this are however too advanced to be given here.

CHAPTER 6—PROBLEMS

6.1 Two identical mixtures of ice and water contained in two similar vessels, A and B, undergo identical changes of state at atmospheric pressure as follows:

(i) A heat transfer of 30 Btu to the contents of vessel A causes some of the ice to melt.

(ii) Stirring work done on the contents of vessel B causes an equal quantity of ice to melt. The stirrer rotates at a speed of 1485 rev/min and operates for 40 minutes. The mean torque imposed by the mixture on the stirrer is 0.75 lb$_f$ in. Vessel B is well insulated.

Evaluate: (*a*) the stirring work done on the contents of vessel B in ft lb$_f$.

(*b*) the mechanical equivalent of heat in ft lb$_f$/Btu and in ft lb$_f$/Chu.

(*c*) the change in the energy of the mixture in each vessel.

Neglect the change of volume due to the melting of the ice.

6.2 A vertical cylinder fitted with a frictionless leakproof piston contains a quantity of gas. The piston is free to move and its weight is such that the gas pressure is 30 psia; the upper surface of the piston is exposed to the atmosphere. The gas executes a cycle by undergoing the following processes in sequence;

(i) With the cylinder well-insulated, 1000 ft lb$_f$ of stirring work are done on the gas by a paddle wheel projecting through the cylinder wall. As a result the gas temperature rises and the piston moves slowly upwards; the increase in the gas volume is 170 in^3.

(ii) With the insulation removed and the paddle wheel stationary, heat transfer from the gas of 1.285 Btu restores the gas on its initial state.

Evaluate (a) the displacement work and hence the net work done by the gas during process (i).

(b) the net work done by the gas in process (ii).

(c) the mechanical equivalent of heat in ft lb_f/Btu.

(d) the increase in energy of the gas in process (i) and in process (ii).

(e) the increase in energy of the gas for the combined process (i) plus (ii).

6.3 In an experiment to determine the mechanical equivalent of heat, a paddle wheel was fixed to the shaft of an engine and rotated in water contained in a well-insulated closed vessel. The vessel was mounted freely on the shaft and prevented from rotating by weights attached to its side.

At an engine speed of 268 rev/min it was found that 381 lb_m of water had increased in temperature by 159°F in 51 min. The weights attached to the vessel exerted a force of 110 lb_f at a distance of 5 ft from the axis of rotation of the engine shaft. Sketch the arrangement and evaluate the mechanical equivalent of heat.

6.4 The working fluid in an engine continuously executes a cyclic process. During one cycle the fluid engages in two work transfers: 11,000 ft lb_f to the working fluid and 32,000 ft lb_f from the working fluid. Also during the cycle there are three heat transfers two of which are known: 74 Btu to the working fluid and 39 Btu from the working fluid.

Determine the magnitude and direction of the third heat transfer.

6.5 Reconsider problem 5.6 and state whether the increase in energy, ΔE, is $+$, $-$, or 0.

6.6 Reconsider problem 5.7 and state whether the increase in energy, ΔE, is $+$, $-$, or 0.

6.7 Reconsider problem 5.8 and state whether the increase in energy, ΔE, is $+$, $-$, or 0.

6.8 A dashpot is a device for controlling the motion of mechanisms. It consists of a cylinder, closed at both ends, fitted with a piston; a piston rod, which protrudes through one of the cylinder covers, connects the piston to the mechanism. Both ends of the cylinder contain oil and are in communication, via a small hole drilled through the piston. As a piston is pushed inward the oil in one end of the cylinder is forced through the hole to the other end.

In a particular dashpot, the mechanism connected to the piston has a kinetic energy of 4000 ft lb_f initially; finally the mechanism is at rest.

Assuming heat transfers to be negligible evaluate the increase in the energy of each of the following systems:

(i) The mechanism-piston combination.

(ii) The oil.

(iii) The mechanism-dashpot combination.

6.9 A gyroscope is set spinning and is placed inside a well-insulated rigid box; initially the gyroscope has a kinetic energy of 1000 ft lb_f. Evaluate the increase in energy (in Btu) of the contents of the box when the speed of the gyroscope has fallen to zero.

6.10 For tests on a turbine rotor to determine the effect of fluid friction on its rotational motion, the rotor is mounted in the turbine casing with the inlet and exhaust flanges blanked-off. After charging the casing with steam, the rotor is accelerated to a specified speed, the drive is disconnected, and the rate at which the rotor decelerates is observed.

In a particular test the rotor has a kinetic energy of 200,000 ft lb_f when the drive is disconnected. Evaluate the increase in energy of the contents of the turbine casing as the rotor decelerates to rest. Neglect bearing friction and assume zero heat transfer.

6.11 (a) A system undergoes a process in which the heat transfer to the system is 40 Btu and the work done by the system is 45,000 ft lb$_f$. Evaluate the increase in the energy of the system.

(b) In a second process between the same initial and final states, the same system does 35,000 ft lb$_f$ of work; there is also heat transfer during this second process. Determine the magnitude and sign of the heat transfer.

6.12 (a) A system comprising 3 lb$_m$ of a mixture of air and water vapour is initially at a pressure of 15 psia and a temperature of 80°F. The mixture undergoes a process to a pressure of 60 psia and a temperature of 200°F. During the process the heat transfer from the mixture is 10 Btu and the work done on the mixture is 64,000 ft lb$_f$. Evaluate the increase in the energy of the mixture.

(b) Following the first process, the mixture undergoes a second process to a pressure of 15 psia and a temperature of 80°F. The work done by the mixture during the second process is 50,000 ft lb$_f$. Determine the magnitude and direction of the heat transfer during the second process.

(c) What is the increase in the energy of the mixture after it has undergone both processes in sequence?

6.13 In a closed-circuit wind tunnel air delivered by a fan circulates in succession through a cooler and the test section and then returns to the suction side of the fan. An electric motor outside the air duct drives the fan by means of a shaft protruding through the air-duct walls. Heat transfer through the air-duct walls is negligible. Assuming that the supply of coolant to the coolers is shut-off and considering the contents of the air-duct as the system, state whether the heat transfer, the work and the increase in energy are +, −, or 0 for the following cases:

(i) when the fan is running continuously;

(ii) when the current is switched-off and the fan speed gradually falls to zero.

6.14 Reconsider problem 6.13 when the motor is mounted within the air duct; in this case the electric supply cables pass through the air-duct walls.

6.15 State whether the heat transfer, the work, and the increase in energy are +, −, or 0 in each of the following cases. The system to be considered is printed in italics.

(a) A *lead-acid secondary cell*, discharging adiabatically, supplies current to a resistor.

(b) A *lead-acid secondary cell*, discharging adiabatically, supplies current to an electric motor.

(c) The *lead acid cell of* (a) undergoes the same change from the same initial state as in (a) while standing on open circuit for a long time.

6.16 A cyclic process, known as the air-standard Otto cycle, is often used as a standard of comparison for reciprocating internal combustion engines. The cycle is executed by unit mass of air contained in a cylinder closed by a frictionless leakproof piston and consists of four processes in sequence, exemplified in the following:

(i) Air initially at a pressure of 15 psia and a specific volume of 13 ft³/lb$_m$ (state 1) undergoes a fully-resisted, adiabatic compression according to the law $pv^{1\cdot4}$ = constant, to a specific volume of 1·8 ft³/lb$_m$ (state 2).

(ii) Heat transfer to air at constant volume of 220 Btu/lb$_m$ causes the air pressure to rise to 500 psia (state 3).

(iii) The air undergoes a fully-resisted, adiabatic expansion according to $pv^{1\cdot4}$ = constant, to the initial specific volume (state 4).

(iv) Heat transfer from the air at constant volume causes the air pressure to fall to its initial value, 15 psia, to complete the cycle.

Sketch the cycle on a pressure-specific-volume state diagram and evaluate:

(a) the work done by the air during each process;

(b) the heat transfer from the air during process (iv);

(c) the increase in the energy of the air in each process.

6.17 (a) An insulated rigid vessel contains some powdered coal and air at a pressure of 10 atm and a temperature of 68°F. The coal is ignited so causing a rise in the pressure and temperature of the contents of the vessel; the final temperature is 1000°F. Taking the vessel and its contents to be the system under consideration, evaluate the increase in the energy of the system.

(b) The insulation is now removed. A heat transfer of 45 Btu from the system causes the temperature to fall to the initial value, 68°F. Evaluate the increase in the energy of the system during this process.

(c) Taking the initial energy of the system as 30 Btu, write down the energy values after process (a) and process (b).

6.18 A 4 in. diameter vertical cylinder, closed by a piston, contains a combustible mixture at a temperature of 60°F. The piston is free to move and its weight is such that the mixture pressure is 40 psia; the upper surface of the piston is exposed to the atmosphere. The mixture is ignited. As the reaction proceeds, the piston moves slowly upwards and heat transfer to the surroundings takes place. When the reaction is complete and the temperature of the contents has been reduced to the initial value, 60°F, it is found that the piston has moved upwards a net distance of 3 in. and that the magnitude of the heat transfer to the surroundings is 4 Btu.

Evaluate the increase in the energy of the contents of the cylinder.

6.19 (a) A system consisting of a mixture of air and petrol vapour at an initial temperature of 60°F is contained in a rigid vessel. The mixture undergoes the following processes in sequence.

(i) The mixture temperature is raised to 400°F by a heat transfer of +3 Btu.

(ii) The mixture is ignited and burns completely; this process is adiabatic and the temperature rises to 2500°F.

(iii) The temperature of the products of combustion is reduced to 250°F by a heat transfer of −32 Btu.

Evaluate the energy of the system after each process given that the initial energy of the system is 10 Btu.

(b) An equal mass of the same mixture is contained in a cylinder closed by a piston. The mixture undergoes the following processes in sequence.

(i) Adiabatic compression to a temperature of 400°F.

(ii) Adiabatic combustion at constant volume until burning is complete.

(iii) Expansion to a temperature of 250°F the work done by the system being 24,100 ft lb$_f$.

(iv) Cooling at constant volume until the temperature is again 60°F.

On the assumption that the energy of the system depends only on its temperature and chemical aggregation (i.e. the way in which the elements are chemically combined), evaluate the work done during process (i) and the heat transfer during process (iii). Also state, with reasons, whether or not the system has executed a cyclic process.

CHAPTER 7

THE PURE SUBSTANCE

INTRODUCTION

In the previous chapter the First Law of Thermodynamics was applied to systems of considerable complexity, involving chemical, mechanical, electrical and other effects. Fortunately the systems encountered in thermodynamics are frequently less complex, and comprise fluids which do not change chemically or exhibit significant electrical, magnetic or capillary effects. Because of this, and because important statements can be made about such relatively simple systems, the present chapter will be devoted to explaining the nature of these systems. They will be given the generic name of *the pure substance*.

One of the important features of the pure substance is that its state can be represented as a point on a graph and, in some circumstances, changes of state can be represented by lines on a graph. The latter part of the present chapter will be devoted to this matter. The opportunity will be taken to define three new properties: the specific heat at constant volume, the specific heat at constant pressure, and enthalpy.

Symbols

a, b	Constants.	U	Internal energy of a pure substance.
c_p	Specific heat at constant pressure.	u	Specific internal energy of a pure substance.
c_v	Specific heat at constant volume.	V	System volume.
E	Energy of a system.	v	Specific volume.
e	Specific energy of a system.	W	Net work done by a system.
H	Enthalpy of a system.	x, y, z	Arbitrary properties of a system.
h	Specific enthalpy of a system.		
p	Pressure.	Δ	Increase in ($=$ Final value
Q	Heat transfer to a system.		$-$ Initial value).
t	Temperature.		

THE PURE SUBSTANCE

Definition of the pure substance

A pure substance is a particular sort of system, characterised by the following definition:

A pure substance is a system which is (a) homogeneous in composition, (b) homogeneous in chemical aggregation, (c) invariable in chemical aggregation.

Explanation of the definition. (a) "Homogeneous in composition" means that the composition of each part of the system is the same as the composition of every other part. "Composition" means the relative

93

proportions of the chemical elements into which the sample can be analysed. It does not matter how these elements are combined.

For example in Fig. 7.1, system (i), comprising steam and water, is

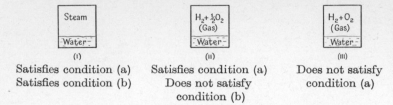

Steam	$H_2 + \frac{1}{2}O_2$ (Gas)	$H_2 + O_2$ (Gas)
Water	Water	Water
(i)	(ii)	(iii)

Satisfies condition (a)   Satisfies condition (a)   Does not satisfy
Satisfies condition (b)   Does not satisfy   condition (a)
                     condition (b)

Fig. 7.1 Illustrating the definition of a pure substance.

System		Homogeneous in composition	Homogeneous in chemical aggregation	Invariable in chemical aggregation	Pure substance
Steam		✓	✓	✓	✓
Steam / Water		✓	✓	✓	✓
Air ($O_2 + N_2$ Gas)		✓	✓	✓	✓
Air / Liquid air	N.B. $O_2 : N_2$ proportions differ in the gas & liquid phase in equilibrium	x	✓	✓	x
Air + fuel vapour	No reaction	✓	✓	✓	✓
Air + fuel vapour / Liquid fuel	No reaction	x	✓	✓	x
Air + fuel vapour — Combustion products / Flame		✓	x	x	x
Gaseous combustion products		✓	✓	✓	✓

Fig. 7.2 Illustrating the application of the definition of a pure substance.

homogeneous in composition, since chemical analysis would reveal that hydrogen and oxygen atoms are present in the ratio 2 : 1 whether the sample be taken from the steam or from the water. The same is true of system (ii) containing uncombined hydrogen and oxygen gas in the atomic ratio 2 : 1 in the upper part, and water in the lower part. System (iii) however, is not homogeneous in composition, for the hydrogen and oxygen are present in the ratio 1 : 1 in the upper part, but in the ratio 2 : 1 (as water) in the lower part.

(b) "Homogeneous in chemical aggregation" means that the chemical elements must be combined chemically in the same way in all parts of the system. Consideration of Fig. 7.1 again shows that system (i) satisfies this condition also; for steam and water consist of identical molecules. System (ii) on the other hand is not homogeneous in chemical aggregation since in the upper part of the system the hydrogen and oxygen are not combined chemically (individual atoms of H and O are not uniquely associated), whereas in the lower part of the system the hydrogen and oxygen are combined to form water.

Note however that a uniform mixture of steam, hydrogen gas, and oxygen gas would be regarded as homogeneous in both composition and chemical aggregation whatever the relative proportions of the components.

(c) "Invariable in chemical aggregation" means that the state of chemical combination of the system does not change with *time* (condition (b) referred to variations with *position*). Thus a mixture of hydrogen and oxygen, which changed into steam during the time that the system was under consideration, would not be a pure substance.

EXAMPLES

Fig. 7.2 contains some examples of systems, some of which are pure substances. The reader should check his understanding of the three qualifications of a pure substance by reference to this diagram.

The Two-Property Rule

It is necessary to be precise about what we mean by a pure substance, because of an important feature of systems which obey the above three conditions. This feature may be expressed by what we shall call the *Two-Property Rule*, namely:

The state of a pure substance of given mass can be fixed by specifying two properties, provided that (i) the system is in equilibrium, (ii) gravity, motion, electricity, magnetism and capillarity are without significant effects.

Remarks on the Two-Property Rule. 1. To give a concrete example, if measurements are made of the pressure and temperature of a system comprising 1 lb_m of gaseous air, all the properties of that system can be deduced; there is only one possible value of the volume of the air, for instance. This does not mean that knowledge of the pressure and temperature alone tells us what the volume is; but it does mean that every time the pressure and temperature are caused to have these particular values, the volume will be the same.

2. The Rule only states "*can* be fixed", because not every pair of properties suffices to specify the state. For example consider a system comprising water and steam. If the pressure is found to be 1 atm. and the temperature is 212°F, reflection will show that a number of states

could exist: the system might consist of pure steam, or of a large proportion of steam with a small proportion of water, or of a little steam with a lot of water, or of pure water. This is because when water is changed into steam at 1 atm. pressure, the temperature remains at 212°F throughout the complete process. In this case the two properties, pressure and temperature, are not independent and therefore count as one property.

The state of a steam-water system at 1 atm. pressure would be fixed however if the volume of the system were measured instead of the temperature; the volume changes greatly according to whether steam or water predominates in the mixture. Pressure and volume (or specific volume) are independent properties in this case.

3. It is necessary for the system to be in equilibrium, as will be seen if we consider a system comprising steam and water, of which the volume and the internal energy are the specified properties. If the steam and water are not initially at the same temperature for example, then at constant volume and constant energy (physically realised by enclosing the system within a rigid, thermally-insulated container) the pressure will gradually change as temperature equilibrium is brought about by heat transfer between the steam and the water. Clearly if several pressures and temperatures can be observed the state of the system is not fixed. The equilibrium requirement also excludes such conditions as "supercooling" from the range of validity of the Two-Property Rule*.

4. Although gravity is always present in terrestrial experiments, its effects can be neglected provided, firstly, that the system is not so large that differences of hydrostatic pressure are significant, and, secondly, that if the system moves the observer moves with it. This second proviso simultaneously excludes other significant effects of motion, like kinetic energy.

5. Capillarity (surface tension), electrical and magnetic effects are all of negligible importance for most of the systems encountered in engineering:— for example, steam, air and combustion products. The restriction involved in condition (ii) of the Two-Property Rule is therefore not a practically hampering one.

6. The Two-Property Rule only applies to liquid and gaseous systems; for solids can have pressures (positive or negative) which differ according to the direction of measurement. It therefore requires more than two properties to specify completely the state of a system comprising a solid.

7. The Two-Property Rule is also obeyed by some systems which are not pure substances. Obedience to the rule is therefore not an infallible sign that a system is homogeneous in composition etc.

8. A symbolic representation of the Two-Property Rule is that, for these systems, three properties x, y, z of a system can be related by expressions of the form

$$z = f(x,y) \qquad \ldots \quad (7.1)$$

* Actually a mixture of H_2 and O_2 gas at room temperature is not in thermodynamic equilibrium, for it tends spontaneously, though very slowly, to react chemically. Nevertheless for many purposes such mixtures can be treated as though they were in equilibrium; the Two-property Rule can be applied to them.

where $f(\ )$ signifies some function. For example, the equation

$$p = \frac{(a + bt)}{v} \qquad \qquad \ldots \quad (7.2)$$

where p, v and t have their usual meanings and a and b are constants, might represent the relation between these three properties for a particular substance. In general however, the function $f(\ )$ will not have any recognisable algebraic form. Eq. (7.1) is then simply another way for saying: "if x and y are fixed, so is z".

The energy of a pure substance: internal energy

It is convenient to have a new symbol for the energy of a pure substance under the conditions required by the Two-Property Rule. This symbol is U; when the system is of unit mass, the lower case, u, will be used.

For a pure substance we can relate E and U by:—

$$E = U + \text{terms accounting for gravity, motion capillarity,}$$
$$\text{electricity and magnetism.} \qquad \ldots \quad (7.3)$$

U may be identified as that mode of energy which can be directly influenced by heat transfer, though not of course only by heat transfer. It is therefore the internal energy referred to in Chapter 6. We continue to refer to it as internal energy below; the proviso that we are dealing with a pure substance in the absence of gravity, etc. will be re-iterated from time to time. u is the *specific internal energy* of the system; the word "specific" is often omitted, however.

The First Law. For a pure substance under these conditions, the First Law of Thermodynamics, eq. (6.5), may now be written as:

$$Q - W = \Delta U \qquad \qquad \ldots \quad (7.4)$$

or, if the system is of unit mass,

$$Q - W = \Delta u \qquad \qquad \ldots \quad (7.5)$$

Tables and diagrams

One reason for the importance of pure substances is that paper is two-dimensional; for if two properties specify the state of a system, a table or diagram on a single sheet of paper can represent all possible states of the system. As examples of what is meant, consider Table 7.1 and Fig. 7.3, both of which convey information about the specific volume of air at various pressures and temperatures. In each case specification of a pressure and a temperature, i.e. of two properties, specifies a definite location on the paper and so a definite value of the specific volume; e.g. at $t = 200°F$ and $p = 50$ psia, the corresponding $v = 4 \cdot 89$ ft³/lb$_m$. In the case of the table, the specific volume is indicated by the number situated in the appropriate pressure column and temperature row. In the case of the graph the specific

TABLE 7.1. *Specific volume of air* (ft^3/lb_m)

$t°F$ \ p	1	5	10	50	100	200 psia
0	170·4	34·08	17·04	3·41	1·70	0·85
100	207·4	41·48	20·74	4·15	2·07	1·04
200	244·4	48·88	24·44	4·89	2·44	1·22
300	281·5	56·30	28·15	5·63	2·82	1·41
400	318·5	63·70	31·85	6·37	3·19	1·59

volume is found by interpolation between the lines of constant specific volume nearest to the point with the appropriate t-ordinate and p-abscissa.

Examples of tables of properties of a pure substance will be found in Appendix B. They will be discussed in more detail in Chapter 9. The remainder of the present chapter will be devoted to discussing some features of processes represented on property diagrams.

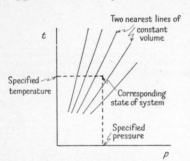

Fig. 7.3 Illustrating interpolation on a property chart.

SOME PROCESSES EXECUTED BY PURE SUBSTANCES

Conditions of validity of diagrammatic representation

Before discussing particular processes, it is important to be clear about the conditions under which states and processes can be represented on diagrams. The first point is that the conditions of the Two-Property Rule must be satisfied; that is to say that we must be dealing with a pure substance, it must be in equilibrium, and effects due to gravity, motion, capillarity, electricity and magnetism must be absent. The most easily overlooked requirement is that for equilibrium.

When these conditions are satisfied a given point on the diagram represents a fixed state of the system; that is to say that all the system properties are determinate there.

Now consider the question of representing a change of state, i.e. a process, on the diagram. The path of this change of state is the succession of states passed through by the system. *If each of these states is an equilibrium state*, each may be represented by a point on the diagram. Since the states merge continuously one into the next, the corresponding points form a continuous line joining the point representing the initial state of the process to that of the final state.

Below, examples will be given of processes the paths of which may be represented by continuous lines. They represent what in Chapter 3 were termed "fully-resisted expansions" (p. 37). An example will also be given of a process of which only the initial and final states can be represented on a property diagram; this is an "un-resisted expansion"; the intermediate states of the system are not equilibrium states, so no line representing the path of the process can be drawn.

The constant-volume process

Fig. 7.4 serves to illustrate processes characterised by constancy of volume: the container enclosing the systems is rigid. A practical example of such a process is that occurring in the cylinder of the Newcomen engine

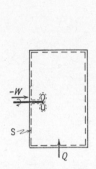

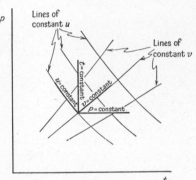

Fig. 7.4 Constant-volume process.

Fig. 7.5 Pressure–temperature diagram showing processes in which p, v, u and t remain constant.

when heat transfer between the injected water and the steam causes the latter to condense; in this case the steam initially in the cylinder is to be taken as the system.

Fig. 7.4 has an arrow indicating heat interaction with the surroundings and another arrow (and symbolic paddle-wheel) indicating that stirring work may in general be done. Displacement work is excluded however by the rigidity of the system boundary. The fluid within the system boundary can be any pure substance.

Figs. 7.5, 7.6 and 7.7 represent respectively p—t, v—u, and p—v diagrams for the substance in question. Each of them has two families of property lines: the p—t diagram has lines of constant specific volume and constant internal energy; and so on.

Provided that the constant-volume process involves a continuous succession of equilibrium states, which is possible even with stirring work provided that the stirring rate is low, the process may be represented on each of the property diagrams by lines such as those marked "$v =$ constant" on Figs. 7.5, 7.6, and 7.7. On Fig. 7.6 the line is horizontal because v is the ordinate of that diagram; on Fig. 7.7 the line is vertical since v is the abscissa.

The specific heat at constant volume. The opportunity will now be taken to define a new property. Although the name will be familiar to those instructed in elementary physics, the definition used in thermodynamics should be carefully noted.

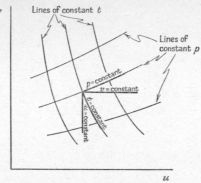

Fig. 7.6 Volume–internal energy diagram showing processes in which p, v, u and t remain constant.

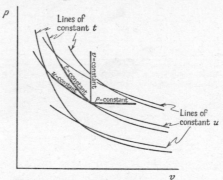

Fig. 7.7 Pressure–volume diagram showing processes in which p, v, u and t remain constant.

Definition. The specific heat at constant volume, c_v, is the rate of change with temperature of the specific internal energy of the system when the specific volume is held constant.

Symbolically, this definition runs

$$c_v \equiv \left[\frac{du}{dt}\right]_v \qquad \ldots \quad (7.6)$$

where du/dt means the rate of change of u with respect to t, as is usual in differential calculus, while the square bracket with the suffix v signifies that the latter property is constant during the change.

Remarks on c_v

1. The significance of c_v is most easily realised by reference to a property diagram with internal energy as ordinate, temperature as abscissa, and lines of constant volume drawn on the body of the graph as in Fig. 7.8. Eq. (7.6) shows that for any state of the system, e.g. that represented by

P in Fig. 7.8 c_v is equal to the slope of the constant-volume line passing through the point P.

2. Evidently there is a unique value of c_v at each point of the diagram. This means that c_v is a *property*, i.e. a function of the state. No matter how one approaches the point P, the constant-volume line always has the same slope there. The slope differs from point to point however; to specify c_v we must specify a point on the diagram, which requires of course two co-ordinates.

3. The great usefulness of the property c_v is that, not withstanding what has just been said about its variability in general, for many substances over a restricted range of conditions c_v can be taken as constant. For example, over an important range of temperatures and pressures, the error in taking c_v for water as 1 Btu/lb$_m$ °F is quite small; this simplifies calculations.

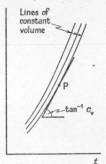

Fig. 7.8 Illustrating the definition of specific heat at constant volume.

4. The name specific "heat" and its commonly used alternative, "heat capacity", must now be regarded as misnomers hallowed by tradition. They derive from a "caloric" view of heat, which is thought to be "absorbed" by the material as a sponge soaks up water.

5. The definition given above in terms of internal energy is slightly preferable to that given in school physics texts in terms of "the heat to raise the temperature one degree at constant volume", because the temperature rise might be brought about by (stirring) work in the absence of heat transfer. Beside this, the fact that c_v is a property is brought out more clearly if it is defined in terms of the two other properties, u and t.

6. It should not be forgotten that u is the internal energy of a pure substance, and it is therefore only for such systems that c_v is defined. In systems which react chemically it is possible to have appreciable temperature changes at constant volume and energy (which might suggest that c_v was zero), and also large energy changes at constant volume and temperature (which might suggest that c_v was infinite). But such systems are not of course pure substances, and therefore have no c_v.

The constant-pressure process

Often processes take place at substantially constant pressure. For example the water in a boiler is at almost the same pressure at entry as when it leaves as steam. Constant-pressure processes in general are illustrated by Fig. 7.9 wherein the fluid system is supposed to be enclosed in a cylinder beneath a frictionless leakproof piston surmounted by a constant weight. For generality, a paddle-wheel is indicated, but this time of course displacement work is done as well as stirring work, since the piston must move in order to keep the pressure constant.

The lines marked "$p = $ constant" in Figs. 7.5, 7.6, and 7.7 indicate the path of a constant-pressure process which passes through a continuous succession of equilibrium states.

The specific heat at constant pressure. We now define another specific heat, namely the specific heat at constant pressure, c_p. Its definition may at first appear even more arbitrary than that for c_v, and involves the

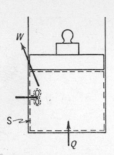

Fig. 7.9 Constant-pressure process.

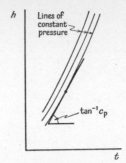

Fig. 7.10 Illustrating the definition of specific heat at constant pressure.

introduction of yet another new property; the *specific enthalpy*, h. We only give a symbolic definition at this stage, namely:

Definition:
$$c_p \equiv \left[\frac{dh}{dt}\right]_p \qquad \ldots \quad (7.7)$$

where
$$h \equiv u + pv \qquad \ldots \quad (7.8)$$

Here dh/dt signifies the rate of change of h with respect to t, while the square bracket with the suffix p indicates that the pressure is held constant during the differentiation.

Remarks on the enthalpy* h

1. The convenience of having a name and symbol for the quantity $(u + pv)$ will not become apparent until steady-flow processes are dealt with in Chapter 8. Nevertheless, it is evident that we are free to define h in accordance with eq. (7.8) and moreover that this quantity represents a *property;* for u, p and v are all properties, and when their values are fixed the value of h is uniquely determined also.

2. The word "enthalpy" is pronounced with the accent on the second syllable: enthálpy. This helps to prevent confusion with "éntropy", introduced in Chapter 13.

3. To be meaningful, the internal energy u and the product pv must be expressed in like units, for example in Btu/lb$_m$ or ft lb$_f$/lb$_m$. The enthalpy h is then in the same units.

4. Since enthalpy is a property, it may be used like other properties as ordinate or abscissa of a property diagram. Fig. 7.10 illustrates an enthalpy-temperature diagram for a pure substance; the lines drawn on it represent states of constant pressure.

---

* As in the case of *specific* internal energy, the qualifying adjective is usually omitted except where emphasis is required.

5. The symbol H is used to denote the enthalpy of a system of mass m; thus $H = mh$. If the system volume is V, it follows from eq. (7.8) that

$$mh = mu + mpv$$

i.e. $$H = U + pV$$

Remarks about c_p

1. The definition of c_p (eq. (7.7)) indicates that this quantity is a slope, namely that of a line of constant pressure on an h—t diagram, e.g. Fig. 7.10. As in the case of c_v, this observation shows that c_p is a property, the value of which varies, in general, according to the state of the substance.

2. In words, the definition of c_p is:

The specific heat at constant pressure, c_p, is the rate of change with temperature of the specific enthalpy of the system when the pressure is held constant.

3. Elementary physics texts ordinarily define c_p as "the heat transfer necessary to raise the temperature of unit mass of the substance through one degree at constant pressure"; the absence of stirring work is understood. While preferring our present definition, which is in terms of properties rather than of a process, we have to demonstrate that it includes the "physics" definition.

Consider the system of Fig. 7.9 which will be supposed to comprise unit mass of a pure substance; let it undergo a small constant-pressure expansion in the absence of stirring work. Let the heat transfer be dQ, and the work transfer dW. Application of the First Law, eq. (7.5), to the system leads to:

$$dQ - dW = du \qquad \ldots \quad (7.9)$$

Since the only work is displacement work, the net work done by the system, dW, is simply equal to the displacement work, $p\,dv$; eq. (7.9) then becomes

$$dQ = du + p\,dv \qquad \ldots \quad (7.10)$$

or

$$\frac{dQ}{dt} = \frac{du}{dt} + \frac{p\,dv}{dt} \qquad \ldots \quad (7.10)$$

where dv is the small increase of the (unit mass) system volume and dt is the small increase in system temperature.

Now the left-hand side of eq. (7.10) is equal to c_p according to the above "physics" definition. We wish to prove that it is also equal to c_p according to eq. (7.7). For this we differentiate the definition of h, eq. (7.8), to get

$$\frac{dh}{dt} = \frac{du}{dt} + \frac{d(pv)}{dt}$$

$$= \frac{du}{dt} + \frac{p\,dv}{dt} + \frac{v\,dp}{dt} \qquad \ldots \quad (7.11)$$

If the pressure is held constant, the last term on the right-hand side of eq. (7.11) is zero. The equation reduces to

$$\left[\frac{\mathrm{d}h}{\mathrm{d}t}\right]_p = \frac{\mathrm{d}u}{\mathrm{d}t} + \frac{p\,\mathrm{d}v}{\mathrm{d}t} \qquad \ldots \quad (7.12)$$

where constancy of pressure is understood on the right hand side also.

Comparison of eq. (7.10), eq. (7.12) and our definition of c_p, eq. (7.7) shows that the latter indeed equals $\mathrm{d}Q/\mathrm{d}t$ in the constant-pressure process. This completes the required proof.

4. Further remarks on c_p parallel those on c_v. Its usefulness derives from the approximate constancy of c_p for many substances over restricted ranges. It has only been defined for pure substances.

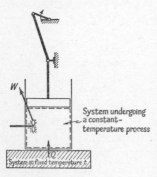

System undergoing a constant-temperature process

System at fixed temperature t

Fig. 7.11 Constant-temperature process.

The constant-temperature process

Fig. 7.11 illustrates a system which undergoes changes at constant temperature. Such processes occur in practice whenever the system changes relatively slowly while in thermal contact with a larger system of uniform temperature. Boiling and condensation processes also occur at constant temperature if the pressure is constant, as has already been mentioned.

If the process is fully-resisted, and so involves solely a succession of equilibrium states, constant-temperature processes can be represented by lines drawn on property diagrams, as illustrated by the lines marked "$t = $ constant" on Figs. 7.5, 7.6 and 7.7.

Constant-temperature processes are often called *isothermal processes;* the constant-temperature lines on the property diagrams are called *isotherms.*

The constant-internal-energy process

Processes involving only equilibrium states in which the heat and work quantities exactly balance at all times are rare in practice. However, if they do occur, they are processes of constant internal energy (since $\mathrm{d}u = \mathrm{d}Q - \mathrm{d}W = 0$) and may be represented by lines on property diagrams. Figs. 7.5, 7.6 and 7.7 show examples.

The most important practical constant—u process happens to be one which cannot be so represented: it is typified by the diaphragm-bursting process of Chapter 3, p. 50. Fig. 7.12 shows the system in its initial position to the left of the diaphragm; the space to the right of the diaphragm is evacuated. The process involves the bursting (or removal) of the diaphragm which allows the fluid to fill the whole space. The container is insulated and rigid so both heat and work are absent. It follows from eq. (7.4) that the internal energy remains constant.

Fig. 7.13 shows, by means of the points marked 1 and 2, all that can be represented of the process on a p-v diagram: the initial and final state points. They have been drawn between the constant internal energy lines of the diagram for clarity. States between 1 and 2 cannot be represented

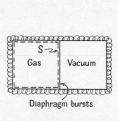

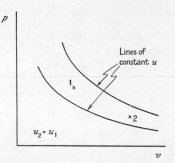

Fig. 7.12 Illustrating a process in which the initial and final internal energies are equal.

Fig. 7.13 Pressure–volume diagram showing the initial and final state-points of the process illustrated in Fig. 7.12.

on the diagram because they are not in equilibrium: the pressure, for example at any intermediate instant in the process, is not uniform throughout the system, so what ordinate could be allotted to the state-point?

Something approaching a continuous line can be obtained by the modified process with the same initial and final states shown in Fig. 7.14

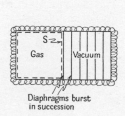

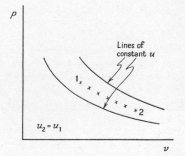

Fig. 7.14 Modified process with the same initial and final states as that shown in Fig. 7.12.

Fig. 7.15. Showing successive equilibrium states of the process illustrated in Fig. 7.14.

where a large number of diaphragms burst successively enabling the whole volume to be filled by the fluid in stages. Then shortly after each diaphragm bursts, but while the next diaphragm is still there, an equilibrium state is arrived at. These are shown as crosses on Fig. 7.15; they all lie on a line of constant internal energy. Nevertheless since each equilibrium state is always separated from the rest by states in which equilibrium does not exist, no matter how many diaphragms are used, the points on Fig. 7.15 can never join up to form a line.

One consequence of this is that $\int_1^2 p \, dv$ for the process has no meaning; for p is not prescribed for each v. However, if anyone with sufficiently blurred vision does evaluate the area under the "line" joining 1 and 2, this will certainly not equal the work done in the process; for the work, it will be remembered, is zero (p. 51).

BIBLIOGRAPHY

Keenan, J. H. and Kaye, J., *Gas Tables*. Wiley & Sons and Chapman & Hall, 1948.
Keenan, J. H. and Keyes, F. G., *Thermodynamic Properties of Steam*. Wiley & Sons and Chapman & Hall, 1936.
Keenan, J. H., *Thermodynamics*. Wiley & Sons and Chapman & Hall, 1941.

CHAPTER 7—PROBLEMS

7.1 A system comprising $2 \cdot 5 \, \text{lb}_m$ of a pure substance is initially at a pressure of 100 psia and a temperature of 400°F; the corresponding specific volume of the substance is $3 \, \text{ft}^3/\text{lb}_m$. The system undergoes a process to a final pressure of 100 psia and a final specific volume of $3 \, \text{ft}^3/\text{lb}_m$.

(a) What is the final temperature of the substance and the increase in its specific internal energy?

(b) During the process the work done by the system is $9000 \, \text{ft lb}_f$. Determine the magnitude and direction of the heat transfer.

7.2 A system comprising a pure substance undergoes a process in which its internal energy decreases by 10 Btu. The heat transfer to the system during the process is 6 Btu.

(a) Determine the magnitude and direction of the work done.

(b) If, in undergoing a different process between the same end-states, the work done had been zero, what would have been the magnitude and sign of the heat transfer?

7.3 A fluid system consisting of $9 \cdot 2 \, \text{lb}_m$ of a pure substance has an energy E of $81 \cdot 2$ Btu. The kinetic energy of the system is $12,900 \, \text{ft lb}_f$ and its gravitational potential energy is $3660 \, \text{ft lb}_f$. The system undergoes an adiabatic process in which the final specific internal energy is $70 \, \text{Btu}/\text{lb}_m$, the final kinetic energy is $1430 \, \text{ft lb}_f$ and the final gravitational potential energy is $900 \, \text{ft lb}_f$. The effects due to electricity, capillarity and magnetism are assumed to be absent.

(a) Evaluate the initial value of the specific internal energy of the fluid.

(b) Determine the magnitude and sign of the work done during the process.

(c) The fluid system undergoes a second adiabatic process between the same initial and final pressures and temperatures as above. In this second process the effects of gravity and motion are negligible. Assuming pressure and temperature to be independent properties, determine the magnitude and sign of the work done during the process.

7.4 A mass of $0 \cdot 3 \, \text{lb}_m$ of a pure substance at a pressure of 14 psia and a temperature of 100°F occupies a volume of $4 \, \text{ft}^3$. Given that the internal energy of the substance is 28·8 Btu, evaluate the specific enthalpy of the substance.

7.5 A pure substance is contained in a cylinder closed by a piston. The substance undergoes a fully-resisted, constant-pressure process in which the only work done is the displacement work at the slowly-moving piston face. Show that the heat transfer during the process is equal to the increase in the enthalpy of the substance.

7.6 A pure substance is contained in a cylinder closed by a piston. A paddle wheel, rotated by means of a shaft protruding through the cylinder wall, causes the substance to undergo a fully-resisted constant-pressure process as the piston moves outwards. There is no heat transfer during the process. Show that the stirring work done on the substance is equal to the increase in the enthalpy of the substance.

7.7 The internal energy and the enthalpy of certain pure substances may be considered to be functions of (i.e. dependent upon) temperature only. Further, over restricted ranges of conditions, the specific heats at constant volume and constant pressure may be assumed to be constant. Show that for *any* process executed by a pure substance satisfying these conditions:

$$\Delta u = c_v \Delta t$$

and

$$\Delta h = c_p \Delta t$$

7.8 Examine the following situations, all of which satisfy the conditions set down in problem 7.7.

(a) The specific heat of water at constant *volume* may be taken as 1 Btu/lb_m°F. Evaluate the increase in internal energy of 1 lb_m of water at atmospheric pressure as its temperature is increased from 32°F to 212°F at constant *pressure*.

(b) The specific heat of ice at constant *pressure* may be taken as 0·5 Btu/lb_m°F. Evaluate the increase in enthalpy of 4 lb_m of ice at atmospheric pressure as its temperature is increased from 0°F to 32°F at constant *volume*.

(c) 5 lb_m of air at a pressure of 60 psia and a temperature of 140°F are contained in a cylinder closed by a piston. As a result of expansion and heat transfer the temperature falls to 40°F and the pressure to 50 psia. For air the specific heat at constant pressure may be taken as 0·24 Btu/lb_m°F and the specific heat at constant volume may be taken as 0·171 Btu/lb_m°F. Evaluate (i) the increase in the internal energy of the air, (ii) the increase in the enthalpy of the air. Can the work or heat transfer be evaluated for this process?

7.9 The relation between the properties of oxygen gas may be expressed over a restricted range by

$$pv = 0·335t + 154.3$$

and

$$t = 6·46u - 460$$

where p is in psia, v in ft³/lb_m, t in °F and u in Btu/lb_m.

(a) Evaluate the specific heat at constant volume and the specific heat at constant pressure in Btu/lb_m°F.

(b) Show that for *any* process executed by unit mass of oxygen $\Delta u = c_v \Delta t$ and $\Delta h = c_p \Delta t$.

(c) 1 lb_m of oxygen at a pressure of 100 psia and a temperature of 540°F is contained in a rigid vessel. Heat transfer to the oxygen increases its enthalpy by 12 Btu/lb$_m$. Evaluate the final temperature, the heat transfer and the final pressure.

7.10 The following data have been extracted from Table IV of the Steam Tables (Appendix B). They show the variation in the enthalpy of steam with temperature at a fixed pressure, 20 psia.

t°F	300	400	600	800	1000	1200	1400	1600
h Btu/lb$_m$	1191·6	1239·2	1334·4	1432·1	1533·0	1637·4	1745·4	1857·2

Plot h versus t and hence obtain values of the specific heat at constant pressure at $t = 400$°F and at $t = 1300$°F for $p = 20$ psia.

7.11 The properties of a certain gas are related by

$$pv = 0\cdot4(t + 460)$$

and
$$u = u_0 + 0\cdot2t$$

where p is in psia, v in ft^3/lb$_m$, t in °F and u in Btu/lb$_m$.

A cylinder fitted with a piston contains 0·8 ft^3 of this gas at a pressure of 50 psia and a temperature of 180°F. As the gas expands to a lower pressure the work done by the gas is 2150 ft lb$_f$ and the heat transfer from the gas is 1·9 Btu.

(a) Determine the temperature of the gas after expansion.

(b) If the gas undergoes a second process between the same end states in which the heat transfer is zero, evaluate the work done by the gas in this case.

THE FIRST LAW APPLIED TO STEADY-FLOW PROCESSES

INTRODUCTION

In the discussion of the First Law of Thermodynamics, we focussed attention on the processes undergone by a fixed body of material, the *thermodynamic system*, and thereby related the heat and work transfers at the system boundary to the changes of energy of the material within the boundary.

In many engineering problems, however, the natural focus of attention is a piece of equipment through which material flows continuously. Examples are:—

(a) A hydro-electric plant comprising a water turbine coupled to a dynamo. Water from a high-level reservoir flows into the turbine continuously, emerging at reduced pressure at the outlet. The flow within the turbine rotor and associated pipes is turbulent and confused, so that it would be difficult to follow the history of an individual particle (system) of water in order to compute its energy changes and the heat and work flows across its boundaries. What we are more directly interested in is how much electrical work flows out along the wires.

(b) A steam turbine in which hot, high-pressure steam enters the casing, passes between alternate rows of fixed and moving blades, and emerges, partially condensed, with a lower internal energy but higher velocity than at entry. Once again the processes undergone by a given particle of steam are too complex to be observed and analysed, and indeed will not be the same for every particle. Yet we need to determine how the average change of state of the steam in its passage through the turbine is related to the shaft work delivered by the turbine to its surroundings, and to the heat transfer from the turbine casing to the atmosphere.

(c) A petrol engine running at constant speed. Air and petrol enter the engine in a more or less pulsating fashion, while combustion products (nitrogen, carbon dioxide, carbon monoxide and steam) pass out of the exhaust pipe, usually pulsating even more violently. Not all the cylinders will receive combustible mixture of quite the same mixture ratio, though this is hard to establish; nor will the ignition and cylinder-cooling arrangements operate uniformly between cylinders. Again, however, we need to find some way of applying the First Law of Thermodynamics so as to relate the changes which have taken place in the petrol and air to the useful work performed by the engine and to the heat transfers to the cooling water and elsewhere.

Despite the complexity of these examples, it will be shown below that, if the system boundaries are chosen judiciously, the analysis of Chapter 6 can be applied directly and in a simple fashion. However, problems of these types occur so frequently in engineering practice that it is found convenient to make a slight re-formulation of the First Law.

An important characteristic of each of the examples cited is that, as far as the inlet and outlet pipes are concerned, the flow of material may be taken as *steady*, i.e., invariant with time. This is true even of the petrol engine, and of other reciprocating machines, provided that conditions are considered at points sufficiently far upstream and downstream for the pulsations to have died away. Our re-formulation of the First Law is therefore called the *Steady-Flow Energy Equation*. In deriving it, a new concept will be introduced, the *control volume;* this is almost as important as the concept of *system*. A new sub-division of work will also be introduced, namely into *flow work* and *external work*.

The chapter comprises the derivation of the new equation, followed by important examples of its use. In the course of one of these the Continuity Equation is introduced (p. 127). There follows a demonstration of how the control-volume concept can be used also in processes where the flow is not steady. Finally, the similarities and differences are explained between the Steady-Flow Energy Equation and two equations which arise in fluid mechanics and which are based on a quite different physical principle: Newton's Second Law of Motion.

Symbols

A Cross-sectional area.

c_v Specific heat at constant volume.

E Energy of a system.

E_C Energy of the material within a control surface.

e Specific energy.

F Force.

g Gravitational acceleration.

g_0 Constant in Newton's Second Law.

h Specific enthalpy of a pure substance.

h_t Stagnation enthalpy of a pure substance.

h' Specific enthalpy of a chemical substance.

L Displacement.

m Mass.

$\dot{m}$ Mass flow rate of fluid.

p Pressure.

Q Heat transfer.

$\dot{Q}$ Heat transfer rate.

t Temperature.

u Specific internal energy of a pure substance.

u' Specific internal energy of a chemical substance.

V Velocity.

v Specific volume.

W Net work done by a system.

W_x External work.

$\dot{W}_x$ External work transfer rate.

z Elevation of a system above an arbitrary datum.

α, β Gas angles (Figs. 8.12b and c).

σ Volume enclosed by a control surface.

τ Time.

Δ Increase in ($=$ Final value $-$ Initial value).

Subscripts

1, 2 Inflow, outflow sections of a control surface.

i, f   Initial, final state of the material within a control surface.

G Flue gas.

S Steam.

THE STEADY-FLOW ENERGY EQUATION

The control volume

Consider as an example the triple-expansion reciprocating steam engine illustrated in Fig. 8.1. We suppose it to be operating at constant r.p.m. and to have been running long enough to be warmed right through.

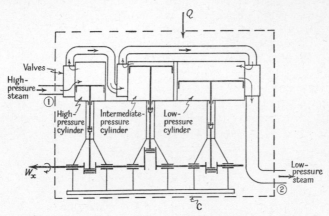

Fig. 8.1 Triple-expansion reciprocating steam engine.

The first and most important step in the analysis is the drawing of an imaginary envelope around the engine, shown dotted in Fig. 8.1, and marked C. This cuts the steam entry and exhaust pipes at the sections marked 1 and 2 respectively, which have been chosen sufficiently far from the valve-gear for the pulsations in steam velocity to be damped out. The steam flow rates therefore can be regarded as steady, and of course equal. The space bounded by the imaginary envelope, C, is called a *control volume*; C is often called a *control surface*.

A control volume is any volume of fixed shape, and of fixed position and orientation relative to the observer.

In addition to the steam flowing across the control-volume boundary in Fig. 8.1, two other flows are important. The first is the *external work* indicated by an arrow and marked W_x; the second is the *heat transfer* likewise indicated by an arrow and marked Q.

External work is all the work transfer across the control surface other than that due to normal fluid forces.

In engineering thermodynamics the only sorts of external work of importance are *shear (shaft or stirring) work and electrical work*. In Fig. 8.1 the only external work occurs where the control surface cuts the engine shaft; in this case, therefore, W_x is the shaft work delivered by the engine.

The heat transfer Q, is indicated by a single arrow, although it may actually be spread over the whole control surface. The sign convention for Q and W_x is the same as for systems (pp. 34 and 71). Thus the Q arrow points inwards although in this example heat is certainly transferred *from* the engine casing *to* the engine-room.

Extension of the definitions of heat and work to control surfaces. Heat and work have so far only been defined as interactions between systems. However, since the parts of the control surface where heat and external work interactions occur can be locally regarded as parts of a system boundary, the previous definitions apply without change.

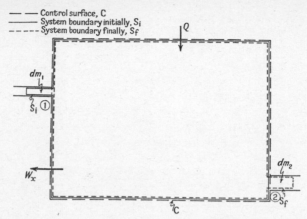

Fig. 8.2   Diagram used in the derivation of the steady-flow energy equation.

Comparison between control volume and system. The control-volume and system concepts have in common that they are both defined by *boundaries*. Further, as will be seen, their use consists in the way we can relate quantitatively the *flows across* the boundaries to the *changes within* them.

However the concepts are distinguished by two features:—

(i) The system boundary may, and usually does, change shape, position and orientation relative to the observer. The control-volume boundary does not by definition.

(ii) Material may, and usually does, flow across the control-volume boundary. No such flow takes place across a system boundary, by definition.

These similarities and distinctions have caused the control volume to be termed an *open system*. This term will not however be used in this book.

Derivation of the Steady-Flow Energy Equation

In order to make use of the First Law as stated in Chapter 6, a system must be chosen. Referring to Fig. 8.2, which shows the control volume C once more, with its contents omitted for clarity, we choose the system which initially has the boundary marked S_i. S_i is identical with C except that it also encloses some material in a short length of the inlet pipe near section 1. The extra material outside C (in this case steam) enclosed by S_i has mass dm_1.

We now consider the later instant of time, at which the mass dm_1 has just completely entered the control volume C; the system boundary now coincides with C at the section 1. Simultaneously, however, material has flowed along the exhaust pipe: the system, which by definition always comprises the same collection of matter, has therefore moved its boundary to the new position marked S_f in Fig. 8.2. S_f coincides with C except at the section 2, where it encloses an additional mass of material dm_2.

Application of the First Law. The system has now undergone a process. Q and W_X will be taken as the heat and external work flows during this process. The First Law may therefore be applied. We have, from eq. (6.5),

$$Q - W = \Delta E \qquad \qquad \dots \quad (8.1)$$

Here the heat transfer Q may be inserted directly. Evaluation of the net work, W, done by the system requires more thought, for, in addition to the external work W_X, the net work W must include the displacement work done by the moving parts of the system boundary. If the specific volumes of the fluid at sections 1 and 2 are respectively v_1 and v_2, the volumes swept out by the corresponding parts of the system boundary are $v_1 \, . \, dm_1$ and $v_2 \, . \, dm_2$. If the local pressures are p_1 and p_2, the corresponding displacement work terms are $-p_1 v_1 \, . \, dm_1$ and $+p_2 v_2 \, . \, dm_2$, the signs being ascribed in accordance with the previous convention. We can therefore write

$$W = W_X - p_1 v_1 \, . \, dm_1 + p_2 v_2 \, . \, dm_2 \qquad \dots \quad (8.2)$$

In seeking an expression for ΔE in eq. (8.1), it is convenient to treat separately the parts of the system within the control volume and the parts outside it. We use the symbols $E_{C,i}$ and $E_{C,f}$ respectively for the initial and final energies of the contents of the control volume; the *specific* energies of the fluid in the pipes at sections 1 and 2 respectively are denoted by e_1 and e_2. It follows that:—
the initial energy of the system is

$$e_1 \, . \, dm_1 + E_{C,i};$$

the final energy of the system is

$$E_{C,f} + e_2 \, . \, dm_2.$$

Eq. (8.1), the First Law for the system in the specified process, can now be written as

$$Q - (W_X - p_1 v_1 \, . \, dm_1 + p_2 v_2 \, . \, dm_2) = E_{C,f} + e_2 \, . \, dm_2 - E_{C,i} - e_1 \, . \, dm_1$$
$$\dots \quad (8.3)$$

Re-arrangement of the equation. Eq. (8.3) will be re-arranged by introducing, (i) the condition that the flow is steady, and (ii) the Conservation-of-Mass principle.

If the flow is steady, so that changes in all measurable quantities within the control volume are either non-existent or cyclic, we can write

$$E_{C,f} = E_{C,i} \qquad \qquad \dots \quad (8.4)$$

wherein it is assumed that, if cyclic changes are in question, an integral number of cycles has taken place during the process considered. Thus, in the reciprocating-steam-engine example, the crank-shaft must be in the same position at the end of the process as at the beginning. Eq. (8.4) holds, even though each non-solid part of the control volume will be occupied by different particles of material at the two instants by reason of the flow; for the states of the particles are identical.

The Conservation-of-Mass principle is invoked to show that the two mass quantities, dm_1 and dm_2, must be equal; for otherwise there would be an accumulation of material within the control volume, which is contrary to the requirement of steady flow. We can therefore write

$$dm_1 = dm_2 = dm, \quad \text{say.} \qquad \dots \text{(8.5)}$$

Insertion of eq. (8.4) and eq. (8.5) in eq. (8.3) simplifies the latter equation, which now becomes

$$Q - W_x - dm(p_2v_2 - p_1v_1) = dm(e_2 - e_1) \qquad \dots \text{(8.6)}$$

It is convenient to collect all the fluid properties on one side of the equation and the two interactions at the control surface on the other side; the equation then becomes

$$Q - W_x = dm(e_2 + p_2v_2 - e_1 - p_1v_1) \qquad \dots \text{(8.7)}$$

Flow work. The pv terms in the above equations have arisen as expressions for the displacement work done at the moving system boundaries. In this connexion they are called *flow work*. Another reason for separating them from W_x in the equation is that it is the latter, the *external work*, that the engineer is interested in practically. It should be noted that pv and $p\,dv$ are *not* related as integral and differential of each other.

A separate misleading line of thought is sometimes provoked by calling pv "pressure energy", which carries with it the suggestions either that pv is already included within e, or that pv ought always to be added to e in order completely to describe the energy, whenever p and v are finite. *Both these suggestions are false.* The only legitimate physical interpretation of pv in this context is that it represents the work done by the adjacent fluid in forcing unit mass of the fluid into or out of the control volume as the flow proceeds. The name "pressure energy" should never be used.

Refinement of e. To proceed with the derivation of the Steady-Flow Energy equation, it is necessary to consider more closely the nature of the energy e for the substances of importance in engineering. For the moment, only *pure substances* will be considered; the extension to substances in which chemical reaction occurs is made on p. 131.

In Chapter 7, eq. (7.3), it was stated that e for a pure substance may be written as:

$$e = u + \text{terms accounting for motion, gravity,}$$
$$\text{capillarity, electricity and magnetism} \qquad \dots \text{(8.8)}$$

For most fluids of interest to the mechanical engineer, capillarity, electricity and magnetism produce negligible effects; their influences will therefore be neglected. In flow problems, however, motion must obviously be considered, and the hydroelectric example given above shows that gravity can be important. We therefore now consider, in turn, the contributions of motion and gravity to the energy. It is possible to treat them separately, and then add the resulting expressions, because both are

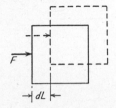

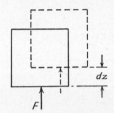

Fig. 8.3   Rigid body accelerated by the force F.

Fig. 8.4   Rigid body raised in a gravitational field.

determined by the relative positions of the system and the observer, which can obviously be altered by choosing a different observer, without altering properties of the system like pressure, temperature and specific volume. Both the results to be derived will be familiar from elementary mechanics; they are given here for formal completeness.

Kinetic energy. Consider the rigid system illustrated in Fig. 8.3. It is acted upon by a single force F, and in the process to be considered moves a small distance dL in the direction of the force. In this process the velocity of the system increases from V to $V + dV$, but there are no changes in other system properties. Heat transfer is absent $(Q = 0)$.

The work done by the system is $-F \, dL$ because the surroundings could have carried out the same process and done work $F \, dL$ by raising weights instead of accelerating the system. The First Law, eq. (6.5), for the process can therefore be written

$$0 - (-F \, dL) = m \, de \qquad \ldots \quad (8.9)$$

where m is the mass of the system and de is the increase in its specific energy.

Now F may be related to the velocity change dV by Newton's Second Law of Motion, eq. (2.2), which runs

$$F = \frac{m}{g_0} \frac{dV}{d\tau} \qquad \ldots \quad (8.10)$$

where τ stands for time so that $dV/d\tau$ is the acceleration.

From the theory of kinematics, we have

$$\frac{dV}{d\tau} = \frac{V \, dV}{dL} = \frac{1}{2} \frac{d(V^2)}{dL} \qquad \ldots \quad (8.11)$$

whence

$$F = \frac{m}{g_0} \cdot \frac{1}{2} \frac{(\mathrm{d}V^2)}{\mathrm{d}L} \qquad \qquad \ldots \quad (8.12)$$

Substituting eq. (8.12) in eq. (8.9) and re-arranging, we have the required relation between the changes in specific energy and in the velocity, as

$$\mathrm{d}e = \frac{1}{2g_0} \, \mathrm{d}(V^2) \qquad \qquad \ldots \quad (8.13)$$

For a large change of the above type (adiabatic, rigid system boundary), eq. (8.13) integrates to

$$e_2 - e_1 = \frac{V_2^2}{2g_0} - \frac{V_1^2}{2g_0} \qquad \qquad \ldots \quad (8.14)$$

where suffixes 1 and 2 denote the initial and final states.

Gravitational potential energy. To account for the contribution of gravity, we consider the rigid system of mass m shown in Fig. 8.4, executing an adiabatic process in which it is raised slowly and vertically upwards by a force F through a small distance dz in a gravitational field which is such that freely-falling bodies have an acceleration g.

The First Law for the process is

$$0 - (-F \, \mathrm{d}z) = m \, \mathrm{d}e \qquad \qquad \ldots \quad (8.15)$$

by the same reasoning as before.

From Newton's Second Law and the statement about the gravitational field (p. 22), we know that the force executed by the latter, i.e., the weight of the body, which must be numerically equal to F, is given by

$$F = \frac{mg}{g_0} \qquad \qquad \ldots \quad (8.16)$$

Combining eq. (8.15) and eq. (8.16), and re-arranging, the required relation between the increase in specific energy and the increase in elevation is found to be

$$\mathrm{d}e = \frac{g \, \mathrm{d}z}{g_0} \qquad \qquad \ldots \quad (8.17)$$

For a large adiabatic change of elevation of a rigid body in a *uniform* gravitational field, eq. (8.17) integrates to

$$e_2 - e_1 = \frac{gz_2}{g_0} - \frac{gz_1}{g_0} \qquad \qquad \ldots \quad (8.18)$$

The new expression for e. By reason of the two results just derived, we can now re-write eq. (8.8) for a pure substance as

$$e = u + \frac{V^2}{2g_0} + \frac{gz}{g_0} + \text{terms accounting for capillarity,} \\ \text{electricity and magnetism} \qquad \ldots \quad (8.19)$$

Here z is to be measured, like e itself, from some arbitrary base state. V, the velocity, is measured relative to the observer. The terms $V^2/2g_0$ and gz/g_0 are known respectively as the kinetic energy and the gravitational potential energy of the system per unit mass.

The Steady-Flow Energy Equation for a pure substance. Eq. (8.19) will now be inserted, with the omission of the usually negligible capillarity, electricity and magnetism terms, in eq. (8.8), which it will be recalled represents the application of the First Law of Thermodynamics to steady flow through a control volume. Eq. (8.8) then becomes

$$Q - W_x = dm\left(u_2 + p_2v_2 + \frac{V_2^2}{2g_0} + \frac{gz_2}{g_0} - u_1 - p_1v_1 - \frac{V_1^2}{2g_0} - \frac{gz_1}{g_0}\right)$$

$$\ldots \ (8.20)$$

Here the terms u and pv have been placed together in order to make obvious the next step: their substitution by the enthalpy h, defined by eq. (7.8) as

$$h \equiv u + pv \qquad \ldots \ (8.21)$$

Simultaneously with this substitution we change the meanings of Q and W_x slightly, so that they now stand for heat transfer and external work *per unit mass flowing*. dm can therefore be dropped from the equation, which becomes

$$Q - W_x = h_2 + \frac{V_2^2}{2g_0} + \frac{gz_2}{g_0} - h_1 - \frac{V_1^2}{2g_0} - \frac{gz_1}{g_0}$$

or $$Q - W_x = \Delta\left(h + \frac{V^2}{2g_0} + \frac{gz}{g_0}\right) \qquad \ldots \ (8.22)$$

where $\Delta(\ldots)$ stands for "increase in ..." as before.

Eq. (8.22) is the *Steady-Flow Energy Equation* for a pure substance. It is one of the most useful results of engineering thermodynamics and should be learned by heart. Its name is abbreviated below to S.F.E.E.

An example using the S.F.E.E.

Problem. Suppose that measurements made at the inlet and outlet to the triple-expansion steam engine of Fig. 8.1, together with reference to tabulated properties of steam, establish the pressures, temperatures, enthalpies, velocities, elevations and mass-flow rate as those shown on Fig. 8.5. The shaft power is also known. We wish to establish the heat transfer per hour from the engine casing and associated ducting as part of an analysis of whether further lagging of the engine is economically worth while. The S.F.E.E. can be used for this calculation. The pressures and temperatures do not feature in this calculation: they are listed on the diagram since the enthalpies will normally be evaluated by their aid.*

* Though they do not suffice if the steam is wet. See p. 156.

Solution. The first step is to decide on the units in which the equation will be expressed. Here we choose ft lb_f/lb_m steam. Then W_x is given by

$$W_x = \frac{1000 \times 550 \times 60}{275} = 1 \cdot 20 \times 10^5 \text{ ft } lb_f/lb_m$$

where 550×60 is the number of ft lb_f/min equivalent to 1 horse-power.

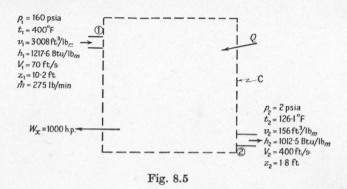

$p_1 = 160$ psia
$t_1 = 400°F$
$v_1 = 3 \cdot 008$ ft^3/lb$_m$
$h_1 = 1217 \cdot 6$ Btu/lb$_m$
$V_1 = 70$ ft/s
$z_1 = 10 \cdot 2$ ft
$\dot{m} = 275$ lb/min

$W_x = 1000$ h.p.

Q

C

$p_2 = 2$ psia
$t_2 = 126 \cdot 1°F$
$v_2 = 156$ ft^3/lb$_m$
$h_2 = 1012 \cdot 5$ Btu/lb$_m$
$V_2 = 400$ ft/s
$z_2 = 1 \cdot 8$ ft

Fig. 8.5

Inserting the values shown on Fig. 8.5, with the enthalpy terms multiplied by the mechanical equivalent of heat, 778 ft lb_f/Btu, and with g_0 given the appropriate value $32 \cdot 17$ lb_m ft/lb_f s^2, the S.F.E.E., eq. (8.22), becomes

$$Q - 1 \cdot 2 \times 10^5 = \left(1012 \cdot 5 \times 778 + \frac{(400)^2}{2 \times 32 \cdot 17} + \frac{g \times 1 \cdot 8}{32 \cdot 17} \right)$$

$$- \left(1217 \cdot 6 \times 778 + \frac{(70)^2}{2 \times 32 \cdot 17} + \frac{g \times 10 \cdot 2}{32 \cdot 17} \right)$$

Taking $g = 32 \cdot 2$ ft/s^2 we get

$$Q - 1 \cdot 2 \times 10^5 = (8 \times 10^5 + 2 \cdot 5 \times 10^3 + 1 \cdot 8) - (9 \cdot 47 \times 10^5 + 76 \cdot 1 + 10 \cdot 2)$$

$$\therefore \qquad Q = -3 \cdot 79 \times 10^4 \text{ ft } lb_f/lb_m \text{ steam.}$$

Since the required answer should be in heat units per hour, we multiply Q by the steam mass flow rate and divide by J, giving

$$\text{Heat transfer} = -\frac{3 \cdot 79 \times 10^4 \times 275 \times 60}{778}$$

$$= -8 \cdot 05 \times 10^5 \text{ Btu/h.} \qquad \dots \textit{Answer}$$

Remarks. 1. The negative sign denotes that the heat transfer is from the steam to the surroundings.

2. Examination of the individual terms in the equation shows that the contribution of the gravitational potential energy terms is quite negligible. This is almost always the case when gases and vapours are in question.

The kinetic energy terms are also small; one is negligible. However, in many cases this is not so. For example, the kinetic energy of the steam leaving a turbine is usually appreciable.

Basis and units: various forms of the S.F.E.E.

Time basis. In the above example the working would have been slightly shorter had the basis of the equation been 1 hour. In that case Q and W_x would have stood respectively for the heat and external work transfers in ft lb_f/h. Introducing the symbol $\dot{m}$ for the steam flow rate in lb_m/h, the equation would be written

$$Q - W_x = \dot{m}\Delta\left(h + \frac{V^2}{2g_0} + \frac{gz}{g_0}\right) \qquad \ldots \quad (8.23)$$

In this equation each term within the brackets, including h, would still have the units of ft lb_f/lb_m of steam. If the enthalpy h is looked up in steam tables as Btu/lb_m, it must be multiplied by the mechanical equivalent of heat, 778 ft lb_f/Btu.

Sometimes, when using a time basis, the heat and work flow rates are given the symbols $\dot{Q}$ and $\dot{W}_x$ instead of Q and W_x. This has advantages. However, it is impossible to introduce different symbols for every unit system, so it is necessary to examine the units in each case. Examples of unit systems in common use now follow.

Heat units. Whether work or heat units are used in the S.F.E.E. is a matter of convenience. In the latter case, with Q and W_x both as Btu/lb_m, the equation may be written

$$Q - W_x = \Delta\left(h + \frac{V^2}{2g_0J} + \frac{gz}{g_0J}\right) \qquad \ldots \quad (8.24)$$

It may be thought inconsistent that J is here introduced in the denominator of the kinetic and gravitational potential energy terms but not as a divisor of W_x, nor, in eq. (8.23), as a multiplier of h. It *is* inconsistent. The practice is justified on the grounds that we have become accustomed to the fact that Q, W_x and h may be in heat or work units, but that the form of the kinetic and gravitational terms so obviously suggests ft, lb_f, and lb_m that J seems definitely called for. The individual can, of course, please himself in this matter.

Practice in mechanics and fluid mechanics. In subjects involving a large amount of algebra, anything that reduces the number of symbols is advantageous. Rigid-body and fluid mechanics are such subjects, and moreover they are largely concerned with Newton's Second Law of Motion. As a result it is usual to use unit systems in which g_0 is numerically unity. If this practice is followed, g_0 may be omitted from the equation. The S.F.E.E. then becomes

$$Q - W_x = \Delta\left(h + \frac{V^2}{2} + gz\right) \qquad \ldots \quad (8.25)$$

Each term then has the units of, for example, ft poundals/lb_m or ft lb_f/slug (see Chapter 2). If finally numerical evaluation in terms of lb_f and lb_m is required, g_0 must of course appear again as $32 \cdot 17 \, lb_m$ ft/lb_f s^2.

Practice in hydraulics. Although logically a branch of fluid mechanics, hydraulics has historically a different origin. Moreover, being particularly concerned with flowing water, an important property of which is its "head", measured in vertical feet, a unit system is often adopted which results in the S.F.E.E. being written as

$$Q - W_x = \Delta \left(\frac{hg_0}{g} + \frac{V^2}{2g} + z \right) \qquad \ldots \quad (8.25)$$

Here the units are feet, as is obvious from the gravitational term. This arises because the energy terms are in ft lb$_f$ per "lb wt" of material, and lb wt is just a different name for lb$_f$ (see p. 21). The enthalpy h in eq. (8.25) is left as ft lb$_f$/lb$_m$ to emphasise that thermal properties are always tabulated with a mass unit as basis so that they should be valid for all points of the earth's gravitational field. h must therefore be multiplied by g_0/g.

What not to do. Because in common unit systems g and g_0 are often nearly the same *numerically*, slipshod use of units has become common. Thus the S.F.E.E. may be found written as

$$"Q - W_x = \Delta \left(h + \frac{V^2}{2g_0} + z \right)" \qquad \ldots \quad (8.26)$$

Unfortunately the user often gets the right answer and is confirmed in his error. But his confusion of thought always catches up with him in the end.

Final general remarks on the S.F.E.E.

Before considering particular engineering applications, a few more points need to be made about the validity of the S.F.E.E.

Identification of steady flow. For purposes of applying the S.F.E.E. the foregoing discussion shows that steady flow can be deemed to exist if:—

(i) The states and rates of the material streams crossing the control volume boundaries do not change with time.

(ii) *Either*, the state at each point within the control volume does not change with time,

    or, only cyclic variations of these states occur.

(iii) *Either*, the heat and work flow rates do not change with time,

    or the heat and work flow rates, averaged over a single cycle, do not change with time.

Control volume with many streams of material. When deriving the S.F.E.E. a single entering stream and a single leaving one were considered. The form for the more general case where there are many such streams is obvious without further proof. In this case it is convenient to adopt a time basis, whereupon the S.F.E.E. becomes

$$\dot{Q} - \dot{W}_x = \sum_{\text{out}} \dot{m} \left(h + \frac{V^2}{2g_0} + \frac{gz}{g_0} \right) - \sum_{\text{in}} \dot{m} \left(h + \frac{V^2}{2g_0} + \frac{gz}{g_0} \right) \quad \ldots \quad (8.27)$$

where $\sum_{\text{out}}$ and $\sum_{\text{in}}$ stand respectively for the summations of all the out-flowing and in-flowing fluxes of enthalpy, kinetic energy and gravitational potential energy.

The significance of non-uniform entering streams. In deriving the S.F.E.E. we have supposed that, for example, the velocity of the entering stream at the control volume boundary has a unique value. On reflection, however, we remember that the velocity varies across the pipe cross-section, as seen in Fig. 3.23. The usual practice is to use the mean value of velocity obtained from the equation

$$\dot{m} = \frac{AV}{v} \qquad \qquad \dots \quad (8.28)$$

where $\dot{m}$ is the mass flow rate, A is the cross-sectional area, and v is the specific volume (which is also *assumed* uniform). This involves a negligible error in most cases.

In fluid mechanics problems, however, for example when studying the flow of air from a cascade of compressor or turbine blades, the non-uniformity is all-important. We then imagine an infinite number of streams to be crossing the control volume boundary. The summations of eq. (8.27) now become integrals, and the S.F.E.E. is written as

$$\dot{Q} - \dot{W}_x = \int_C \left(h + \frac{V^2}{2g_0} + \frac{gz}{g_0} \right) d\dot{m} \qquad \dots \quad (8.29)$$

where $d\dot{m}$ is the mass flow rate in an infinitesimal stream, positive if outwards, negative if inwards, and $\int_C$ means that the integral is carried over the whole control volume boundary,

Extension to flow processes involving chemical reaction. So far we have supposed the flowing material to be a pure substance. Provided an extended definition for enthalpy is used, a form of the S.F.E.E. covering chemically-reacting substances can also be derived. This is done in connexion with one of the particular examples below (p. 131).

PARTICULAR EXAMPLES OF STEADY FLOW

We now apply the Steady-Flow Energy Equation to a number of common engineering examples. Incidentally more general matters will be touched on, namely the Continuity Equation and the aforesaid extension to reacting substances.

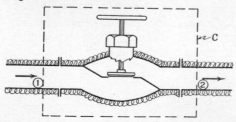

Fig. 8.6   Throttling. A partially open valve in a pipe line.

Throttling

When a fluid flows through a restriction such as an almost closed valve or a plug of porous material placed in a pipe-line, there is an appreciably lower pressure on the downstream than on the upstream side of the restriction. The flow is then said to have been *throttled*. Fig. 8.6 illustrates the situation in an insulated pipe. The S.F.E.E. can be applied to relate the downstream conditions to those upstream, provided that a control volume is chosen sufficiently large so that the outgoing stream, at section 2 in Fig. 8.6, is reasonably uniform.

Since in this example the process may be taken as adiabatic and there is no external work, the S.F.E.E., eq. (8.22) becomes

$$0 = h_2 + \frac{V_2^2}{2g_0} - h_1 - \frac{V_1^2}{2g_0} \qquad \ldots \quad (8.30)$$

wherein the gravitational potential energy terms have been ignored as being too small.

Often the pipe velocities in throttling are so low that the kinetic energy terms are also negligible. We then have

$$h_2 = h_1 \qquad \ldots \quad (8.31)$$

signifying that the enthalpy is unchanged.

Of course the friction forces on the wall of a long insulated pipe cause a fall of pressure even in the absence of restrictions like valves. This can also be classified as throttling. In these cases however it is often not permissible to neglect the change in kinetic energy. For the reduced pressure causes the specific volume of the fluid to increase. This increase may be so large, in the case of a vapour or gas, that the fluid must flow much faster at the downstream end than does the relatively dense in-flowing material. In an extreme case the velocity at the downstream end can reach the velocity of sound. Taking this at a typical value of 1000 ft/sec, we have

$$\frac{V_2^2}{2g_0} = \frac{(1000)^2}{2 \times 32 \cdot 17} = 15{,}600 \text{ ft lb}_f/\text{lb}_m$$

$$= 20 \text{ Btu/lb}_m$$

In general, if the downstream state has been calculated from eq. (8.31) it is always necessary to check the downstream kinetic energy to make sure that the change of kinetic energy is indeed negligible.*

Adiabatic machines

Under this title we consider such apparatus as turbines and reciprocating engines which give a positive power output, and rotary or reciprocating compressors which absorb power. Often these are well-lagged, so that the heat transfer can be neglected.

With *reciprocating machines*, the flow velocities are often small and the kinetic energy terms can be neglected. The S.F.E.E., eq. (8.22) then becomes

$$-W_x = h_2 - h_1 \qquad \ldots \quad (8.32)$$

* End note 5.

wherein the gravitational term is omitted as usual. It is evident that if the power output is positive, the enthalpy of the leaving fluid is less than that of the entering fluid by the amount of the work done per lb_m of fluid. With compressors, on the other hand, the leaving fluid has the higher enthalpy.

EXAMPLE

Problem. At entry to the reciprocating compressor of a refrigerator, the refrigerant, Freon 12, has a pressure and temperature of 30 psia and 12°F respectively. At exit from the compressor the Freon has a pressure of 120 psia and a temperature of 112°F. The flow is steady.

Evaluate the external work per lb_m of Freon assuming the compressor to be adiabatic and the kinetic and potential energies to be negligible.

Solution. Since the machine is adiabatic and changes of velocity and height are negligible, the form of S.F.E.E. given in eq. (8.32) is appropriate. To obtain W_x we therefore require the values of h_1 and h_2, the enthalpy of the Freon at entry to and exit from the compressor respectively. These are obtained from tables of properties of Freon and are as follows:—

At $\qquad p_1 = 30$ psia, $\qquad t_1 = 12$°F: $\quad h_1 = 79 \cdot 5$ Btu/lb$_m$

$\qquad\qquad p_2 = 120$ psia, $\qquad t_2 = 112$°F: $\quad h_2 = 91 \cdot 3$ Btu/lb$_m$

Inserting these values in eq. (8.32) we get

$$-W_x = 91 \cdot 3 - 79 \cdot 5 = 11 \cdot 8$$

or $\qquad\qquad$ External work $= -11 \cdot 8$ Btu/lb$_m$ $\qquad$ ... *Answer.*

Rotary machines usually cause the fluid to flow at high velocity, so the kinetic energies cannot be neglected. We then have, from eq. (8.22) with $Q = 0$, that

$$-W_x = h_2 + \frac{V_2^2}{2g_0} - h_1 - \frac{V_1^2}{2g_0} \qquad \text{...} \quad (8.33)$$

In the case of steam turbines, the velocity of the dense in-flowing steam is often small so that $V_1^2/2g_0$ is negligible.

EXAMPLE

Problem. The turbine of a jet engine receives a steady flow of gases at a pressure of 104 psia, a temperature of 1590°F and a velocity of 540 ft/s. It discharges the gases at a pressure of 31·5 psia, a temperature of 1155°F and a velocity of 1000 ft/s.

Evaluate the external work output of the turbine per lb_m of gas. The process may be assumed to be adiabatic.

Solution. In this case the effect of kinetic energy is important. We must therefore use the form of S.F.E.E. given in eq. (8.33) to analyse the conditions in this adiabatic machine. To evaluate W_x we need the enthalpy of the gas entering and leaving the turbine; these are obtained from property tables:

At $\quad p_1 = 104$ psia, $\qquad t_1 = 1590$°F: $\quad h_1 = 427 \cdot 5$ Btu/lb$_m$ of gas

At $\quad p_2 = 31 \cdot 5$ psia, $\qquad t_2 = 1155$°F: $\quad h_2 = 308 \cdot 0$ Btu/lb$_m$ of gas

Inserting these values in eq. (8.33), together with the values of velocity, the appropriate values of g_0, 32·17 lb_m ft/lb_f s², and of J, 778 ft lb_f/Btu, we get

$$-W_x = \left(308·0 + \frac{(1000)^2}{2 \times 32·17 \times 778}\right) - \left(427·5 + \frac{(540)^2}{2 \times 32·17 \times 778}\right)$$

$$= (308·0 + 20) - (427·5 + 5·8)$$

$$= -105·3 \text{ Btu/}lb_m \text{ of gas.}$$

i.e.   External work, $W_x = 105·3$ Btu/lb_m of gas.   ... *Answer*

Heat transfer equipment

Boilers and condensers have, as their main purpose, heat transfer to or from a steadily-flowing material. An example is the evaporator of a refrigerating plant shown in Fig. 8.7, in which liquid Freon enters a coil

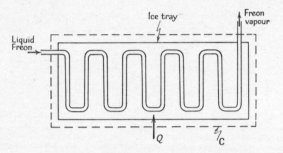

Fig. 8.7   Evaporator of a refrigerator.

in contact with the air in a refrigerator cabinet and leaves as vapour. The velocities are small, we suppose; there is no external work; and the gravitational terms are negligible. The S.F.E.E. (unit mass basis, eq. (8.22)) therefore may be written as

$$Q = h_2 - h_1 \qquad\qquad ... \quad (8.34)$$

It should be noted that there is no need to specify that the pressure should be uniform; in general, friction at the pipe walls causes the pressure at outlet to be somewhat below that at inlet. The frictional shear stresses on the wall of course do no external work: their points of application do not move.

The superheater. To illustrate the use of the S.F.E.E. in a situation where there are more than two entering streams, Fig. 8.8 shows the superheater of a boiler (N.B. a superheater raises the temperature of the steam above that of the boiling water). If a control volume were drawn to fit tightly over the superheater tubes, eq. (8.34) would be applicable. We choose however to consider a larger control volume, enclosing the insulated duct through which the flue gases from the furnace pass. Examination of the control volume boundary shows that there is no heat or external work transfer, but that there are four material streams: steam enters at S, and leaves at S_2; gases enter at G_1 and leave at G_2.

Assuming that the stream properties are uniform at the four cross-sections, that the steam and gas flow rates are $\dot{m}_S$ and $\dot{m}_G$ respectively, and that kinetic and gravitational potential energies are small, the S.F.E.E. (time basis, eq. (8.27)) gives

$$0 = \dot{m}_S(h_{S_2} - h_{S_1}) + \dot{m}_G(h_{G_2} - h_{G_1}) \qquad \ldots \ (8.35)$$

where the subscripts have obvious meanings.

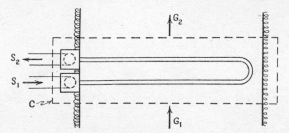

Fig. 8.8   Superheater of a boiler.

Re-arranging eq. (8.35), we have

$$\dot{m}_S(h_{S_2} - h_{S_1}) = \dot{m}_G(h_{G_1} - h_{G_2}) \qquad \ldots \ (8.36)$$

which shows that the increase in enthalpy of the steam flow is exactly equal to the enthalpy decrease of the gas stream. This is to be expected because the right- and left-hand sides of eq. (8.36) are respectively equal, numerically, to the heat transfer between the steam and gas streams.

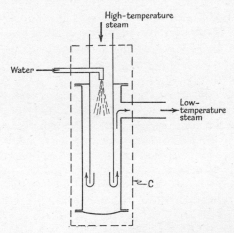

Fig. 8.9   Steam de-superheater.

The steam de-superheater. As a final example of equipment of this character, chosen to show that there is no necessity for the two streams to remain separate, Fig. 8.9 shows a steam de-superheater in which the steam has its temperature reduced by being mixed with water which is sprayed in from a hot-water main. This practice is adopted in chemical processing plant where accurate control of temperature is required, and also in boiler plant.

In this case it is impossible to draw a control volume around either of the two streams which enter, for the steam and injected water become completely mixed. However, the control volume C shown in Fig. 8.9

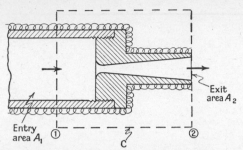

Fig. 8.10   Convergent-divergent nozzle.

provides all the information which is ordinarily required. If the mass flow rates of the injected water, of the steam entering, and of the steam leaving are $\dot{m}_W$, $\dot{m}_{S_1}$ and $\dot{m}_{S_2}$ respectively, and kinetic and gravitational energies are neglected as before, the S.F.E.E. eq. (8.27) gives

$$0 = \dot{m}_{S_2} h_{S_2} - (\dot{m}_{S_1} h_{S_1} + \dot{m}_{W_1} h_{W_1}) \qquad \dots \ (8.37)$$

The mass flow rates are obviously connected, by the mass-conservation principle, in the form

$$\dot{m}_{S_2} = \dot{m}_{W_1} + \dot{m}_{S_1} \qquad \dots \ (8.38)$$

Eq. (8.37) and eq. (8.38) are used, in conjunction with tabulated properties of water and steam, to determine how much water must be supplied in order to bring about a given temperature change in the steam.

The adiabatic nozzle

An example in which the kinetic energy terms are definitely not negligible is provided by the *nozzle*, the whole purpose of which is to cause the fluid to leave with a higher velocity than that with which it enters. A nozzle is a specially-shaped pipe. If only small velocity changes are to be caused, i.e., such that the associated pressure changes cause only small density changes, the nozzle is *convergent*, i.e., its cross-sectional area decreases in the direction of flow. For larger pressure differences, such as are encountered in steam turbines or in the exhaust jet of a rocket motor, the cross-section at first decreases and later increases; this is the case of the *convergent-divergent nozzle*, also called the *Laval nozzle* after its inventor. Fig. 8.10 shows an example.

If the nozzle is insulated ($Q = 0$) and the gravitational terms are neglected, the S.F.E.E. (unit mass basis, eq. (8.22)) relates the entering and leaving conditions in the form

$$0 = h_2 + \frac{V_2{}^2}{2g_0} - h_1 - \frac{V_1{}^2}{2g_0} \qquad \dots \ (8.39)$$

wherein W_x has of course been put equal to zero because there is no external work.

The meaning of eq. (8.39) can be seen more clearly by re-arranging as

$$\frac{V_2{}^2}{2g_0} - \frac{V_1{}^2}{2g_0} = h_1 - h_2 \qquad \ldots \quad (8.40)$$

which shows that the increase of kinetic energy is equal to the decrease of enthalpy.

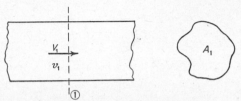

Fig. 8.11 Steady flow in a duct.

It should be noted that the equation holds whether the friction at the wall is appreciable or not. It is indeed identical with that which holds for an adiabatic throttling process in which the kinetic energy is not neglected.

Stagnation enthalpy. It is sometimes convenient to unite h and $V^2/2g_0$ in a single term. We therefore define the *stagnation enthalpy*, h_t, by

$$h_t \equiv h + \frac{V^2}{2g_0} \qquad \ldots \quad (8.41)$$

The term stagnation derives from the fact that h_t and h are identical if the fluid is made stagnant, i.e., if it is brought to rest in an adiabatic steady-flow process without external work.

The S.F.E.E. (unit mass basis, eq. (8.22)) can be re-written in terms of h_t as

$$Q - W_x = \left(h_t + \frac{gz}{g_0} \right) \qquad \ldots \quad (8.42)$$

The results derived for adiabatic throttling and the adiabatic nozzle can be summarised in the statement:—

In an adiabatic steady-flow process, with zero external work and negligible gravitational potential energy change, the stagnation enthalpy of the fluid remains constant. Symbolically,

$$Q = 0, \quad W_x = 0, \quad \Delta\left(\frac{gz}{g_0}\right) = 0: \quad h_{t2} = h_{t1} \qquad \ldots \quad (8.43)$$

The continuity equation. We have mentioned above the need to check the magnitude of the kinetic energy term even when neglecting it, but have not so far indicated how to do so. The influence of the cross-sectional area has also been mentioned. This is an appropriate point to introduce the *continuity equation*, which is an expression of the *conservation-of-mass principle*.

Consider the duct shown in Fig. 8.11 which at the section 1 has the cross-sectional area A_1. Let the velocity of flow have the uniform value

V_1; let the specific volume of the fluid be v_1 and its mass flow rate be $\dot{m}$. Then the above four quantities are related by

$$\dot{m} = \frac{V_1 A_1}{v_1} \qquad \ldots \ (8.44)$$

The truth of this is most readily perceived by imagining the fluid to be at rest while the section 1 travels to the left at velocity V_1. Then in time $d\tau$ it travels a distance $V_1 \, d\tau$. Since the area is A_1, the volume swept out is $A_1 V_1 \, d\tau$. The mass of fluid contained in this volume is $A_1 V_1 \, d\tau / v_1$. The mass of fluid crossing the imaginary surface 1 in unit time is therefore $(A_1 V_1 \, d\tau)/(v_1 \, d\tau)$, i.e., it is $V_1 A_1 / v_1$. This is the required result, eq. (8.44).

Considering now steady flow through a control volume such as that of Fig. 8.10 for example, and noting that the conservation of mass requires that the mass flow rates at sections 1 and 2 must be identical, we have

$$\frac{V_1 A_1}{v_1} = \frac{V_2 A_2}{v_2} \qquad \ldots \ (8.45)$$

This equation can also be applied at any section intermediate between 1 and 2, and in fact is so applied in designing the nozzle.

We note that at any section

$$A = \frac{\dot{m} v}{V} \qquad \ldots \ (8.46)$$

In a nozzle the velocity V increases continuously; this tends to require a decreasing area in the flow direction, a requirement that predominates at first. But the pressure decreases continuously. When the pressure fall becomes appreciable, the consequent increase in the specific volume v becomes more important, so that the ratio v/V begins to increase. This is the reason for the convergent-divergent form of nozzles for gases when the ratio of inlet pressure to outlet pressure is large.

The impulse turbine wheel

In this section an example is chosen which, as well as being immediately interesting to engineers, also illustrates that a control volume can be in motion relative to the earth and that the magnitude of the external work term depends on this motion.

Description. Fig. 8.12a illustrates a section through a turbine wheel. This consists of a rotating disc (rotor), to the periphery of which are fitted blades R which are curved so that the gas, which flows from left to right through the annular gap, has its angle of swirl (about the rotor axis) altered. The initial swirl is given to the gas by fixed blades or nozzles N situated to the left, i.e., upstream, of the rotor.

Fig. 8.12b shows more clearly the geometry of the nozzles N and rotor blades R. It represents a developed section along the cylindrical surface marked A in Fig. 8.12a. The nozzles, N, are to be regarded as at rest, while the rotor blades, R, are moving vertically upwards.

The velocity relationships are shown by the velocity diagram of Fig. 8.12c, which employs the convention usual in the kinematics of machines. Points r and n represent respectively the velocities of the rotor and the nozzles; the line joining them therefore represents the magnitude and

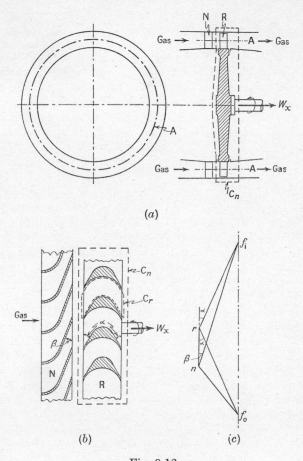

(a)

(b)   (c)

Fig. 8.12
(a) Single-stage impulse turbine.
(b) Impulse turbine blading.
(c) Velocity vector diagram for impulse blading.

direction of the velocity of R relative to N. It is assumed that the flowing gas leaves the nozzles and both enters and leaves the rotor blade passages in directions parallel to the adjacent surfaces. Then if f_i and f_o represent respectively the velocity vectors of the gas entering and leaving the rotor, these points must be situated such that $\angle f_i nr = \beta$ and $\angle f_o rn = \alpha$ in Fig. 8.12c corresponding to the angles β and α shown on Fig. 8.12b.

The turbine chosen for illustration is of the *impulse* type and has negligible friction: for present purposes this means that the gas experiences no change of pressure or temperature in passing through the rotor passages, and that the velocity *relative to the rotor* is unchanged, i.e., $f_i r = f_o r$. It also means that the inlet and outlet gas angles, α, are identical and that the axial velocities of the entering and leaving gas are identical so that on Fig. 8.12c f_o is vertically below f_i.

The reader is asked to accept the above brief description as sufficient for the time being. Fuller discussion can be found in more advanced texts.

Application of the S.F.E.E. We first consider the control volume marked C_n in Figs. 8.12a and b. This is supposed to be at rest relative to the nozzles and relative to the earth. Examination of its boundaries shows that there is an external work transfer W_x and a steady flow of gas. Since heat transfer is absent (we assume), and the enthalpies of the entering and leaving gases are equal (because it is an impulse turbine), the S.F.E.E. eq. (8.22) becomes

$$-W_x = (V_{nf_o}^{21} - V_{nf_i}^2)/2g_0 \qquad \ldots \quad (8.47)$$

Here the suffix nf_o means "leaving gas relative to nozzles (rest)" and nf_i means "entering gas relative to nozzles (rest)". The velocities are represented respectively by the lengths nf_o and nf_i in Fig. 8.12c, where it is evident that the outlet velocity is considerably smaller than the inlet velocity. Eq. (8.47) shows that the external work per lb_m of gas is equal to the decrease in its kinetic energy measured relative to the control volume at rest (C_n).

We now consider a second control volume: that marked C_r in Fig. 8.12b. This encloses one passage between the rotor blades, *and moves with the rotor*. Examination of its boundary shows that not only is there no heat transfer, but there is *no external work either;* for no shaft protrudes through the boundary of C_r as it did through that of C_n. How has this result, apparently contradictory to eq. (8.47), come about?

The explanation becomes clear when we apply the S.F.E.E. to the moving control volume C_r. As before, Q and the enthalpy change are zero. With W_x also zero we have

$$0 = (V_{rf_o}^2 - V_{rf_i}^2)/2g_0 \qquad \ldots \quad (8.48)$$

i.e. $\qquad\qquad V_{rf_o} = V_{rf_i} \qquad\qquad\qquad \ldots \quad (8.49)$

Here the *relative* velocities between rotor and gas have been used because the control volume moves with the rotor.

Eq. (8.49) shows that, relative to the rotor, the gas leaves with the same velocity* as that with which it enters. But this we already knew: it is a consequence of having an impulse or constant-pressure turbine wheel. There is therefore no contradiction between the two applications of the S.F.E.E.: the work terms are different because of the different frame of reference (see pp. 23 and 35); but so are the kinetic energy changes for the same reason. ·

* In magnitude, not direction.

Further analysis in terms of the momentum change. The reader who is still worried by the difference between the above two results may find the following analysis helpful:—

Application of Newton's Second Law of Motion to control volume C_r for the direction of blade movement (see fluid mechanics texts for justification) yields

$$F = \frac{\dot{m}}{g_0} \left(V_{\text{rf}_1} \cos \alpha - V_{\text{rf}_0} \cos (-\alpha) \right) \qquad \ldots \text{(8.50)}$$

where F is the force exerted on the blades in the direction of motion, $\dot{m}$ is the mass flow rate of the gas, and the cosines are introduced to give the velocity components of the gas in the direction of rotor movement. The right-hand side is the difference between the entering and leaving momentum fluxes.

Shifting now to a co-ordinate system at rest relative to the earth, i.e., relative to the nozzles, and introducing the blade speed V_{nr}, the rate at which the gases do work on the rotor becomes

$$\text{rotor power} = F V_{\text{nr}} \qquad \ldots \text{(8.51)}$$

Expressing F in terms of gas velocities from eq. (8.50) and dividing by $\dot{m}$ to get the work per unit mass of gas, we obtain

$$\text{work on rotor per lb}_m \text{ of gas} = \frac{V_{\text{nr}}}{g_0} \left(V_{\text{rf}_1} + V_{\text{rf}_0} \right) \cos \alpha \qquad \ldots \text{(8.52)}$$

But this must equal W_x which has already been expressed by eq. (8.47). Equating the right-hand sides of the two equations,

$$\frac{V_{\text{nf}_0}^2 - V_{\text{nf}_1}^2}{2g_0} = \frac{V_{\text{nr}}}{g_0} \left(V_{\text{rf}_1} + V_{\text{rf}_0} \right) \cos \alpha \qquad \ldots \text{(8.53)}$$

Each of the velocities in eq. (8.53) is represented by a length in Fig. 8.12c. Application of trigonometry to the velocity diagram should enable us to check the correctness of our analysis. This is left as an exercise for the student.

Steady-flow combustion processes

The First Law, as introduced in Chapter 6, is valid for all types of systems and processes. In introducing the Steady-Flow Energy Equation, however, only pure substances were considered. We now remove this restriction to the extent of allowing chemical reaction to occur. This may be done simply by replacing u and h by the new symbols u' and h', where the prime signifies that we are concerned with substances which may react chemically, i.e., with materials which are not pure substances (see definition on p. 329).

We now have, in the absence of capillarity, electricity and magnetism,

$$e = u' + \frac{V^2}{2g_0} + \frac{gz}{g_0} * \qquad \ldots \text{(8.54)}$$

and

$$h' = u' + pv * \qquad \ldots \text{(8.55)}$$

* These equations should be compared with the corresponding ones for pure substances, viz., eq. (8.19) and eq. (7.8).

For such substances, more than two independent properties will be needed to specify the state, but this is not required in the derivation of the S.F.E.E. The latter now runs, for unit mass of flowing material,

$$Q - W_x = \Delta\left(h' + \frac{V^2}{2g_0} + \frac{gz}{g_0}\right) \qquad \ldots \quad (8.56)$$

In this form the S.F.E.E. may be applied to an internal-combustion engine for example. Considering the diesel engine shown in Fig. 8.13,

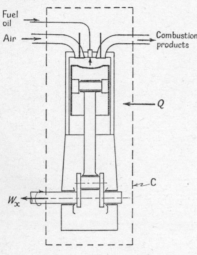

Fig. 8.13   Diesel engine.

and noting that the material flows crossing the boundaries are air and fuel oil flowing inward, and combustion products outwards, the S.F.E.E. (time basis, eq. (8.27)) becomes

$$\dot{Q} - \dot{W}_x = \dot{m}_p h'_p - (\dot{m}_a h'_a + \dot{m}_t h'_t) \ldots \quad (8.57)$$

where the suffixes p, a, and f refer to products, air and fuel respectively, $\dot{m}$ signifies mass flow rate, $\dot{Q}$ and $\dot{W}_x$ are per unit time, and the kinetic and gravitational terms have been neglected. Normally in internal combustion engines $\dot{Q}$ will be negative; it comprises the heat "losses" from the engine to the cooling water and atmosphere.

The subject of combustion will be returned to in Chapter 16. In the meantime we emphasise that $\dot{Q}$ is *not* the "calorific value" of the fuel.

EXAMPLE

Problem. A petrol engine consumes 34 lb$_m$ of fuel per hour and develops 70 brake horse-power. The air mass flow rate into the engine is 470 lb$_m$ per hour, the temperature of the fuel-air stream entering the engine is 60°F and the temperature of the exhaust gases leaving the engine is 1650°F. The heat transfer rate to the jacket cooling water and surroundings is 3500 Btu/min.

Evaluate the increase in the specific enthalpy of the entering fuel-air stream, assuming the kinetic and potential energies to be negligible.

Solution. The problem requires the evaluation of $\Delta h'$ in eq. (8.56). Basis: 1 lb$_m$ of (fuel + air) entering the engine and leaving it as combustion products.

$$\text{Fuel} + \text{air} = 34 + 470 = 504 \text{ lb}_m/\text{h}$$

$$\dot{W}_x \equiv 70 \text{ h.p.} \equiv \frac{70 \times 550 \times 3600}{778} \text{ Btu/h}$$

$$= 178,200 \text{ Btu/h}$$

$$W_x = \frac{178,200}{504} = 353 \text{ Btu/lb}_m \text{ of (fuel + air)}$$

where 550×3600 ft lb$_f \equiv 1$ horse-power hour and 778 ft lb$_f$/Btu is the mechanical equivalent of heat.

$$\dot{Q} = -3500 \text{ Btu/min}$$

$$Q = -\frac{3500 \times 60}{504} = -416 \text{ Btu/lb}_m \text{ of (fuel + air)}$$

where the negative signifies that the heat transfer is *from* the fuel-air stream as it passes through the engine. Inserting these values in eq. (8.56) we get

$$-416 - 353 = \Delta h' + 0 + 0$$

whence $\qquad \Delta h' = -769 \text{ Btu/lb}_m \text{ of (fuel + air)} \qquad \ldots \text{ Answer}$

Remarks. 1. The negative sign indicates that the enthalpy of the fuel-air stream *decreases* even though the temperature *increases*.

2. The "calorific value" of the fuel does not appear in the analysis.

COMPARISON OF THE STEADY-FLOW ENERGY EQUATION AND THE EULER AND BERNOULLI EQUATIONS OF FLUID MECHANICS.

Several mentions of the science of *fluid mechanics* have already been made, and it is clear that the thermodynamics and mechanics of flow processes are intimately related. In this section a short digression will be made in order to clarify the distinction between the Steady-Flow Energy Equation and two equations which belong to fluid mechanics: the *Euler Equation* and *the Bernoulli Equation*. Emphasis is given to this matter because the S.F.E.E. is often confused with, i.e., thought to be identical with, one or other of these equations.

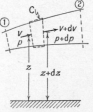

Fig. 8.14 Steady flow in a stream-tube.

The Euler Equation. Fig. 8.14 shows a fluid flowing steadily along a "stream-tube", which for our purposes we can regard as an imaginary pipe enclosing the flow and of sufficiently small cross-section for the velocity to be taken as uniform across a cross-section. We consider the thin control volume C at rest, shown by the dotted line. This has two faces at right angles to the flow direction while the remainder of the control-volume boundary coincides with the surface of the stream-tube.

At the upstream face the stream velocity is V and the pressure is p; the mean elevation of the fluid above some arbitrary datum is z. At the downstream face the values of the corresponding quantities are $V + dV$, $p + dp$, and $z + dz$. Shear forces on the control surface boundaries are supposed absent.

Application of Newton's Second Law of Motion. It is shown in fluid mechanics texts that application of Newton's Second Law, i.e., the momentum principle, to this control volume yields the relationship

$$v \, dp + \frac{V \, dV}{g_0} + \frac{g \, dz}{g_0} = 0 \qquad \ldots \quad (8.58)$$

In words, this equation states that the sum of the forces acting on the fluid in the control volume, resolved in the direction of motion, is equal to the rate of flow of momentum out of the control volume minus the rate of flow of momentum into the control volume.

Eq. (8.58) is the *Euler Equation*.

Restrictions on the validity of the Euler Equation. The conditions under which eq. (8.58) is valid will now be summarised. They are:—

(i) Steady flow.

(ii) No shear forces, i.e., no friction,
no shaft or stirring work.

(iii) No electrical, magnetic or capillary forces.

It is not necessary that heat transfer should be absent however. For that matter an electric current acting in a purely dissipative (ohmic) manner may also be present.

The Bernoulli Equation. The thickness of the control volume of Fig. 8.14 in the stream direction was infinitesimal. A control volume of finite thickness may be considered however. Newton's Second Law for such a control volume is given by *integrating* the Euler Equation in the stream direction. We note first that the term $V\,dV/g_0$ can be regarded, according to the rules of differentiation, as $d(\frac{1}{2}V^2)/g_0$. Denoting the upstream face of the finite control volume by suffix 1 and the downstream face by suffix 2 (Fig. 8.14), integration of eq. (8.58) yields

$$\int_1^2 v\,dp + \frac{V_2^2}{2g_0} - \frac{V_1^2}{2g_0} + \frac{gz_2}{g_0} - \frac{gz_1}{g_0} = 0 \qquad \ldots \quad (8.59)$$

This is known as the *Bernoulli Equation*. Its conditions of validity are the same as those of the Euler Equation.

The Bernoulli Equation for an incompressible fluid. The Bernoulli Equation is frequently required for a fluid such as water which can be regarded as *incompressible;* that is to say that the fluid density may be regarded as constant. Gases may also be treated as incompressible if the pressure changes are small. Since the specific volume v is the reciprocal of the density, it too is constant; v can therefore be taken outside the integral sign in eq. (8.59), which can consequently be written as

$$p_2 v - p_1 v + \frac{V_2^2}{2g_0} - \frac{V_1^2}{2g_0} + \frac{gz_2}{g_0} - \frac{gz_1}{g_0} = 0 \qquad \ldots \quad (8.60)$$

For comparison with the S.F.E.E., we write this as

$$0 = \Delta\left(pv + \frac{V^2}{2g_0} + \frac{gz}{g_0}\right) \qquad \ldots \quad (8.61)$$

wherein v is constant and $\Delta(\ldots)$ means "increase in . . ." as before.

Comparison of the Bernoulli Equation and the S.F.E.E. In order to show how the confusion of eq. (8.61) with the S.F.E.E. has come about, the latter will be written with $(u + pv)$ substituted for h. Eq. (8.22) then becomes

$$Q - W_x = \Delta\left(u + pv + \frac{V^2}{2g_0} + \frac{gz}{g_0}\right) \qquad \ldots \quad (8.62)$$

Comparison of eq. (8.61) and eq. (8.62) shows that they have several terms in common. This has led to the suggestion that the S.F.E.E. is merely an extended form of the Bernoulli Equation. That this is not so may be seen by noting the restricted conditions under which the Bernoulli Equation is valid. The most striking are:—

(i) Shear forces must be absent.

(ii) The flow must be incompressible (i.e., v = constant).

The S.F.E.E. on the other hand is valid whether friction is present or not, and regardless of how the density of the fluid changes.

The S.F.E.E. is therefore not an extended form of the Bernoulli Equation.

Combination of the Euler Equation with the S.F.E.E.

To emphasise the distinction between the Euler Equation, which is based on Newton's Second Law of Motion only, and the S.F.E.E., which is based on Newton's Second Law of Motion *and* the First Law of Thermodynamics, the equations will be combined. Since the Euler Equation is more general than the Bernoulli Equation for an incompressible fluid, the former will be used. It is therefore necessary to express the S.F.E.E. in differential form, i.e., to consider the form valid for a control volume of infinitesimal thickness in the flow direction. Differentiating eq. (8.62), we have

$$dQ - dW_x = du + p\,dv + v\,dp + \frac{V\,dV}{g_0} + \frac{g\,dz}{g_0} \quad \ldots \quad (8.63)$$

For comparison with eq. (8.58), dW_x must be put equal to zero. We then note that the Euler Equation states that the last three terms of eq. (8.63) are zero. *If the Euler Equation is valid*, therefore, the S.F.E.E. reduces to

$$dQ = du + p\,dv \quad\quad\quad \ldots \quad (8.64)$$

At first sight eq. (8.64) appears merely to be the First Law of Thermodynamics written for unit mass of fluid. Further thought reveals that eq. (8.64) is the particular form of the First Law valid for a pure substance, in the absence of gravity, motion, electricity, magnetism and capillarity in a process where the only work is displacement work.

Comments on equation (8.64)

1. The restriction to a pure substance was of course introduced in the way the S.F.E.E. was written. A more general form could have been used.

2. The required "absence" of gravity and motion appears more surprising. This merely means however that, in deriving eq. (8.64) from the First Law, the evaluation of the energy change and the work is done *with reference to a frame which moves with the fluid*.

3. The significant implication of eq. (8.64) is that the conditions for validity of the Euler Equation imply that only displacement work is done by the fluid particles in their travel. This is another way of saying that friction is absent and that all expansions of the fluid particles are fully-resisted.

4. In Chapter 11, p. 191, where we return to this subject, it will be shown that the condition that friction should be absent signifies that the flow is "reversible".

5. The most important lesson to learn from the present section is:— *The Steady-Flow Energy Equation is general; the Euler and Bernoulli Equations are not.*

FURTHER USES OF THE CONTROL-VOLUME CONCEPT

In the final section of this chapter we discuss the extension of the control-volume concept to unsteady flow processes. So far, the First Law has been applied to general processes by focussing attention on a fixed body of material, the system; only for steady-flow processes has the control volume been used. These procedures are still recommended for most problems encountered in engineering thermodynamics. However, in more advanced work, for example the theory of unsteady compressible fluid flow, the control-volume analysis is simpler than the system analysis. We lay the foundations for such advanced work in the subsequent paragraphs.

The First Law of Thermodynamics for unsteady processes: control-volume analysis

We return to eq. (8.3), which expresses the First Law written for the control volume shown in Fig. 8.2. Re-arranging, and writing $u + V^2/2g_0 + gz/g_0$ for e, this equation becomes

$$Q - W_{\mathrm{x}} = E_{\mathrm{C,f}} - E_{\mathrm{C,i}} + \mathrm{d}m_2\left(h_2 + \frac{V_2^2}{2g_0} + \frac{gz_2}{g_0}\right)$$

$$- \mathrm{d}m_1\left(h_1 + \frac{V_1^2}{2g_0} + \frac{gz_1}{g_0}\right) \qquad \ldots \quad (8.65)$$

Since the flow is not steady, we cannot this time write $E_{\mathrm{C,f}} = E_{\mathrm{C,i}}$ and $\mathrm{d}m_2 = \mathrm{d}m_1$. Instead we generalise eq. (8.65) to the case where there are arbitrary numbers of entering and leaving streams instead of the two streams of Fig. 8.2. Then eq. (8.65) becomes

$$Q - W_{\mathrm{x}} = E_{\mathrm{C,f}} - E_{\mathrm{C,i}} + \sum_{\mathrm{out}} \mathrm{d}m\left(h + \frac{V^2}{2g_0} + \frac{gz}{g_0}\right)$$

$$- \sum_{\mathrm{in}} \mathrm{d}m\left(h + \frac{V^2}{2g_0} + \frac{gz}{g_0}\right) \qquad \ldots \quad (8.66)$$

Here $\sum_{\mathrm{out}} \mathrm{d}m(\ldots)$ represents the sum of all the out-going fluxes of enthalpy, kinetic energy and gravitational potential energy, each h, V^2 and z being appropriate to the particular $\mathrm{d}m$ which it multiplies, while $\sum_{\mathrm{in}} \mathrm{d}m(\ldots)$ represents the sum of all the in-going fluxes in the same way. $E_{\mathrm{C,f}}$ and $E_{\mathrm{C,i}}$ represent as before respectively the final and initial energy contents of the control volume, it being understood that the material in the control volume at the end of the process differs from that there initially, both in its identity and its total mass. E_C includes the kinetic and gravitational potential energies of the material in the control volume, which in general comprises solids (pistons, springs, etc.) as well as fluid, but *there is no pv term* for either the solid or the fluid material. Thus, if only a pure substance is present within the control volume, we should evaluate the energy E_C of the material in the control volume at any instant by

$$E_C = \int_\sigma \left(u + \frac{V^2}{2g_0} + \frac{gz}{g_0} \right) \frac{d\sigma}{v} \qquad \dots \quad (8.67)$$

where $d\sigma$ is a volume element of the control volume, v is the local specific volume so that $d\sigma/v$ represents the mass of substance in the element $d\sigma$, u, V and z are the local values of these quantities, and $\int_\sigma$ means that the integral is carried out over the whole volume.

A warning example: the thermostatically-controlled tank

Use of eq. (8.66) is not recommended for elementary problems of unsteady flow: the system analysis is safer and just as simple. We conclude discussion of the First Law for the present by an illustration of the dangers of confusing the two approaches.

Fig. 8.15 shows a hot-water tank which has an electrical heating element which is controlled by a thermostat so as to maintain the water temperature at the constant value t_1. Cold water can enter from the supply pipe where the temperature is t_0. We wish to calculate the heat transfers from the heating element which ensue when (*a*) water is supplied to the tank, (*b*) when it is drawn off.

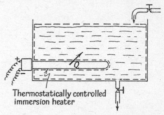

Thermostatically controlled immersion heater

Fig. 8.15 Thermostatically controlled hot-water tank.

How not to do it. A careless reading of the foregoing chapter might lead the student to write

$$\text{"First Law: } \dot{Q} = \frac{d}{d\tau}(mu)\text{"} \qquad \dots \quad (8.68)$$

where $\dot{Q}$ is the rate of heat supply, m is the mass of water in the tank and u is its internal energy per unit mass. Loosely, eq. (8.68) might be put into words as "heat transfer rate equals rate of change of internal energy", which has a convincing ring.

Since for water we can write

$$u = c_V(t - t_0) \qquad \dots \quad (8.69)$$

where c_V is the (nearly constant) specific heat at constant volume, t is the water temperature at any time, and t_0 is the temperature adopted for the base of enthalpy, eq. (8.68) can be written as

$$\dot{Q} = c_V \frac{d}{d\tau} m(t - t_0)$$

$$= c_V(t - t_0) \frac{dm}{d\tau} + c_V m \frac{dt}{d\tau} \qquad \dots \quad (8.70)$$

Now $dt/d\tau$, the time variation of tank water temperature, is made zero by the action of the thermostat. Our false form of the First Law therefore reduces to

$$Q = c_v(t - t_0)\frac{dm}{d\tau} \qquad \dots \quad (8.71)$$

Since in the present case the tank temperature is t_1 we have

$$Q = c_v(t_1 - t_0)\frac{dm}{d\tau} \qquad \dots \quad (8.72)$$

Case (a): In a filling process, the rate of increase of mass in the tank, $dm/d\tau$, is positive. We therefore find that the rate of heat input is also positive, as is to be expected; its magnitude can be evaluated from eq. (8.72). The heat transfer rate evaluated in this way is indeed *correct*, if the small flow work term is neglected. Perceiving this, the student may gain confidence in his formulation, eq. (8.68), of the First Law. A surprise awaits him however.

Case (b): Consider now the drawing off of water from the tank, no replacement by fresh water being provided. In this case $dm/d\tau$ is *negative*. Since $(t_1 - t_0)$ is still positive, the evaluation of Q from eq. (8.72) shows that this quantity is also negative, i.e., drawing off water from the tank apparently causes heat to flow *from* the tank *to* the heater element. This definitely does not correspond to reality.

The absurd result derives from the incorrect formulation of the First Law given in eq. (8.68).

Correct method. The problem may be correctly solved by either the system or control-volume analysis. In the former case, it is necessary to draw a system boundary, which of course moves during filling and emptying, and to apply the First Law directly to the material within this boundary. In the latter case, a suitable fixed control surface is chosen, for example surrounding the tank, and eq. (8.66) is applied; watch has to be kept on the boundaries of this control volume in order to note what material crosses it, a precaution omitted in writing eq. (8.68).

Analysis of the problem by these two correct methods is left as an exercise for the reader.

Final remarks on control volume and system

In conclusion it must be emphasised that the *explicit* use of the system and control volume is among the most important techniques, not only of thermodynamics, but of engineering analysis generally. The extent to which they assist in clarifying thought and separating the relevant from the irrelevant can only be appreciated by those who were taught thermodynamics without ever being enjoined to relate the fluxes across a boundary to the changes within.

Two remarks will indicate the wide relevance of the concepts:—

(i) In *structural analysis*, the "method of sections" is nothing else than the drawing of a system boundary around a part of the structure and requiring that the forces crossing its boundaries should be in equilibrium with the gravitational forces on the material within the boundary.

(ii) In *economics*, a control-volume boundary drawn around a country permits the rate of internal consumption of goods to be related to their rate of production in the country's factories and to their transport across the frontier. Subsidiary boundaries enclosing various classes of the community help in the analysis of the internal transfer of goods. Explicit use of the boundary concept can go far to demolish unsound economic (and thermodynamic) arguments.

BIBLIOGRAPHY

Shapiro, A. H., *Dynamics and Thermodynamics of Fluid Flow*, Ronald Press Co., Vol. I, 1953, Vol. II 1954.

CHAPTER 8—PROBLEMS

Note. Unless otherwise stated assume changes in elevation to be negligible and the gravitational acceleration to be standard.

8.1 (a) A system comprising $2 \cdot 1$ lb_m of a pure substance has a specific internal energy of 8 Btu/lb_m. The system is moving with a velocity of 400 ft/sec at an elevation 5000 feet above sea level. Evaluate the energy of the system relative to an observer at rest at sea level.

(b) The system undergoes a process to a final specific internal energy of 9 Btu/lb_m, a final velocity of 700 ft/s and a final elevation of 1000 feet. The work done on the system during the process is 1600 ft lb_f. Evaluate the magnitude and direction of the heat transfer during the process.

8.2 A steady flow of water at a temperature of 139°F and a pressure of 45 psia ($h = 106 \cdot 9$ Btu/lb_m) enters a section of the heating plant of a building in which there are no pumps. The water leaves the section at a temperature of 118°F and at a pressure of 40 psia ($h = 85 \cdot 9$ Btu/lb_m). The exit pipe is 85·5 ft above the entry pipe. Evaluate the heat transfer from the water, per pound of water flowing, assuming changes in kinetic energy to be negligible.

8.3 The gas leaving the turbine of an aero-gas-turbine jet engine flows steadily into the engine jet-pipe at a temperature of 1660°F, a pressure of 27·8 psia and a velocity of 900 ft/s relative to the pipe. The gas leaves the jet-pipe at a temperature of 1500°F and a pressure of 15·2 psia. Heat transfer from the gas is negligible. Using the following data evaluate the relative velocity of the gas leaving the jet-pipe.

For the gas   At $t = 1500°F$: $h = 369 \cdot 2$ Btu/lb_m

$t = 1660°F$: $h = 411 \cdot 8$ Btu/lb_m

8.4 A gas flows steadily through a rotary compressor. The gas enters the compressor at a temperature of 62°F and pressure of 15 psia with an enthalpy of 125·2 Btu/lb_m. The gas leaves the compressor at a temperature of 475°F and a pressure of 90 psia with an enthalpy of 225 Btu/lb_m. There is no net heat transfer to or from the gas as it flows through the compressor.

(a) Evaluate the external work done per pound of gas assuming the gas velocities at entry and exit to be negligible.

(b) Evaluate the external work done per pound of gas when the gas velocity at entry is 300 ft/s and that at exit is 550 ft/s.

8.5 Steam flows steadily into a condenser at the rate of 10,000 lb_m/h. The enthalpy of the steam at entry is 980 Btu/lb_m and its specific volume is 294 ft^3/lb_m. The condensed steam ('condensate') has an enthalpy of 80 Btu/lb_m and leaves with negligible velocity. The heat transfer from the condensing steam to the atmosphere is 4,000 Btu/min.

(a) Given that the flow area at entry is 2 ft^2 evaluate the steam velocity at entry.

(b) Evaluate the heat transfer to the cooling water per pound of steam condensed.

8.6 A valve is fitted in a 2 in. diameter horizontal pipe-line; the valve and the pipe-line are well insulated. The valve, which is partially open, throttles the steam flowing steadily along the pipe-line from a pressure of 400 psia to a pressure of 20 psia. The enthalpy of the steam approaching the valve is 1192 Btu/lb_m and the steam mass flow rate is 10 lb_m/min.

(a) Assuming the change in the kinetic energy of the steam to be negligible, evaluate the enthalpy of the steam downstream of the valve.

(b) Verify that the kinetic energies are negligible by evaluating the steam velocity upstream and downstream of the valve. The specific volumes of the steam upstream and downstream of the valve are 7·14 ft^3/lb_m and 22·36 ft^3/lb_m respectively.

8.7 An air turbine forms part of an aircraft refrigerating plant. Air at a pressure of 42·5 psia and a temperature of 136°F flows steadily into the turbine with a velocity of 150 ft/s. The air leaves the turbine at a pressure of 16·6 psia, a temperature of 36°F and a velocity of 500 ft/s. The shaft work done delivered by the turbine, per pound of air flowing through it, is 18,000 ft lb_f. Neglecting changes in elevation, determine the magnitude and sign of the heat transfer per pound of air flowing.

For air take $c_p = 0.24$ Btu/lb_m °F and assume that the enthalpy of air is a function of temperature only (see problem 7.7 and Chapter 14).

8.8 A long, well-insulated pipe-line consists of two pipes connected in series, the internal diameters of which are 3 in. and 1 in. respectively. A steady flow of steam enters the 3 in. diameter pipe at a pressure of 500 psia, a specific volume of 1·08 ft^3/lb_m, and an enthalpy of 1266·8 Btu/lb_m. At a point downstream in the 1 in. diameter pipe the pressure is 450 psia, the specific volume is 1·18 ft^3/lb_m and the enthalpy is 1259·1 Btu/lb_m.

Determine the velocity of the steam at the two points in the pipe-line and the steam mass flow rate.

8.9 A simple impulse turbine has a single nozzle and one row of rotating blades.

(a) Steam flows steadily into the nozzle with negligible velocity. Given that the decrease in the enthalpy of the steam in flowing through the nozzle is 50 Btu/lb_m and that the flow is adiabatic, evaluate the velocity of the steam leaving the nozzle.

(b) The nozzle is set at an angle of 20 degrees to the plane of rotation; the outlet angle of the rotor blades is 35 degrees measured from the plane of rotation; the blade speed is 714 ft/s. Assuming ideal conditions across the rotor blades, i.e. no change in the steam velocity relative to the rotor blades, construct the velocity triangles and hence evaluate the absolute velocity of the steam leaving the rotor blades.

(c) Apply the S.F.E.E. to a control volume rotating with the rotor blades to find the increase in the enthalpy of the steam across the rotor blades. Assume the flow to be adiabatic.

(*d*) Apply the S.F.E.E. to a control surface enclosing the whole machine and fixed with respect to the nozzles to evaluate the external work delivered by the turbine.

(*e*) Given that the steam mass flow rate is 300 lb_m/h, evaluate the power developed.

(*f*) Evaluate the stagnation enthalpies at each condition given that the initial specific enthalpy of the steam is 1100 Btu/lb_m.

8.10 A jet condenser consists of a vessel into which a steady stream of exhaust steam is discharged. A spray of water, injected at the top of the vessel, mixes with the exhaust steam and subsequently flows out with the condensed steam at the base of the vessel. The vessel is well lagged.

In a particular installation, exhaust steam enters the condenser with an enthalpy of 1000 Btu/lb_m at the rate of 500 lb_m/h. The mixed stream of water leaves the condenser with an enthalpy of 150 Btu/lb_m.

Given that the enthalpy of the injected water is 30 Btu/lb_m and that changes in kinetic energy and in elevation are negligible, determine the quantity of water injected.

8.11 The steam supply to an engine comprises two streams which mix before entering the engine. One stream is supplied at the rate of 1 lb_m/min with an enthalpy of 1269 Btu/lb_m and a velocity of 60 ft/s. The other stream is supplied at the rate of 10 lb_m/min with an enthalpy of 1105 Btu/lb_m and a velocity of 400 ft/s. At exit from the engine the fluid leaves as two streams, one as water at the rate of 0·1 lb_m/min with an enthalpy of 180 Btu/lb_m and the other as steam; the fluid velocities at exit are negligible. The engine develops a shaft power of 25 horse-power; the heat transfer is negligible. Evaluate the enthalpy of the second exit stream.

8.12 A steady stream of air is supplied to the combustion chamber of a gas turbine engine at the rate of 30 lb_m/s. The temperature of the air is 375°F, its velocity is 300 ft/s and its enthalpy is 76·2 Btu/lb_m. Liquid fuel at a temperature of 60°F flows into the combustion chamber with negligible velocity at the rate of 1580 lb_m/h. The products of combustion leave the chamber at a temperature of 1380°F, a velocity of 650 ft/s and an enthalpy of 337·4 Btu/lb_m. Heat transfer to the atmosphere is negligible. Evaluate the specific enthalpy of the entering fuel stream. The datum temperature for enthalpy is to be taken as 60°F.

8.13 A petrol engine has a specific fuel consumption of 0·5 lb_m/hp h. The stream of air and petrol vapour in the ratio 14 : 1 by mass enters the engine at a temperature of 85°F and leaves as combustion products at a temperature of 1460°F. The net heat transfer rate from the fuel air stream to the jacket cooling water and to the surroundings is 2000 Btu/min. The shaft power delivered by the engine is 35 horse-power. Evaluate the increase in the specific enthalpy of the fuel-air stream assuming the changes in kinetic energy and in elevation to be negligible.

CHAPTER 9

PROPERTIES OF PURE SUBSTANCES

INTRODUCTION

The First Law of Thermodynamics, either in its original or its steady-flow form, suffices for the solution of a great many practical problems in engineering. It involves, it will be realised, the relation of the heat and work transfer, at the system or control volume boundary, to the changes in energy or enthalpy occurring within the system or control volume.

Now energy and enthalpy are not amenable to direct measurement in the same way as are, for example, pressure and temperature. In order to make the First Law applicable to practical apparatus therefore, it is necessary to see how energy and enthalpy are related to more easily measurable properties. Provided that pure substances are in question, we are assured that relatively simple relations exist by the Two-Property Rule. Finding the relations however is an experimental matter which will now be discussed.

The present chapter starts with a description of experiments on a pure substance and of the results that are typically obtained. This leads to a more detailed discussion of property diagrams than was possible in Chapter 7, and to such concepts as *phase, saturation,* and *intensive* and *extensive property.* Thereafter Steam Tables are discussed.

Since experiments take time to do, knowledge of the thermodynamic properties of substances has always lagged behind engineering need. For example it was not until 1760 that Black discovered the "latent heat" of vaporisation of water. Yet steam engines had been operating since the beginning of the century. Even now (1958) knowledge of the properties of steam is insufficient to enable some advanced projects to be designed with certainty, and experimental research on steam properties is being actively pursued. Knowledge of other substances is in a far less complete state.

Symbols

H	Enthalpy of a system comprising a pure substance.	v	Specific volume.
h	Specific enthalpy of a pure substance.	W_x	External work.
		x	Dryness, dryness fraction.
m	Mass.	τ	Time.
p	Pressure.		
Q	Heat transfer.	*Subscripts.*	
t	Temperature.	f	Saturated liquid (fluid).
U	Internal energy of a system comprising a pure substance.	g	Saturated vapour (gas).
		s	Solid.
u	Specific internal energy of a pure substance.	fg	Saturated liquid to saturated vapour.
		sf	Solid to saturated liquid.
V	System volume.	sg	Solid to saturated vapour

FACTS ABOUT PURE SUBSTANCES

Constant-pressure experiments: temperature-pressure (*t-p*) diagram

Consider the apparatus shown in Fig. 9.1, comprising a cylinder mounted on an electrically heated hot-plate, a frictionless leak-proof piston surmounted by a weight, and a thermometer for measuring the temperature of the contents of the cylinder.

The cylinder contains a pure substance; for definiteness this may be thought of as water,* though of course any substance can be chosen.

The experiment to be carried out is as follows:—With a fixed weight on the piston, and so a fixed pressure beneath it, the heater is caused to transfer heat to the cylinder contents at a steady rate. Initially the system temperature is low, but it rises as a result of the heat transfer. The temperature is observed and plotted as a function of time.

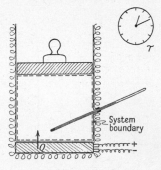

Fig. 9.1 Heat transfer at constant pressure.

The temperature-time curves. Fig. 9.2 shows a series of temperature-time curves obtained in this way. Their relative horizontal positions are without significance since the setting of the clock at the beginning of an experiment is, of course, arbitrary. The only

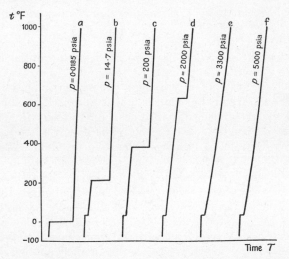

Fig. 9.2   Temperature–time curves for H_2O at constant pressure (approximately to scale).

difference between the conditions of the experiments lies in the size of the weight on the piston, i.e. in the system pressure: the pressure is

---

* We use the word 'water' to denote the chemical substance H_2O, regardless of whether it is in the form of ice, liquid water or steam.

lowest for curve (a) on the left, and increases steadily for curves (b) through to (f).

The notable feature of all the curves is that they show horizontal steps, signifying that the temperature suddenly stops rising for a period and then picks up again. All the curves exhibit steps, but those at intermediate pressures (b, c and d) have two each, whereas the low-pressure (a) and high-pressure (e and f) curves have only one each.

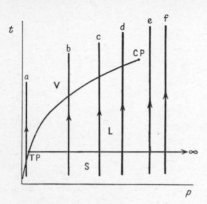

Fig. 9.3   Temperature–pressure diagram showing the phase boundaries.

If the temperatures at which the steps occur are noted and plotted against the appropriate pressures, the points lie on lines such as are shown in Fig. 9.3. There is a steeply sloping line terminating suddenly at the point marked C.P.; another line starts from the point marked T.P. on the first line and travels indefinitely to the right in a more or less horizontal direction (sloping downwards slightly in the case of water). Comparison of Figs. 9.2 and 9.3 shows that experiment (a) must have been carried out at a pressure less than that of T.P., while experiments (e) and (f) must have been at pressures higher than that of C.P., in order that the number of temperature-steps should be correct.

The three phases: solid, liquid, vapour. If a window in the cylinder wall permits observation of the cylinder contents, it is found that, during the time in which the system is traversing a temperature-step, its appearance changes. The nature of the changes is best described by the statements that in experiment (a) the substance changes gradually from a solid to a vapour state during the step, that in experiments (b) (c) and (d) the lower step corresponds to a change from solid to liquid while the higher corresponds to a change from liquid to vapour, and that in experiments (e) and (f) the step corresponds to a change from solid to liquid but that no subsequent vaporisation occurs however high the temperature is raised.

The three conditions of the system, solid, liquid and vapour (or gas), are known as *phases*; we have the following formal, though scarcely informative, definition:—**A phase is any physical homogeneous aspect of a system.**

The transitions from one phase to another, namely melting and freezing, vaporisation and condensation, are known as *changes of phase*. They correspond to changes in the types of force dominant between the individual molecules. The phase of the substance at any temperature and pressure is indicated on Fig. 9.3 by the letters S (for solid), L (for liquid) and V (for vapour) marking the various regions. The phase changes occur when the state-point crosses the lines on Fig. 9.3 mentioned above, which are therefore known as *phase boundaries*.

More careful experiments will indicate that, in general, small temperature steps occur along several lines within the general region marked S. This means that there are several solid phases, corresponding to the various crystalline states of matter. In engineering thermodynamics the solid phase is of relatively small importance for the good reason that engines will not work if the fluid within them freezes. We shall therefore not distinguish between the various solid phases. The distinctions are however very important in the subject of *metallurgy*.

The solid-vapour phase change. Examination of Fig. 9.3 shows that, to the left of T.P., the solid and vapour regions are contiguous: experiment (a) exhibited a change direct from the solid to the vapour phase. Such a change is known as *sublimation*. An example is the gradual "disappearance" of fallen snow in prolonged dry, cold weather, without intermediate melting; this occurs because, even though the pressure of the atmosphere exceeds that of T.P. for water,* the *partial* pressure of the vapour, which is what matters in this case, is below that of T.P. (See Chapter 15 for explanation of the term "partial pressure".) Another example is the sublimation of solid carbon dioxide ("dry ice") at atmospheric pressure.

An example of the reverse of sublimation is the formation of hoar frost, which is the transition direct from water vapour to ice without intermediate condensation and freezing.

The triple point, T.P. The point marked T.P. on Fig. 9.3 is known as the *triple point*. It is the only combination of pressure and temperature at which it is possible for the solid, liquid and vapour phases to exist side-by-side in equilibrium. For water the triple point occurs at a temperature of $32 \cdot 02°F$ and a pressure of $0 \cdot 088$ psia.

Note that at this pressure the freezing point is $0 \cdot 02°F$ above the freezing point at atmospheric pressure. This corresponds with the slight downward slope of the solid-liquid phase boundary of water as it travels to the right, a tendency which is also responsible for making ice-skating possible; for an increase of pressure (beneath the blades of the skates) at constant temperature causes a transition from the solid to the liquid phase, so that the water lubricates the motion.

The critical point, C.P. The upper termination of the liquid-vapour phase boundary, C.P., is known as the *critical point*. For water the relevant temperature and pressure are respectively $705 \cdot 4°F$ and $3206 \cdot 2$ psia. The corresponding temperatures and pressures for substances which are vapours at atmospheric conditions are considerably lower, as is shown by Table 9.1.

A consequence of the existence of the critical point which often puzzles students is that at higher pressures and temperatures there is no demarcation between the liquid and the vapour states. This means that it is possible, for example, to vaporise a substance repeatedly without ever condensing it. The cyclic process ABCDA shown in Fig. 9.4a indicates how this may be done:—Starting at state A, where the substance is a liquid, constant-pressure heating is carried out. The crossing of the liquid-vapour

---

* See footnote on page 143.

phase boundary is marked by all the features which we understand under boiling, i.e. bubbling and agitation. Let the heating be continued until the temperature of the substance, which is now entirely vapour, has risen

TABLE 9.1: *Critical point data.*

Substance	Critical temperature	Critical pressure
Water	705·4°F	3206·2 psia
Carbon dioxide	87·8°F	1069·4 psia
Oxygen	−181·8°F	730·6 psia
Hydrogen	−399·8°F	188·2 psia

above the critical temperature; the state-point is now that marked B on Fig. 9.4a. The system is now compressed at constant temperature to a pressure in excess of the critical pressure; the state-point shifts from B to C; no phase boundary is crossed and no change takes place in the appearance of the substance. The system is now cooled to the original temperature at constant pressure, the state-point moving down the vertical CD; again no change takes place in the appearance of the substance, so the observer concludes that it is still vapour. To complete the cycle, the substance is expanded at constant temperature until the state A is reached once more at the original (lower) pressure; there has still been no change in the appearance. Is the substance still a vapour? The answer seems to be "yes"; but if we now repeat the constant-pressure heating process AB, the substance boils again! So in the process BCDA the substance has changed from vapour back to liquid without our noticing. Of course it is equally possible to carry out the reverse cyclic process ADCBA, and so to get repeated condensation without intermediate vaporisation.

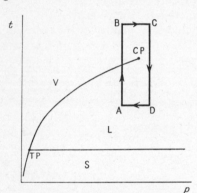

Fig. 9.4a Temperature–pressure diagram showing a cyclic process which involves states above and below the critical point.

The apparent paradox results from the unwarranted expectation that hard-and-fast distinctions between phases must always exist. The following analogy may prove helpful in understanding this:—Fig. 9.4b illustrates an extensive escarpment which forms a boundary between a plateau called Upland and a low-lying country called Downland. Tribe A living at the foot of the cliff have no frontier disputes with tribe B living on the plateau, for the cliff forms an obvious boundary and peace is ensured by the agreement that "Up is up, and down is down". Later however, tribesmen from B form a settlement at C in a region where the escarpment has tapered away and disappeared, while tribesmen from A form a nearby settlement at D. The consequences of continued attempts to adhere to the "Up is up" formula can readily be imagined.

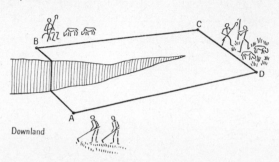

Fig. 9.4b   Topographical analogy of conditions close
to the critical point.

It may be asked whether the solid-liquid phase boundary also disappears at sufficiently high pressure. The answer is "not as far as is known". For water, this phase boundary is known to exist up to pressures of 6.4×10^5 psia.

The enthalpy-pressure (h-p) diagram

A main purpose of the present chapter is to show how the "First Law" properties of pure substances, internal energy and enthalpy, are related to the easily measurable properties, pressure, temperature and specific volume. Enthalpy changes can be determined from the constant-pressure experiments already described if measurement of the heat transfer to the system is made; this may be done by measuring the electrical power to the heater and allowing for the heat transfer to the cylinder walls and piston.

Since in the processes under consideration we have a pure substance in the absence of gravity, motion, etc., and friction and stirring work are absent, the First Law eq. (7.5) written for unit mass is

$$dQ = du + p\,dv \qquad \ldots \quad (9.1)$$

where dQ is an elementary heat transfer, du the elemental change in the internal energy and $p\,dv$ the displacement work done in the fully-resisted expansion.

Eq. (9.1) may be written in terms of enthalpy, h, as follows:

By definition, $\qquad\qquad h = u + pv \qquad\qquad \ldots \quad (9.2)$

Differentiating eq. (9.2), we have

$$dh = du + p\,dv + v\,dp$$

Eq. (9.1) then becomes

$$dQ = dh - v\,dp \qquad\qquad \ldots \quad (9.3)$$

Now pressure changes are absent, so $v\,\mathrm{d}p = 0$ in eq. (9.3), which then runs

$$\mathrm{d}Q = \mathrm{d}h$$

Thus the heat transfer measures the change in enthalpy of the substance in the constant-pressure process, so an enthalpy-pressure diagram can be constructed from the experimental observations.

Strictly, in addition to the constant-pressure experiments, enthalpy changes during the shift from one pressure to the next must be calculated in order to construct the h-p diagram. This is done by means of eq. (9.3).

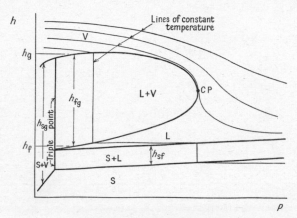

Fig. 9.5 Enthalpy–pressure diagram showing the phase boundaries and isotherms.

Phase boundaries. The results of such experiments for a typical pure substance are indicated in Fig. 9.5. It is evident that the h-p diagram is more complicated than the p-t diagram. This is a consequence of the fact that whereas the system temperature does not vary during the change of phase, the enthalpy does (the heat transfer is continuous); the result is that now the phase boundaries have been broadened into bands of finite vertical height. These bands are indicated on Fig. 9.5 by the letters $V + S$, $L + S$, and $L + V$, signifying the two phases which are present in the corresponding regions. The regions of pure solid, liquid and vapour phase are marked S, L and V, as before.

The triple and critical points. The triple point, like all other points (but one) on the p-t phase boundaries, has been extended vertically, so that now it is a line. This is the boundary between the $S + V$, $S + L$ and $L + V$ regions of Fig. 9.5, these letters emphasising that it is in the nature of the triple point to have all three phases in contact.

The critical point is the exception to the rule that phase-boundary points become extended vertically; or rather its extension is zero. The critical point is on the extreme right of the $L + V$ envelope of Fig. 9.5; to the right of it there is no such envelope. It corresponds to the point in Fig. 9.4b at which the escarpment vanishes.

The "latent heats". The vertical height of a two-phase region (S + V, L + V or S + L) represents the enthalpy increase of the fluid when it changes from one phase to the other. This enthalpy increase is known as the *latent heat of sublimation, vaporisation or melting* (fusion) as the case may be. The name "latent heat" is of course a legacy of the caloric theory which led to the idea that the "heat" was "hidden", i.e. it did not cause the expected temperature rise.

Taking the liquid-vapour transition as an example, it is evident from Fig. 9.5 that the latent heat of vaporisation varies with pressure, decreasing rapidly to zero as the critical pressure is approached. This latter feature is an expression of the fact that the difference in enthalpy between the liquid and vapour states becomes smaller the nearer is the critical state, and corresponds to the fact that the escarpment height must decrease gradually before it disappears altogether.

The latent heats, being enthalpy changes, are given the symbol h with the subscripts sg, sf or fg, where s stands for solid, f stands for liquid (i.e. fluid; l might be mistaken for 1), and g stands for vapour (or gas). Thus the latent heat of vaporisation has the symbol h_{fg}.

It may be seen from the geometry of Fig. 9.5 that, at the triple point conditions, $h_{sg} = h_{sf} + h_{fg}$.

Saturated liquid and vapour. Liquid at any state lying on the lower part of the L + V envelope is called *saturated liquid*. The name arises because liquid at a lower enthalpy and the same pressure could "soak up" steam if it were added: the steam would condense. Saturated liquid on the other hand does not cause steam of the same temperature to condense; the two phases can co-exist in equilibrium. The enthalpy of saturated liquid is designated h_f.

Vapour at any state lying on the upper part of the L + V envelope is correspondingly called *saturated vapour;* for whereas vapour lying above this line would cause liquid added to it to vaporise, saturated vapour can "soak up" no more, but co-exists in equilibrium with the liquid. Sometimes saturated vapour is termed *dry* saturated vapour to emphasize that it carries no suspended liquid particles. The symbol h_g is used to denote the enthalpy of (dry) saturated vapour.

The whole of the L + V envelope is commonly called the *saturation line*.

Isotherms. A few lines corresponding to states of constant temperature are drawn on Fig. 9.5. Several features may be remarked:—

(i) The isotherms are vertical (i.e. coincident with constant-pressure lines) in the two-phase regions S + V, S + L, and L + V, signifying of course that no temperature change occurs during a constant-pressure phase change.

(ii) Outside the two-phase regions the isotherms have a generally horizontal tendency except in the neighbourhood of the critical point. The isotherm through the critical point actually has a vertical tangent there.

(iii) The higher temperatures correspond to the higher enthalpies. Particularly at high temperatures it is notable that the isotherms become closely horizontal, signifying that the enthalpy at given temperature is only weakly dependent on pressure. This will assume considerable significance in discussion of Ideal Gases (Chapter 14). The isotherms are also practically horizontal in the pure liquid and pure solid regions.

Superheat. In power-plant practice it is customary to call vapour at states lying above the saturated vapour line *superheated vapour*. This has arisen because for a long time boilers produced steam which, being in contact with water at the same pressure, was saturated. Later (1827) the *superheater* was devised, which caused the steam to be heated to a higher temperature out of contact with the water. Sometimes the difference of temperature between the superheated vapour and saturated vapour at the same pressure is referred to as the *superheat* or *degrees superheat* of the vapour.

It may be as well to remark that "super-cooling" does not have the corresponding meaning. Instead, "super-cooled" vapour means vapour which has an enthalpy sufficiently low that, at the prevailing pressure, some of it ought to condense; yet it does not condense because of the absence of nuclei around which the droplets can form. Such states cannot be represented on property diagrams, for the latter only describe equilibrium states; super-cooled vapour is not in equilibrium, for it has a tendency to spontaneous change. This phenomenon is of some importance in the design of steam nozzles.

The pressure-volume (*p-v*) diagram

As well as enthalpy, internal energy has to be related to the other properties of the substance. One way of doing this is to make volume (piston-position) measurements during the course of the constant-pressure experiments described above. Then internal energy is deducible from the definitional relation

$$u = h - pv \qquad \qquad \text{... (9.4)}$$

We first consider the way in which the specific volume depends on other properties.

Diagram for a substance which contracts on freezing. If volume measurements are made during the constant-pressure experiments, a pressure-volume diagram can be plotted. Fig. 9.6 shows an example. In general shape it is similar to the *h-p* diagram with the ordinate and abscissa interchanged; it is conventional for *p* to be the ordinate in the present case. The single-phase and two-phase regions are indicated by letters as before. A constant-pressure process is now represented by a horizontal line; so the isotherms are horizontal in the two-phase regions. Far from the critical point, however, in contrast to their behaviour on the *h-p* diagram, the isotherms tend to become rectangular hyperbolae with the *p* and *v* axes as asymptotes. This will also assume particular significance in discussion of the Ideal Gases (Chapter 14).

The triple point is again a line, and the critical point occurs at the apex of the L + V bulge, this time on the top instead of at the side.

In conformity with the symbols used earlier, v_f and v_g respectively denote the specific volumes of saturated liquid and of saturated vapour; $v_{fg} = v_g - v_f$.

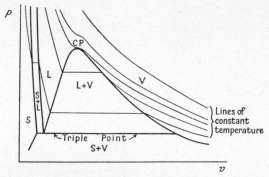

Fig. 9.6   Pressure volume diagram for a substance
which contracts on freezing.

Diagram for a substance which expands on freezing. Traversing a horizontal line on Fig. 9.6 from left to right indicates that, when the system undergoes a constant-pressure heating process, the volume increases at each phase change. This is not always the case however. Water, for example, *contracts* as it changes, at constant-pressure, from the solid to the liquid state, and indeed continues to contract until (at atmospheric pressure) the temperature has risen to 39·2°F.

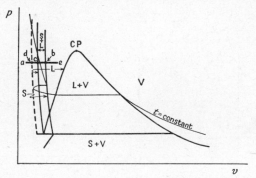

Fig. 9.7   Pressure–volume diagram for a substance
which expands on freezing.

Such behaviour makes the p-v diagram considerably more complicated in the $S + L$ region, for the solid and liquid phase regions overlap. Fig. 9.7 illustrates schematically the p-v diagram for a substance like water; it is not to scale for the reason that liquid and solid specific volumes are very much smaller than vapour specific volumes at a given pressure. The dotted line on the extreme left indicates that the liquid volume can be less than that of the liquid in equilibrium with the solid phase.

Fig. 9.8 shows, to scale, the specific volume of water plotted against temperature at a pressure of 14·7 psia. Corresponding points abcde are shown on Figs. 9.7 and 9.8.

Constant-volume processes. A constant-volume process is represented by a vertical straight line on a *p-v* diagram. Fig. 9.9 shows three such processes, a, b and c. In case a, we suppose that a mixture of liquid and

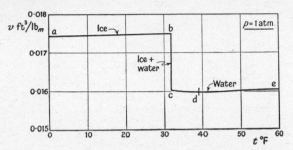

Fig. 9.8   Volume–temperature diagram for water showing that water expands on freezing (to scale).

vapour in a closed container (Fig. 9.10) is gradually heated. The initial ratio of liquid to vapour is relatively small. As the temperature (and pressure) rises, the state-point approaches and then crosses the saturated vapour line on Fig. 9.9, signifying that the meniscus separating liquid and vapour in the vessel falls to the bottom. Finally only vapour is present; the liquid has boiled away.

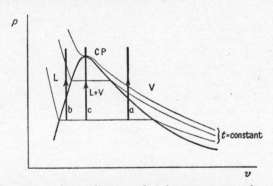

Fig. 9.9   Pressure–volume diagram showing constant–volume processes.

In case b the initial ratio of liquid to vapour is large. This time the heating process causes the state-point to approach and cross the *saturated-liquid* line, signifying that the meniscus rises to the top. This means that finally only liquid is present; the heating has caused all the vapour to *condense*. This surprising result may be interpreted as due to the fact that the rise of pressure consequent on heating at constant volume outweighs, in its effect on the vapour condition, the rise of temperature.

In case c the initial ratio of liquid to vapour has been so chosen that the system, when heated, passes through the critical point. In this case the meniscus neither falls to the bottom nor rises to the top but merely fades away, disappearing completely as the critical pressure is reached. The meniscus becomes hard to see even before this, because all the

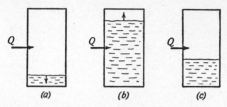

Fig. 9.10 Showing the direction of motion of the meniscus when different liquid–vapour mixtures are heated at constant volume.

properties of the saturated liquid and saturated vapour approach each other; in particular the refractive index difference, which enables the separation surface to be observed visually, becomes steadily smaller.

The internal energy-volume (u-v) diagram

Combination of information about enthalpy and specific volume by way of eq. (9.4) enables diagrams to be constructed with internal energy as one co-ordinate. The u-p diagram is similar to that for enthalpy plotted against pressure. As our last example we therefore show the u-v diagram instead (Fig. 9.11). This exhibits some new features.

Fig. 9.11 holds for a substance which contracts on freezing (i.e. not

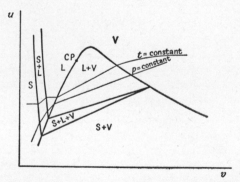

Fig. 9.11 Internal energy–specific volume diagram for a substance which contracts on freezing.

water). The most notable feature is that this time the triple point has expanded to an area, the reason being that both u and v increase during a phase change. Constant-pressure and constant-temperature lines are indicated on the diagram. Corresponding lines coincide in the regions where two phases are present.

11

The whole diagram exhibits a "sloping" appearance, when compared for example with the p-v diagram. In particular the critical point is situated on the flank of the L + V envelope.

The isotherms tend to be horizontal in the vapour region far from the critical point, signifying that the internal energy tends to be a function of the temperature alone. This again is a feature of relevance to the behaviour of Ideal Gases.

Two sorts of properties: dryness

It will be recalled that the p-t diagram was rather simple; when temperature was replaced by enthalpy or specific volume, more complex diagrams appeared; and substitution of u for p brought yet more complexity in the triple-point region. This arose because pressure and temperature are a different sort of property from h, u and v.

The difference lies in the fact that the units of h and u are Btu *per unit mass* and of v, ft³ *per unit mass;* whereas pressure and temperature per unit mass have no meaning. Another way of putting it is that enthalpy, internal energy and specific volume are additive; pressure and temperature are not.

The difference is made explicit by calling p and t *intensive properties*, and h, u and v *extensive properties*. Other examples of intensive properties are viscosity, thermal conductivity and refractive index; other extensive properties are concentration (of some component of a mixture) and entropy (Chapter 13).

The additive nature of extensive properties makes it possible to write their values for a large system, through which the properties are not homogeneous, in the form of integrals. Thus

$$H = \int h \, dm \qquad \qquad \ldots \quad (9.5)$$

$$U = \int u \, dm \qquad \qquad \ldots \quad (9.6)$$

$$V = \int v \, dm \qquad \qquad \ldots \quad (9.7)$$

where H, U and V are respectively enthalpy, internal energy and volume of the whole system; h, u and v are the specific values of these properties for an element dm of the mass of the system; and the integral signs signify summation over all the mass elements.

Dryness. A particular example of this sort of addition is useful in relating the extensive properties of a mixture of two phases to the properties of the pure saturated phases at the same pressure; such a mixture of liquid and vapour phases is often called a *wet* mixture. To describe this we introduce first the concept of *dryness* or *dryness fraction* as a measure of the relative proportions of vapour and liquid phases in a mixture.

Definition. If the dryness of an equilibrium liquid-vapour mixture is x, there are x lb$_m$ of vapour in each lb$_m$ of mixture.

It follows that the vapour-to-liquid mass ratio is given by

$$\frac{\text{mass of pure vapour phase}}{\text{mass of pure liquid phase}} = \frac{x}{1 - x} \qquad \ldots \quad (9.8)$$

Saturated vapour correspondingly has a dryness of unity, or 100%. Saturated liquid has a dryness of zero.

Extensive properties in the liquid-plus-vapour region. We can now write relations between h, u and v for a mixture of liquid and vapour, and h_g, u_g, v_g, h_f, u_f and v_f, the properties of the saturated phases. These are

$$h = xh_g + (1 - x)h_f \qquad \ldots \quad (9.9)$$

$$u = xu_g + (1 - x)u_f \qquad \ldots \quad (9.10)$$

$$v = xv_g + (1 - x)v_f \qquad \ldots \quad (9.11)$$

It is sometimes more convenient to write these expressions in a way that brings the dryness in only once, namely

$$h = h_f + xh_{fg} = h_g - (1 - x)h_{fg} \qquad \ldots \quad (9.12)$$

$$u = u_f + xu_{fg} = u_g - (1 - x)u_{fg} \qquad \ldots \quad (9.13)$$

$$v = v_f + xv_{fg} = v_g - (1 - x)v_{fg} \qquad \ldots \quad (9.14)$$

which is permissible since we have the definitions

$$h_{fg} = h_g - h_f \qquad \ldots \quad (9.15)$$

$$u_{fg} = u_g - u_f \qquad \ldots \quad (9.16)$$

$$v_{fg} = v_g - v_f \qquad \ldots \quad (9.17)$$

For substances such as water, at pressures far below the critical, the specific volume equations may often be simplified to

$$v \approx xv_g \qquad \ldots \quad (9.18)$$

because v_f is so much less than v_g as to be negligible. This is not of course permissible when x is very small.

Geometrical interpretation of mass ratio. Equations (9.8) to (9.11) are capable of geometrical interpretation. Fig. 9.12 will exemplify this. B is the state-point of a mixture of steam and water, the states of the saturated vapour and saturated liquid of which the mixture is composed are respectively represented by points A and C. Examination of the diagram shows that we can write

$$\frac{\overline{AB}}{\overline{BC}} = \frac{h_g - h}{h - h_f} \qquad \ldots \quad (9.19)$$

Substitution of h from eq. (9.9) leads to

$$\frac{\overline{AB}}{\overline{BC}} = \frac{1 - x}{x} = \frac{\text{mass of liquid in mixture}}{\text{mass of vapour in mixture}} \qquad \ldots \quad (9.20)$$

Thus the ratio of the distances of B from the saturation lines is equal to the *reciprocal* of the mass ratio of the respective pure phases. Thus nearness to the saturated vapour line signifies a high proportion of vapour, i.e. a large dryness.

This can be remembered if it is seen that B is in the right position for the fulcrum of a balance which carries the vapour mass at A and the liquid mass at C. Fig. 9.13 illustrates this.

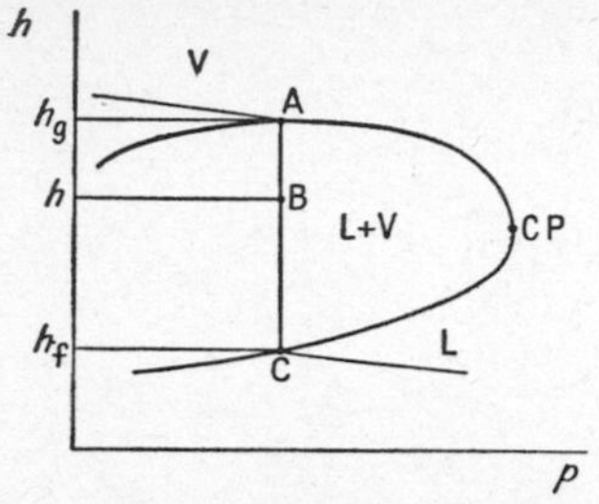

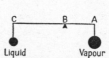

Fig. 9.12   Enthalpy–pressure diagram showing the state point of a wet mixture.

Fig. 9.13   Mechanical analogy of the liquid: vapour mass ratio in a wet mixture.

The throttling calorimeter

Providing that only one phase is present, a property diagram can be used for the determination of, say, enthalpy from measurements of pressure and temperature. For example the h-p diagram of Fig. 9.5 could be used: specification of p gives the horizontal position of the state-point; t locates the appropriate isotherm, so fixing the point; then h can be read from the vertical scale.

However if the state-point is within a two-phase region (the L + V region, for example) specification of pressure and temperature is insufficient: t gives the same information as p does, namely the horizontal position, but neither help in determining the required vertical position. The state could be determined by a volume measurement, but this is not always easy, particularly when the substance is flowing. This problem often arises in boiler practice, where it is necessary to establish the condition of the steam produced by a boiler lacking a superheater; such steam will always be slightly wet, partly because of carry-over of water droplets from the boiler itself and partly because of condensation resulting from heat transfer through the walls of the steam main.

We now discuss a device which enables the condition of the wet steam to be determined provided that the dryness is fairly close to unity. This is the *throttling calorimeter* illustrated in Fig. 9.14. A sampling tube, suitably positioned in the steam main for the steam entering it to be a representative sample, communicates through a throttle with a region of lower pressure. Upstream of the throttle, at point 1, either the pressure or the temperature is measured; downstream of the throttle, at point 2, both pressure and temperature are measured. Flow through the throttle is steady, but the velocities are sufficiently small for the kinetic energy terms to be neglected. The throttle is thermally insulated.

Application of the Steady-Flow Energy Equation, eq. (8.22), to the throttling process leads to

$$Q - W_x = 0 = h_2 - h_1 \qquad \cdots \quad (9.21)$$

from which we deduce that the enthalpy at state 2 equals the enthalpy at state 1,

$$h_2 = h_1 \qquad \cdots \quad (9.22)$$

Now examination of the shape of the saturated steam line on an h-p diagram shows that in the range of common steam pressures it slopes downwards to the left. Fig. 9.15 shows the relevant portion of the

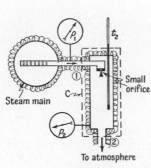

Fig. 9.14 Throttling calorimeter.

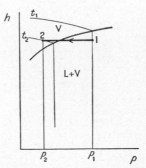

Fig. 9.15 Enthalpy–pressure diagram showing state points before and after throttling.

diagram; on it are drawn the two state-points 1 and 2 of the throttling process. These are at the same height because of eq. (9.22). It is evident that, provided p_2 is sufficiently low, the state-point 2 lies in the superheat region.

Since state 2 is a single-phase state, the measurements of pressure and temperature, p_2 and t_2, suffice to specify the state as explained above. In particular the enthalpy h_2 is known. But this is the same as the enthalpy of the steam at state 1, h_1, which is supposed to be representative of the steam in the main. Now we have two *independent* properties at state 1, h_1 and, say, p_1, which is therefore completely specified. The geometry of Fig. 9.15 explains this more simply than words can do. In particular it is evident that the measurements determine the initial dryness of the steam.

It is not necessary to plot an h-p diagram in order to evaluate measurements made on a throttling calorimeter: Steam Tables suffice. An example is given below (p. 163).

Throttling in general. In the case of the throttling calorimeter when the steam enters wet and leaves superheated, there is an appreciable temperature difference between the two states. It should be realised that this is generally the case even if the throttle does not cause any phase change;

the slope of the isotherms on an h-p diagram ensures that a horizontal shift of the state-point brings it into a region of different temperature. Both temperature rises and temperature falls are observed in such experiments, which have been widely used in determinations of the properties of substances since their introduction by Joule and Thomson in 1852. This matter is referred to again in Chapter 14, p. 244. Further, the above analysis has neglected the effect of kinetic energy; if velocity changes are appreciable, allowance must be made as indicated in Chapter 8, p. 121.

STEAM TABLES

The most compact method of recording information about the thermodynamic properties of a substance is by means of tables. Examples are the Steam Tables given in Appendix B. Although insufficiently detailed for engineering use, they suffice for instructional purposes. The present section will be devoted to their explanation. It is important for an engineer to become thoroughly familiar with the use of these tables in order that his attention should not be diverted from thermodynamic subtleties by the purely mechanical difficulty of looking up numbers in the tables.

The datum state

It has been stated above that only differences of internal energy are defined by the First Law of Thermodynamics; it is necessary to state arbitrarily that the internal energy shall be zero at some definite condition, or *datum state*. Fixing the zero of internal energy fixes that of enthalpy. In practice we choose the reverse procedure: the enthalpy of saturated water is arbitrarily chosen to be zero at a temperature of 32°F.

Since internal energy is related to enthalpy by

$$u = h - pv \qquad \qquad \dots \quad (9.23)$$

it follows that the internal energy of saturated water is slightly negative at 32°F because of the (small) pv term.

Actually this datum state is a fictitious one because the saturated water line stops at the triple point which, as stated above, is at a temperature of 32·02°F. So an extrapolation through 0·02°F is necessary.

The entropy of saturated water (see Chapter 13) is also chosen as zero at 32°F. However the entropy values in the Steam Tables will be ignored for the time being. After entropy has been discussed in Chapter 13 it will be seen that its treatment in the Tables is the same as that of the other extensive properties h, u and v.

Table I: The triple point

Some of these data have already been discussed. Note that enthalpy is tabulated, but not internal energy. The latter property can always be deduced from the former by way of eq. (9.23). Where a choice has to be made to economise in space, enthalpy is usually preferred because of the great importance of steady-flow processes.

EXAMPLE

Problem. What is the internal energy of (*a*) saturated water (*b*) saturated steam, at the triple point?

Solution (*a*)

From equation (9.23)

$$u = h - pv$$
$$= 0 \cdot 02 - \frac{0 \cdot 088 \times 144 \times 0 \cdot 01602}{778}$$
$$= 0 \cdot 01974 \text{ Btu/lb}_m \qquad \qquad \ldots \text{ } Answer \text{ } (a)$$

Solution (*b*)

$$u = h - pv$$
$$= 1075 \cdot 8 - \frac{0 \cdot 088 \times 144 \times 3303}{778}$$
$$= 1022 \cdot 0 \text{ Btu/lb}_m \qquad \qquad \ldots \text{ } Answer \text{ } (b)$$

Note the conversion factors 144 in^2/ft^2 and 778 ft lb$_f$/Btu, needed to make the units consistent.

Tables II and III: Saturated water and steam data

These tables cover the same ground, but differ in that in Table II temperature is the independent variable, whereas in Table III pressure is the independent variable. Of course, for saturated states, p and t are uniquely linked, so only one of the tables is strictly necessary. However interpolation is easier if both are available.

The data in these tables enable the saturation line to be plotted on a property diagram (see exercises).

Remarks 1. The tables contain redundant information, for example v_f, v_g and v_{fg}; h_f, h_g and h_{fg}; u_g, h_g and p and v_g. The reader should sample the data and check their consistency.

EXAMPLE

Problem. In Table III for $p = 10$ psia, $u_g = 1072 \cdot 2$ Btu/lb$_m$ and $v_g = 38 \cdot 42$ ft^3/lb$_m$. Evaluate h_g.

Solution.
$$h_g = u_g + pv_g$$
$$= 1072 \cdot 2 + \frac{10 \times 144 \times 38 \cdot 42}{778}$$
$$= 1072 \cdot 2 + 71 \cdot 1$$
$$= 1143 \cdot 3 \text{ Btu/lb}_m \qquad \qquad \ldots \text{ } Answer.$$

This agrees with tabulated value of h_g.

2. For the saturated liquid, enthalpy and internal energy are nearly equal, so only the former is tabulated. In many cases it is permissible to neglect the difference between them, which is small because of the small value of the specific volume of water. The example about the triple point above exemplifies this.

3. u_{fg} and h_{fg} differ by the amount of the term pv_{fg}. This is definitely not negligible. For example at 60 psia it amounts to $60 \times 144 \times 7 \cdot 158/778 = 79 \cdot 5$ Btu/lb$_m$.

4. As the critical point is approached (bottom of the tables) v_{fg}, u_{fg} and h_{fg} all tend to zero.

5. Since for liquid H_2O, $c_v \approx c_p \approx 1$ Btu/lb$_m$°F, and h and u are scarcely influenced by pressure, we may write for water:

$$h \approx u \approx (t - 32) \text{ Btu/lb}_m$$

where $t =$ temperature of the water in °F.

6. If the data are required for intermediate temperatures or pressures, linear interpolation is normally sufficiently accurate.

EXAMPLE

Problem. Determine h_g at a pressure of 17 psia.

Solution.

Table III is the more convenient in this case.

For 15 psia we have $h_g = 1150\cdot8$ Btu/lb$_m$

For 20 psia we have $h_g = 1156\cdot3$ Btu/lb$_m$

Interpolating,

$$\text{at 17 psia, } h_g = \frac{17 - 15}{20 - 15} \times (1156\cdot3 - 1150\cdot8) + 1150\cdot8$$

$$= \left(\frac{2}{5} \times 5\cdot5\right) + 1150\cdot8$$

$$= 1153\cdot0 \text{ Btu/lb}_m \qquad \ldots \text{ \textit{Answer}.}$$

Note that it is never wise to drop the numbers after the decimal point, because in First Law calculations *differences* of enthalpy or internal energy are involved. Though small compared with the actual values of h (or u), the numbers after the decimal point may not be negligible compared with the differences of h (or u).

7. There is no need to provide tables for the properties of steam in the two-phase (L + V) region: the saturation data suffice. Properties of mixtures of saturated steam and water, i.e. of wet steam, can be obtained by introducing the data of Tables II and III into the equations (9.9) to (9.14).

EXAMPLE INVOLVING WET STEAM AND THE CRITICAL POINT.

Problem. 1 lb$_m$ of wet steam is contained in a rigid container at 60°F. What should be (*a*) the volume of the container, (*b*) the initial dryness, (*c*) the proportion of the volume initially occupied by water, if the meniscus should neither rise to the top nor fall to the bottom when the system is heated to 750°F.

Solution. (*a*) The requirement is that the system should pass through the critical point. Since the volume of the vessel is fixed and contains 1 lb$_m$, its volume must equal 1 times the specific volume at the critical point (705·4°F, 3206·2 psia). From Table II (or III) $v_g = v_f = 0\cdot0503$ ft^3/lb$_m$ at the critical point. Therefore

volume of container $= 0\cdot0503$ ft^3 $\qquad \ldots$ *Answer* (*a*)

Solution. (*b*) If the initial dryness is x, and the initial specific volumes of liquid and vapour are v_t and v_g, we have from eq. (9.11)

$$0 \cdot 0503 = (1 - x)v_t + xv_g$$

v_t and v_g are found from Table II. The equation then runs

$$0 \cdot 0503 = (1 - x) \times 0 \cdot 01604 \times x \times 1206 \cdot 7$$

$$\therefore \qquad x = \frac{0 \cdot 0503 - 0 \cdot 01604}{1206 \cdot 7 - 0 \cdot 01604}$$

$$= 2 \cdot 84 \times 10^{-5} \qquad \ldots \quad Answer \ (b)$$

Thus the initial dryness is very small indeed. In this case it is certainly not permissible to neglect the volume of the water in comparison with that of the steam.

Solution. (*c*) The volume of the steam at 60°F is

$$xv_g, = 2 \cdot 84 \times 10^{-5} \times 1206 \cdot 7$$

$$= 0 \cdot 0343 \text{ ft}^3.$$

The volume of the water at 60°F,

$$(1 - x)v_t = (1 - 2 \cdot 84 \times 10^{-5}) \times 0 \cdot 01604 = 0 \cdot 01600 \text{ ft}^3.$$

giving of course a total volume of $0 \cdot 0503$ ft^3 as in answer (*a*).
The proportion of the total volume occupied by water is

$$\frac{0 \cdot 01600}{0 \cdot 0503} = 0 \cdot 318: \qquad \ldots \quad Answer \ (c)$$

Therefore the vessel should be slightly less than one third full of water.

Table IV: Superheated steam

This table gives data for the pure vapour. h, v and s (entropy, Chapter 13) are contained in the body of the table, for various values of pressure and temperature.

In general data will be required for combinations of pressure and temperature which do not appear explicitly. Then interpolation is necessary. Linear interpolation is sufficiently accurate for most purposes.

EXAMPLE OF INTERPOLATION WHERE THE PRESSURE APPEARS IN THE TABLE BUT THE TEMPERATURE DOES NOT.

Problem. What are h, v and u for $p = 180$ psia, $t = 929$°F?

Solution. At $p = 180$ psia, $t = 900$°F, we have $h = 1476 \cdot 8$ Btu/lb$_m$
(from Table IV)

At $p = 180$ psia, $t = 1000$°F, we have $h = 1528 \cdot 6$ Btu/lb$_m$
(from Table IV)

Therefore at $p = 180$ psia, $t = 929$°F, we have

$$h = 1476 \cdot 8 + \frac{929 - 900}{1000 - 900} \times (1528 \cdot 6 - 1476 \cdot 8)$$

$$= 1476 \cdot 8 + \frac{29 \times 51 \cdot 8}{100}$$

$$= 1476 \cdot 8 + 15 \cdot 0 = 1491 \cdot 8 \text{ Btu/lb}_m \qquad \ldots \quad Answer.$$

Similarly for v we have:

At $p = 180$ psia, $t = 900°F$, $v = 4\cdot452$ ft^3/lb$_m$ (from Table IV)

At $p = 180$ psia, $t = 1000°F$, $v = 4\cdot792$ ft^3/lb$_m$ (from Table IV)

Therefore at $p = 180$ psia, $t = 929°F$, we have:

$$v = 4\cdot452 + \frac{929 - 900}{1000 - 900}(4\cdot792 - 4\cdot452)$$

$$= 4\cdot452 + \frac{29}{100} \times 0\cdot340$$

$$= 4\cdot452 + 0\cdot099 = 4\cdot551 \text{ ft}^3/\text{lb}_m \qquad \dots \quad Answer.$$

Now $\qquad u = h - pv$

$$= 1491\cdot8 - \frac{180 \times 144 \times 4\cdot551}{778}$$

$$= 1491\cdot8 - 151\cdot7 = 1340\cdot1 \text{ Btu/lb}_m \qquad \dots \quad Answer.$$

Note the conversion factors 144 in^2/ft^2 and 778 ft lb$_f$/Btu needed to make the units consistent.

EXAMPLE OF INTERPOLATION WHERE NEITHER THE PRESSURE NOR THE TEMPERATURE APPEARS IN THE TABLE.

Problem. What is h for $p = 187$ psia, $t = 929°F$?

Solution. We first obtain the values of h at $t = 929°F$ for $p = 180$ psia and for $p = 200$ psia using the method given in the previous problem,

At $t = 929°F$, $p = 180$ psia: $\qquad h = 1491\cdot8$ Btu/lb$_m$ (see above)

At $t = 929°F$, $p = 200$ psia:

$$h = 1476\cdot2 + \frac{929 - 900}{1000 - 900}(1528\cdot0 - 1476\cdot2)$$

$$= 1476\cdot2 + \frac{29}{100}(51\cdot8)$$

$$= 1476\cdot2 + 15 = 1491\cdot2 \text{ Btu/lb}_m$$

We now interpolate linearly between the values of h at 180 psia and 200 psia to obtain the value of h corresponding to 187 psia, as follows:

At $t = 929°F$, $p = 187$ psia:

$$h = 1491\cdot8 - \frac{187 - 180}{200 - 180}(1491\cdot8 - 1491\cdot2)$$

$$= 1491\cdot8 - \frac{7}{20} \times 0\cdot6$$

$$= 1491\cdot8 - 0\cdot21 = 1491\cdot6 \text{ Btu/lb}_m \qquad \dots \quad Answer.$$

Remarks about Table IV. 1. The saturation temperatures corresponding to the various pressures are shown in brackets. They are necessary for finding the properties corresponding to states just to the left of those tabulated in Table IV, i.e. of only slightly superheated steam. They are also needed when the temperature quoted is not the true temperature but the "degrees superheat" (see p. 150).

EXAMPLE

Problem. A boiler, fitted with a superheater, generates steam at 140 psia with 20°F superheat. What is the enthalpy of the steam?

Solution. At 140 psia, the saturation temperature of steam $t_g = 353 \cdot 02$°F (from Table III or Table IV).

Therefore the temperature, t, of the steam produced by the boiler is given by

$$t = 353 \cdot 02 + 20°F$$

$$= 373 \cdot 02°F$$

This temperature is less than the lowest tabulated temperature at $p = 140$ psia, in Table IV. Therefore to obtain the required value of h we have to interpolate between Tables III and IV as follows:

From Table III: At $p = 140$ psia, $t_g = 353 \cdot 02$°F, $h_g = 1193 \cdot 0$ Btu/lb$_m$

From Table IV: At $p = 140$ psia, $t = 400$°F, $h = 1221 \cdot 1$ Btu/lb$_m$

$\therefore$ At $p = 140$ psia, $t = 373 \cdot 02$°F we have

$$h = 1193 \cdot 0 + \frac{400 - 373 \cdot 02}{400 - 353 \cdot 02} (1221 \cdot 1 - 1193 \cdot 0)$$

$$= 1193 \cdot 0 + \frac{26 \cdot 98}{46 \cdot 98} (28 \cdot 1)$$

$$= 1193 \cdot 0 + 16 \cdot 1 = 1209 \cdot 1 \text{ Btu/lb}_m \qquad \ldots \quad Answer$$

2. At high temperatures and low pressures it will be seen from Table IV that h varies only slightly with p at a fixed temperature. For example at $t = 1600$°F, $h = 1857 \cdot 5$ Btu/lb$_m$ when $p = 1$ psia, and $1852 \cdot 5$ Btu/lb$_m$ when $p = 400$ psia.

3. The internal energy is not tabulated. When it is needed, it must be derived from eq. (9.23) as before.

4. Linear interpolation may become rather inaccurate when applied to specific volume at low pressures. Rather than use more precise interpolation formulae, it is best to turn to more detailed tables, for example those of Keenan and Keyes (see bibliography) from which the tables in Appendix B are extracted.

THROTTLING CALORIMETER EXAMPLE.

Problem. A throttling calorimeter is used to measure the dryness fraction of the steam in a steam main, Fig. 9.14. The calorimeter readings are: pressure, 14·7 psia; temperature, 250°F. The main pressure is 85 psia. Calculate the dryness fraction of the steam in the main.

Solution. In the throttling calorimeter, it has been shown that the enthalpies of the steam before and after throttling are equal (see p. 157, eq. (9.22)). The downstream (state 2) measurements enable h_2, and hence h_1, to be evaluated as follows:

At state 2: $\qquad\qquad\qquad p_2 = 14\cdot7$ psia; $\qquad t_2 = 250°$F.

Since t_2 is greater than 212°F, the saturation temperature corresponding to $p_2 = 14\cdot7$ psia, the steam is superheated downstream of the throttle; therefore we have to use Table IV to evaluate h_2. However, on consulting Table IV we see that t_2 is less than the lowest tabulated temperature at 14·7 psia, namely 300°F; this means we have to interpolate between Tables III and IV to obtain h_2, as illustrated in the previous example. Thus we have,

From Table III: At $p = 14\cdot7$ psia, $t_g = 212°$F, $h_g = 1150\cdot4$ Btu/lb$_m$

From Table IV: At $p = 14\cdot7$ psia, $t = 300°$F, $h = 1192\cdot8$ Btu/lb$_m$.

$\therefore\qquad\qquad$ At $p_2 = 14\cdot7$ psia, $t_2 = 250°$F

$$h_2 = 1150\cdot4 + \frac{250 - 212}{300 - 212}(1192\cdot8 - 1150\cdot4)$$

$$= 1150\cdot4 + \frac{38}{88}(42\cdot4) = 1168\cdot7 \text{ Btu/lb}_m$$

$\therefore\qquad\qquad h_1 = 1168\cdot7$ Btu/lb$_m$

Now this value of enthalpy is less than h_g at 85 psia, namely, 1184·2 Btu/lb$_m$ (from Table III); the steam in the main is wet (Fig. 9.15). We use eq. (9.12) to evaluate the dryness fraction, for we have

$$h_1 = h_g - (1 - x_1)h_{fg} \quad \text{at 85 psia}$$

$$1168\cdot7 = 1184\cdot2 - (1 - x_1)897\cdot8 \quad \text{from Table III}$$

whence $\qquad\qquad x_1 = 0\cdot983 \qquad\qquad\qquad\qquad\qquad$ ... *Answer.*

Compressed liquid states

Symmetry demands that having dealt first with the saturated phases and so with the L + V region, and second with the superheat (V) region, we should now turn to the compressed liquid (L) states. However no table for these states is provided in the Appendix since the dependence of the properties of liquid water on pressure is quite small, at least when far from the critical point. It is sufficiently accurate for the examples in this book, and for many practical problems also, to use the saturated water data for the *temperature* in question as valid even though the pressure exceeds the saturation pressure for that temperature. For h and u of liquid H_2O it is often satisfactory to use the expression given in note 5, p. 160.

In professional work of course it is never permissible to make this assumption without examination of the inaccuracy involved. Data for compressed liquid water will be found in the Steam Tables of Keenan and Keyes just mentioned.

BIBLIOGRAPHY

Perry, J. H., *Chemical Engineers Handbook*. McGraw-Hill, 1953.
International Critical Tables. McGraw-Hill.
Keenan, J. H., and Keyes, F. G., *Thermodynamic Properties of Steam*. Wiley & Sons and Chapman & Hall, 1936.

CHAPTER 9—PROBLEMS

9.1 Using the Steam Tables given in Appendix B write down the symbol, the magnitude and the units for each of the following:

(a) Specific volume of saturated water at a pressure of 1 psia.

(b) Specific volume of dry saturated steam at a temperature of 300°F.

(c) Temperature of saturated water at a pressure of 14·696 psia.

(d) Temperature of dry saturated steam at a pressure of 14·696 psia.

(e) Temperature of wet steam, dryness 0·9 at a pressure of 14·696 psia.

(f) Latent heat of vaporisation at a pressure of 106 psia.

(g) Enthalpy of dry saturated vapour at a temperature of 212°F.

(h) Internal energy of saturated water at a pressure of 525 psia.

(i) Specific volume, enthalpy and internal energy of steam at a pressure of 60 psia and a temperature of 700°F.

(j) Temperature and specific volume of steam at a pressure of 1000 psia and an enthalpy of 1255 Btu/lb$_m$.

(k) Pressure and internal energy of steam at a temperature of 600°F and a specific volume at 4 ft^3/lb$_m$.

9.2 Using the Steam Tables given in Appendix B, sketch, approximately to scale, the boundaries of the liquid- and vapour-phase regions of H$_2$O on charts with the following coordinates:

(a) t–p; (b) h–p; (c) h–t; (d) p–v; (e) u–v. On sketches (b) and (d) show a few lines of constant t and on (c) a few lines of constant p. Mark the triple and critical points in each case.

9.3 Using the Steam Tables given in Appendix B, determine the value of the enthalpy, the internal energy and the specific volume of a mixture of 0·1 lb$_m$ of saturated water and 0·9 lb$_m$ of saturated steam at (a) a pressure of 250 psia and (b) a temperature of 500°F.

9.4 A vessel of volume 0·8 ft^3 contains a mixture of saturated water and saturated steam at a temperature of 480°F; the mass of liquid present is 10 lb$_m$. For the mixture, evaluate the pressure, the mass, the specific volume, the enthalpy and the internal energy.

9.5 (a) Use Table II of the Steam Tables to find the mass, the enthalpy and the internal energy of a system comprising 1 ft^3 of wet steam at a temperature 370°F and a dryness fraction of 0·94.

(b) The system undergoes a fully-resisted expansion at constant pressure to a temperature of 500°F. During the process there is heat transfer between the system and its surroundings. Show the path of this process on a sketch of the p–v diagram and evaluate the increase in enthalpy, the increase in internal energy, the work done and the heat transfer.

9.6 (a) A rigid vessel of volume 7 ft^3 contains 1 lb$_m$ of steam at a pressure of 60 psia. Evaluate the specific volume, the temperature, the dryness fraction, the internal energy and the enthalpy of the steam.

(b) Heat transfer to the steam causes its temperature to rise to 310°F. Show the path of this process on a sketch of the p–v diagram and evaluate the pressure, the increase in enthalpy, the increase in internal energy of the steam and the heat transfer. Evaluate also the pressure at which the steam becomes dry and saturated.

9.7 A rigid vessel contains 1 lb$_m$ of a mixture of saturated water and saturated steam at a pressure of 20 psia. When the mixture is heated the state passes through the critical point.

Evaluate:
- (a) the volume of the vessel;
- (b) the mass of liquid and vapour in the vessel initially;
- (c) the temperature of the contents of the vessel when the pressure has risen to 4000 psia;
- (d) the heat transfer required to produce the final state (c).

9.8 A vertical cylinder, fitted with a frictionless leak-proof piston, contains 0·06 lb$_m$ of dry saturated steam. The upper face of the piston is exposed to the atmosphere; the weight of the piston is such that the steam pressure is 40 psia. A quantity of water is introduced into the cylinder and mixes thoroughly with the steam. When the mixture is heated subsequently, with the piston held stationary, its state passes through the critical point. Find the mass of water injected assuming the heat transfer between the contents of the vessel and its surroundings to be zero during the injection process.

9.9 A throttling calorimeter sampling the steam generated by a boiler at a pressure 120 psia gives readings of pressure, 14·7 psia and temperature, 235°F. Evaluate the dryness fraction of the boiler steam.

9.10 A combined separating and throttling calorimeter is often used to measure the dryness fraction of very wet steam. The separator is a rigid vessel fitted in the steam-sampling pipe between the steam main and the throttling calorimeter; the steam sample flows through the separator before entering the calorimeter. The purpose of the separator is to remove some of the suspended water particles from the sample which otherwise would not become superheated in passing through the throttle. A test is carried out by measuring, over a specified period of time, the mass of water drained from the separator and the mass of steam flowing through the throttle. In addition the main pressure and the pressure and temperature after the throttle are recorded.

A particular test gave the following results:

Main pressure: 485·1 psig.

Mass of water drained from the separator: 0·73 lb$_m$.

Mass of steam condensed after passing through the throttle: 10·34 lb$_m$.

Throttling calorimeter readings:
  pressure, 2 in. water gauge
  temperature, 300°F.

Barometer reading: 30·4 in. mercury abs.

Evaluate the dryness fraction of the steam in the main and state, with reasons, whether the throttling calorimeter alone could have been used for this test.

9.11 A sample of wet steam from a steam main flows steadily through a partially open valve into a pipeline in which is fitted an electric coil; the valve and the pipeline are well-insulated. The steam mass flow rate is 0·91 lb$_m$/min while the coil takes 3·78 amps at 230 volts. The main pressure is 40 psia and the pressure and temperature of the steam downstream of the coil are 20 psia and 310°F respectively.

(a) Evaluate the dryness fraction of the steam in the main.

(b) State, with reasons, whether an insulated throttling calorimeter could have been used for this test.

9.12 An 11 in. diameter cylinder fitted with a frictionless leakproof piston contains 0.04 lb$_m$ of steam at a pressure of 80 psia and a temperature of 400°F. As the piston moves slowly outwards through a distance of 9.3 in., the steam undergoes a fully-resisted expansion during which the steam pressure p and the steam volume V are related by $pV^n = $ constant where n is a constant. The final pressure of the steam is 20 psia.

Determine:

(a) the value of n

(b) the work done by the steam

(c) the magnitude and sign of the heat transfer.

9.13 A pound of steam at a pressure of 100 psia and a temperature of 400°F is contained in a cylinder closed by a piston. The steam is compressed by the motion of the piston inwards until the pressure is 200 psia. The work done on the steam is 194,500 ft lb$_f$ and the heat transfer from the steam is 350 Btu.

Find the final steam temperature if superheated or the dryness fraction if wet.

9.14 Water flows steadily into a domestic radiator at a temperature of 180°F and leaves at a temperature of 160°F.

Evaluate the heat transfer from the water per pound of water flowing, assuming:

(a) the specific heat of water at constant pressure to be constant and equal to 1 Btu/lb$_m$ °F;

(b) the enthalpy of water at a given temperature to be equal to the enthalpy of saturated water at that temperature.

Neglect changes in kinetic and gravitational potential energies.

9.15 (a) Steam enters a convergent-divergent nozzle with a velocity of 200 ft/s., a pressure 100 psia and with 172.2°F superheat. The steam leaves the exit section of the nozzle at a pressure of 20 psia with a dryness fraction of 0.96. The cross-sectional area of the exit section is 2 in^2. The flow is adiabatic.

Determine the steam velocity at the exit section and the steam mass flow rate.

(b) The exhaust steam from the nozzle flows into a condenser and leaves it as water with negligible velocity at a temperature of 200°F. Determine the mass flow rate of cooling water required if it enters the condenser at a temperature of 50°F and leaves at a temperature of 80°F.

9.16 Steam at a pressure of 300 psia and a temperature of 500°F flows steadily into a turbine with negligible velocity. The steam leaves the turbine at a pressure of 2 psia with a velocity of 650 ft/s. The heat transfer rate from the turbine casing to the atmosphere is 9000 Btu/min. The power developed by the turbine is 4,600 horse-power. The mass flow rate is 804 lb$_m$/min. Determine the dryness fraction of the steam leaving the turbine and the cross-sectional area of the exit section.

9.17 A well-insulated rigid vessel of volume 10 ft^3 contains 18 lb$_m$ of liquid water and steam at 200°F. A coiled tube within the vessel, immersed in the mixture, is supplied with a steady flow of steam at a pressure of 60 psia and a dryness fraction of 0.9. The flowing steam condenses in the coil and leaves as saturated water at a pressure of 60 psia. Changes in velocity and elevation are negligible.

(a) Evaluate the maximum pressure reached by the mixture.

(b) Calculate the quantity of steam condensed in the coil to achieve this maximum pressure.

9.18 A well-insulated pressure vessel of volume 200 ft^3 is connected, via a valve, to a steam main in which the pressure and temperature are maintained at 400 psia and 500°F respectively. Initially the vessel contains water and steam at a pressure of 40 psia in the proportion 1 : 2 by volume. The valve is opened so allowing steam from the main to flow into the vessel. Determine the increase in the mass of the contents of the vessel and the proportions by volume of liquid and vapour finally in the vessel when the pressure has risen to 400 psia. (The arrangement described is known as a *steam accumulator*.)

9.19 Two rigid vessels are connected by a short pipe and a valve, initially shut. One vessel has a volume of 1·95 ft³ and is evacuated. The other vessel has a volume of 0·32 ft³ and contains dry and saturated ammonia at a temperature of 120°F.

The valve is opened and when conditions throughout the two vessels have become uniform it is found that the pressure and temperature of the ammonia are 48·2 psia and 100°F respectively.

Determine the heat transfer to the ammonia, using the data shown below for ammonia.

Pressure psia	Saturation temperature °F	Specific volume ft³/lb$_m$		Enthalpy, Btu/lb$_m$		
				Saturated		Superheated by 100°F
p	t	v_f	v_g	h_f	h_g	h
48·2	20	0·0247	5·910	64·7	617·8	675·0
286·4	120	0·0284	1·047	179·0	634·0	708·2

THE SECOND LAW OF THERMODYNAMICS

INTRODUCTION

We now return to the subject of producing mechanical power. The First Law of Thermodynamics shows that there is a fixed rate of exchange between heat and work. Since by burning fuel, either chemical or nuclear, high temperatures can be obtained and heat transfer caused, all that the engineer has to do, it might be thought, is to convert the heat into the corresponding amount of work.

In this chapter some of the means for producing work from heat will be examined, and it will be seen that they do not by any means effect a complete conversion. Is this because so far engineers have been insufficiently skilful? The answer to this question confronts us with the Second Law of Thermodynamics.

Symbols

C_{hp} Coefficient of performance of a heat pump.

C_{ref} Coefficient of performance of a refrigerator.

q Heat transfer.

q_1 Heat transfer between a system (heat engine) and a hot reservoir.

q_2 Heat transfer between a system (heat engine) and a cold reservoir. Heat transfer from an internal combustion engine to the atmosphere.

t_1 Temperature of a hot reservoir.

t_2 Temperature of a cold reservoir.

w Net work done by (on) a system.

w_p Shaft work input to a feed pump.

w_t Shaft work delivered by a turbine.

w_x External (shaft) work.

w_{100} Net work done by a one-hundred-per-cent-efficient heat engine.

η Efficiency of a heat engine, thermal efficiency.

ENGINES

The steam power plant

A large proportion of the world's power is produced by steam power plants. The four elements of such plants are illustrated in Fig. 10.1:— the boiler, turbine, condenser and feed pump. The working fluid, H_2O (vapour and liquid), flows steadily through these components in turn, thus executing a cyclic process. Entering the boiler as water, the working fluid is vaporised and passes into the turbine. Emerging from there still as steam but at a lower temperature and pressure, the working fluid enters the condenser. There it becomes water once again, and, after being compressed to boiler pressure by the feed pump, is returned to the boiler ready to begin the circuit once more.

A system boundary has been drawn around the power plant in Fig. 10.1. Four interactions occur across it:—in unit time, q_1 is the heat transfer from the hot fuel products to the steam in the boiler; w_t is the external work done by the turbine; q_2 is the heat transfer from the condensing steam to the cooling water, drawn perhaps from a river; while w_p is the external work driving the feed pump. The small letters, q and w, used for these heat and work quantities indicate that the earlier sign convention has

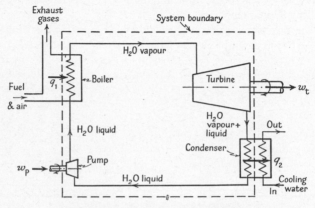

Fig. 10.1   Steam power plant.

been dropped; here the quantities are positive in the directions of the arrows.*

Application of the First Law, eq. (6.2), to this system, bearing in mind that conditions are steady, leads to an expression for the net work in unit time, namely

$$w_t - w_p = q_1 - q_2 \qquad \dots \quad (10.1)$$

Normally w_p is very much smaller than the turbine output w_t. q_2 on the other hand may amount to more than two-thirds the magnitude of q_1. This means that the work quantity obtained is less than one-third of that which the First Law would permit if the entire heat input, q_1, were converted. Why do engineers put up with this?

An immediate answer to the question is that it is only by transferring heat q_2 that the steam is condensed. If it were not condensed, the pump would have to raise the pressure of the exhaust steam to that of the boiler in order that the steam should work in a cycle. To do this the pump would have to do very much more work than when pumping condensed steam, i.e. water, back into the boiler; so much more, in fact, that w_p would exceed w_t and the net work output of the plant would be negative.

It might be thought that this is an idiosyncrasy of steam which could perhaps be avoided by using a different working fluid; alternatively one

* i.e. $q_1 \equiv Q_1$, $q_2 \equiv -Q_2$.

might look for a different way of using steam in order to avoid wasting the heat quantity q_2. The reader is invited to try to invent such a power plant arrangement before finishing this chapter.

In the subsequent discussion it will be important to note a difference between plants like the steam power plant, in which combustion occurs, if at all, external to the working fluid, and other power plants in which the working fluid itself takes part in combustion. We therefore now discuss the internal-combustion engine.

The internal-combustion engine

The important features of these engines will be described by reference to Fig. 10.2, which represents a petrol engine for a road vehicle. Petrol

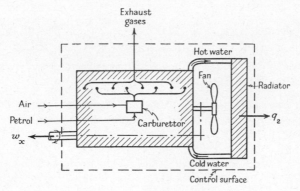

Fig. 10.2   Petrol engine.

and air pass, via the carburettor, into the engine cylinders, where, after combustion and expansion, the resulting exhaust gases (i.e. carbon dioxide, carbon monoxide, nitrogen and steam) flow out to atmosphere. The engine cylinder block is maintained at a reasonable working temperature by the circulation of cooling water between it and the engine "radiator". A fan, driven by the engine, draws atmospheric air through the radiator which cools the water circulating through it.

The dotted boundary of Fig. 10.2, though drawn as a rectangle, should be thought of as fitting over the metal surfaces. It encloses a control volume, not a system, for its contents change continuously as air and petrol flow in and exhaust gases flow out; the cooling air, on the other hand flows *past* the surface, not *through* it. In addition to the material flows, there are two interactions with the surroundings: the shaft work output, w_x and the heat output from the cooling water and exposed hot surfaces to the atmosphere, q_2.

Application of the First Law to the control volume, eq. (8.57), and neglecting kinetic energy and gravitational potential energy, yields,

$$w_x + q_2 = \text{enthalpy decrease of fuel-air-products stream} \quad \dots \quad (10.2)$$

so this time the algebraic sum of the heat and work quantities is not equal to zero. A further difference from the steam power plant is that there is no heat input, only an output from the radiator. The flow of petrol into the engine is not a heat transfer, nor is the outflow of hot exhaust gases; for neither of them is an interaction between systems by reason of a temperature difference. It should be noted also that although the engine works cyclically, i.e. it executes the same periodic sequence of events, the air and petrol do not execute a cycle—the exhaust gases leaving the engine are never returned to it as air and petrol to repeat the process.

Analysis of the performance of internal combustion engines and comparison of their work output with the theoretical maximum is an important part of thermodynamics, but is not treated until the end of the present book. For the moment we merely note the differences between I.C. engines and systems of the steam power plant type, and restrict discussion to the latter, to which we will give the name *heat engine*.

THE HEAT ENGINE

A definition which is logically sufficient is:—

A heat engine is any continuously operating thermodynamic system across the boundaries of which flow only heat and work.*

Explanatory remarks. 1. "Continuously operating" means that its state exhibits only periodic changes; the phrase covers both rotary and reciprocating machines. If a working fluid is present it must undergo cyclic processes.

2. Since a system is in question, the internal-combustion engine cannot be classed as a heat engine. Matter flows continuously into and out of an internal-combustion engine.

3. The steam power plant, as described above, is covered by the definition; the system enclosed by the boundary in Fig. 10.1 is a system. If, however, the boundary were enlarged to include the combustion space of the boiler, it would enclose a control volume, not a system; for, in addition to the heat and work interactions at the boundary, the air, fuel and flue gases would flow across it. The plant enclosed by this enlarged boundary would cease to be a heat engine in the sense defined above.

4. The turbine by itself is not a heat engine, for steam flows both in and out. A reciprocating steam engine, if understood to comprise merely cylinder, piston, and valve gear, is also not a heat engine for the same reason.

5. The distinction which is being emphasised is neatly illustrated by the two types of gas turbine engine.

The "closed-cycle" gas turbine: a heat engine

This power plant is illustrated in Fig. 10.3. Its four elements correspond to those of the steam plant:—the heater, turbine, cooler and compressor. The working fluid, a gas such as air, flows steadily into the heater, from which it emerges at a higher temperature. After expansion in the turbine, it passes to the cooler where its temperature is reduced before re-compression in the compressor. The heating and cooling are effected in order

* End note 6.

that the specific volume of the gas in the turbine should exceed that in the compressor; then the power output of the turbine can exceed the power consumption of the compressor and allow a net output of work.

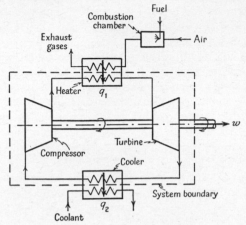

Fig. 10.3 "Closed-cycle" gas turbine

Examination of the dotted boundary in Fig. 10.3 shows that only work, w, and the two heat transfers, q_1 and q_2, cross the boundary. The "closed-cycle" gas turbine is therefore a heat engine.

Despite being more modern, this power plant has not managed to dispense with the "wasteful" heat output q_2, which may amount to 75% of q_1 in practice.

The "open-cycle" gas turbine: not a heat engine

A plant which is similar in many ways to that last described is the so-called "open-cycle" gas turbine, which is illustrated in Fig. 10.4. This

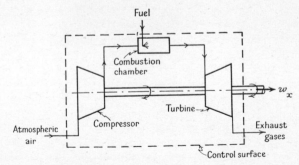

Fig. 10.4 "Open-cycle" gas turbine

has a steady-flow combustion chamber in place of a heater; instead of the cooler the exhaust from the turbine is passed directly to the atmosphere, while the compressor takes in fresh cold air.

Examination of the dotted boundary in Fig. 10.4 shows that this plant is not a heat engine: fresh air and fuel oil flow inwards; hot combustion products flow outwards; the working fluid does not perform a cycle, since nowhere are the combustion products turned back into oil and air. There are no heat transfers across the boundary, apart from minor ones to the atmosphere from exposed hot surfaces ("radiation losses"), but there is, of course, a net work output.

It may be remarked that the features which cause this plant not to be a heat engine are responsible for its popularity as a prime mover. For a combustion chamber is much cheaper to make than the gas-heater of the "closed-cycle" plant, and it is a considerably simpler matter to blow waste gases into the atmosphere than to provide a cooler and a supply of coolant.

The reversed heat engine: refrigerators and heat pumps

Nothing was said in the definition of *heat engine* about the direction of the heat and work transfers. Nevertheless the phrase, when unqualified,

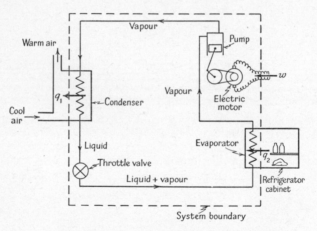

Fig. 10.5   Domestic refrigeration plant.

usually implies that there is a net output of work and correspondingly a net intake of heat; often such engines are called *direct heat engines*. However, there are important engineering applications in which the directions are reversed. These will now be discussed.

Fig. 10.5 illustrates a refrigerator of a type found in many homes. It has four elements corresponding to those of the steam power plant:—a condenser, a vapour compressor, an evaporator, and a throttle. The working fluid, which may be carbon dioxide or ammonia but is more probably Freon,* executes a cycle but in an opposite sense to that executed by the steam (compare Fig. 10.1 and Fig. 10.5.) The condenser is at the higher temperature and pressure. From it liquid flows through the throttle

---

* A commercial refrigerant, e.g. Freon 12, dichlorodifluormethane, CCl_2F_2.

valve to the evaporator which is at a lower pressure and temperature. Thence the vapour passes to the compressor which pumps it into the condenser.

Examination of the dotted boundary in Fig. 10.5 shows that only heat and work cross: the plant is a heat engine. However the work, w, flows inwards, along the wires to the electric motor; the heat transfer q_1, at the higher temperature is *from* the working fluid; the heat transfer q_2, at the lower temperature is *to* the working fluid.

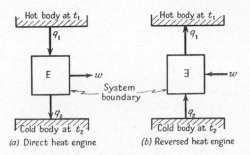

(a) Direct heat engine   (b) Reversed heat engine

Fig. 10.6

If the purpose of the plant is to withdraw heat at the low temperature, it is called a *refrigerator*. If its purpose is to provide heat at the higher temperature, it is called a *heat pump*.

Both refrigerators and heat pumps are *reversed* heat engines. This adjective must not be confused with another, which will be introduced in the next chapter, namely *reversible*. Curiously, thermodynamic usage permits an engine to be reversed without being reversible.

It is customary to represent heat engines diagrammatically as shown in Fig. 10.6. The system boundary encloses the engine; q_1, q_2 and w represent respectively the heat transfers and the work and their direction is indicated by the arrows at the system boundary. Fig. 10.6a shows a direct heat engine (E); Fig. 10.6b shows a reversed heat engine (Ǝ), i.e. a refrigerator or a heat pump.

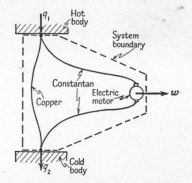

Fig. 10.7   The thermocouple as a heat engine.

The thermocouple as a heat engine

In order to demonstrate that the definition of *heat engine* covers devices which are not ordinarily regarded as engines, we consider the thermocouple system illustrated in Fig. 10.7. Two metal wires of dissimilar composition, for example copper and the copper-nickel alloy, constantan, are connected so that one junction communicates with a hot body and the other one with a cold body. A voltage difference develops and an electric current flows. If a motor is in the circuit this may be used to perform work. The voltage difference increases with the temperature difference but is always very small (millivolts) and permits only tiny power outputs.

As will have been expected, the work output, if maintained, is accompanied by heat transfer from the surroundings to the system. Experimentally it is found that there are two heat transfers: an inward one, q_1, from the hot body, and a very slightly smaller outward one, q_2, to the cold body.

Examination of the dotted system boundary of Fig. 10.7 shows that the thermocouple system should be classed as a heat engine. Indeed it has the feature noted in every other example, though not specified in the definition, of "wasting" a large proportion of the heat input by a heat transfer to a cold body.

HEAT ENGINE PERFORMANCE

Heat engine efficiency

Since the "wastage" of heat by engines is so common, it is convenient to measure it by defining the *efficiency* of a heat engine, η, by

$$\eta \equiv \frac{w}{q_1} \qquad \dots \quad (10.3)$$

where w is the net work output, while q_1 is the heat input at the higher temperature. It is a measure of the excellence of the heat engine in that it compares the work, w, which we want and obtain, with the heat, q_1, which we have to provide. Application of the First Law, eq. (6.2), to the engine gives $w = q_1 - q_2$ and hence

$$\eta = \frac{q_1 - q_2}{q_1} = 1 - \frac{q_2}{q_1} \qquad \dots \quad (10.4)$$

Throughout this chapter, q and w will be expressed in identical units, η is therefore dimensionless.

Actual values of the efficiency of heat engines are given in Table 10.1. It is seen that values above 35% are rare. A significant trend is that η seems to increase with the maximum temperature employed in the cycle.

No internal-combustion plants are included in Table 10.1 because the definition, eq. (10.3), applies only to heat engines. Although it is possible to define an efficiency for an internal-combustion engine, this is a more sophisticated concept; it is discussed in Chapter 16.

Often the efficiency of eq. (10.3) is designated *thermal efficiency* to distinguish it from other "efficiencies".

Eq. (10.3) is only used for heat engines operating "directly", that is to say producing net power. It is convenient at this point to introduce the corresponding quantities used for reversed heat engines.

TABLE 10.1. *Efficiencies of power plants*

Plant	Date of installation	Working fluid	Maximum temperature of the working fluid °F	Efficiency %
Great Britain: central power stations.	1936–40	Steam	800	28
Great Britain: central power stations.	1950–54	Steam	1070	36
United States.	1956	Steam	1200	40
Great Britain: Calder Hall (Nuclear).	1956	Steam	590	22
United States.	1949	Steam + mercury	945	34
Switzerland (Escher Wyss): closed-cycle gas turbine.	1944	Air	1270	32
France: closed-cycle gas turbine.	1950	Air	1250	34

Coefficients of performance of refrigerators and heat pumps

Eq. (10.3) defines efficiency as "what we want" divided by "what we have to pay for". The same principle is adopted for measuring the performance of reversed heat engines.

With refrigerator plants, "what we want" is heat transfer at the low temperature q_2; "what we have to pay for" is the work supply w. Consequently the *coefficient of performance of a refrigerator,** C_{ref}, is defined as

$$C_{ref} \equiv \frac{q_2}{w} \qquad \qquad \dots \quad (10.5)$$

In a heat pump plant the interesting product is heat transfer q_1 at the higher temperature; again w is the commodity which must be supplied. The *coefficient of performance of a heat pump,* C_{hp}, is therefore defined as

$$C_{hp} \equiv \frac{q_1}{w} \qquad \qquad \dots \quad (10.6)$$

---

* Sometimes called performance energy ratio.

TABLE 10.2. *Coefficients of performance*

Plant	Date	Heat pump or refrigerator	Working fluid	Upper temperature °F	Lower temperature °F	Coefficient of performance
Portsmouth, Ohio, U.S.	1940	H.P.	Freon	85 96	27 23	3·6 3·2
Coshocton, Ohio, U.S.	1940	H.P.	Freon	86 90 108	51 51 51	5·0 3·9 3·9
Norwich, Great Britain	1945	H.P.	Sulphur dioxide	120	45	3·5
Zurich, Switzerland	—	H.P.		122 77	River water River water	3·5 7·0
London (Festival Hall), Great Britain	1951	H.P.	Freon	130	65	2·8
Great Britain	1951	Domestic refrigerator	Freon	90 90 90	30 20 −20	4·8 3·8 1·3
Great Britain	1945	Refrigerated rail car	Ammonia	120	−5	1·8

Since the First Law, eq. (6.2), applied to the plant gives $w = q_1 - q_2$ and since the same plant may be regarded as either a refrigerator or a heat pump, we have the relations

$$C_{hp} = \frac{w + q_2}{w}$$

$$= 1 + C_{ref} \qquad \qquad \dots \quad (10.7)$$

Typical practically-obtained values of C_{ref} and C_{hp} are contained in Table 10.2. It may be seen that the coefficients of performance are greatest when the temperature differences are least.

THE 100% EFFICIENT ENGINE, E.100

Returning now to "direct" heat engines, it is clear that all we have to do is to design one like that illustrated in Fig. 10.8. This rejects no heat to a cold body and therefore has an efficiency of 100%. We will designate this engine the E.100.

Before discussing the possibility of attaining this ideal, it should be pointed out that the E.100 is more remarkable than perhaps appears at first sight: it will be unnecessary to buy any fuel for it at all. To show how this comes about, let us suppose that E.100 will work satisfactorily if it communicates with a hot body at a temperature of, say, 1000°F. Rather than burn fuel to provide hot gases at this temperature, it will be cheaper in running costs to employ the arrangement of Fig. 10.9.

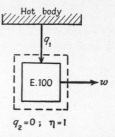

$q_2 = 0$; $\eta = 1$

Fig. 10.8 The 100% efficient heat engine: E.100.

The E.100 drives a reversed heat engine Ǝ which is so arranged that it supplies just as much heat to the 1000°F body as is extracted by E.100. This does not absorb the whole work output of the E.100 however, because we have

For Ǝ: $\qquad w = q_1 - q_2$ where q_2 is positive ... (10.8)

For E.100: $w_{100} = q_1$ $\qquad\qquad\qquad$ ... (10.9)

It follows that there is a net work output from the system within the dotted boundary of Fig. 10.9 of

$$w_{100} - w = q_2 \qquad\qquad ... \quad (10.10)$$

Now examination of the dotted boundary shows that the only heat transfer is that from the river. No heat has to be supplied at 1000°F

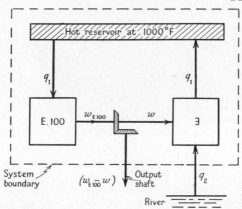

Fig. 10.9 How to make E.100 operate without using fuel.

from outside, and therefore no fuel has to be burned. All that is needed to keep the engine running is a plentiful supply of low-temperature material. Although the large specific heat of water renders it particularly suitable, air or earth could also be used. A ship powered by an E.100 coupled to a heat pump could sail the seas forever.

THE SECOND LAW OF THERMODYNAMICS

All attempts to build an E.100 have failed, and it is now accepted that the task is an impossible one. This fact of nature is embodied in the Second Law of Thermodynamics, which may be expressed as:

It is impossible to construct an engine which will work in a complete cycle and produce no effect except to raise a weight and exchange heat with a single reservoir.

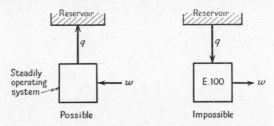

Fig. 10.10   A directional implication of the Second Law.

Explanatory remarks. 1. "Reservoir" means a system at a fixed and uniform temperature. The word is a metaphor, and represents a legacy from the caloric theory which taught that heat could be stored or contained in a body. Usually a reservoir is "large", so that, if its temperature does change, it does so much more slowly than does that of a system communicating with it.

2. The above form of the Second Law is due to Max Planck (1897). Although other forms will be met with later, this one is given prominence here because it most clearly shows the mechanical engineer what he is up against.

3. The Second Law must not be taken merely as an expression of faintheartedness on the part of engine builders. The Law has many consequences, some of which will be discussed below. To disprove the Second Law, it would suffice to disprove just one of its corollaries. No single instance of disproof is on record; as a result the Law is now regarded as among the most firmly established of all the laws of nature.

4. The essential idea of the Second Law was first conceived by Sadi Carnot in 1824, that is to say well before the First Law was established.

5. Whereas the First Law states that heat and work are interchangeable, the Second Law states that complete conversion is only possible in one direction, namely from work into heat. In financial terms, work is a "freely convertible currency"; heat is not. It is for this reason that such care has been necessary to distinguish heat from work in earlier chapters; only with heat and work defined as above is the Second Law true as stated.

6. Note 5 stresses the *directional* implication of the Second Law. This is presented graphically in Fig. 10.10, which reminds us that the entirely possible process on the left, which might for example represent Rumford's cannon-boring experiment, cannot be reversed. The concept of *reversibility* will prove to be of great importance below.

7. The 100% efficient engine, E.100, is sometimes known as a *perpetual motion machine of the second kind* (abbreviated to PMM 2). A perpetual motion machine of the first kind (PMM 1) of course, would be a contravener of the First Law. Fig. 10.11 makes the point. Both are impossible.

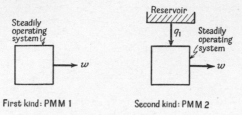

Fig. 10.11   Perpetual motion machines.

8. The Second Law is also the reason for excluding internal-combustion engines from the heat engine class, instead of regarding them as heat engines in which "the heat is in chemical form". For an engine *can* be constructed which converts into work the whole of the "chemical energy", i.e. enthalpy change on complete isothermal reaction, of the fuel (p. 329).

9. The Second Law is a blank statement that the dearest wish of the power plant engineer is unattainable. Of course we cannot leave the matter there, but must go on to ask "Well, how near can we get?" It is in answering this question, and in looking for ways in which to get as near as possible to the unattainable, that the thermodynamicist has had to invent and use the concepts of reversibility, absolute temperature, and entropy. These matters will therefore occupy our attention for the next three chapters.

BIBLIOGRAPHY

Constant, H., *Gas Turbines and their Problems*, Todd Publishing Group Ltd., 1948.

Ewing, Sir J. A., *The Steam Engine and other Heat Engines*, Cambridge University Press, 1926.

Keenan, J. H. and Shapiro, A. H., *History and Exposition of the Laws of Thermodynamics*. Mechanical Engineering, November, 1947.

Ricardo, Sir H. R., *The Internal Combustion Engine*, Blackie and Son Ltd., Vol. I, 1922, Vol. II (4th Edition), 1953.

CHAPTER 10—PROBLEMS

10.1 A heat engine performs many cycles while doing 15,500 ft lb$_f$ of work and receiving a heat transfer of 80 Btu. Evaluate the efficiency of the engine and the heat transfer from the working fluid.

10.2 A heat engine working at the rate of 100 horse-power has an efficiency of 20 per cent. Evaluate the magnitudes of the heat transfer rate to and from the working fluid.

10.3 The efficiency η of a certain type of ideal closed-cycle gas-turbine engine (Fig. 10.3) is given by

$$\eta = 1 - \frac{1}{(r)^{\gamma-1}}$$

where r is the 'pressure ratio, i.e. the ratio of the pressures at outlet from and at inlet to the compressor and γ is the c_p/c_v, the ratio of the specific heats of the working fluid.

(a) Evaluate η for $r = 7$ assuming air (for which $\gamma = 1\cdot4$) to be the working fluid.

(b) The heat transfer rate from the air in the cooler is 3200 Btu/s. Evaluate the heat transfer rate to the air in the heater and the power developed, assuming all other heat transfers to be negligible.

10.4 A steam power plant (Fig. 10.1), incorporating a reciprocating steam engine gave the following results during a test under steady conditions:

Boiler:

Steam outlet conditions: pressure, 100 psia; temperature 400°F.

Feed water: temperature, 130°F; mass flow rate $3\cdot52$ lb_m/min.

Engine:

Shaft power: 9 horse-power.

Steam inlet conditions: as for boiler outlet.

Condenser:

Cooling water: flow rate, 101 lb_m/min; temperature rise, 34°F.

There are unmeasured heat transfers to the atmosphere from the exposed hot surfaces of the plant. Fluid velocities may be assumed to be negligible.

Evaluate, per pound of working fluid (H_2O):

(a) the heat transfer to the H_2O in the boiler;

(b) the external work done by the H_2O in the engine;

(c) the heat transfer from the condensing steam in the condenser, assuming the heat transfer from the condenser casing to the atmosphere to be zero;

(d) the heat transfer to the atmosphere assuming the feed-pump work to be zero;

(e) the efficiency of the plant.

10.5 In a steady-flow closed-cycle gas-turbine engine (Fig. 10.3) the temperature and velocity of the working fluid (air) between the various components are as follows:

Cooler and compressor:	90°F,	300 ft/s.
Compressor and heater:	450°F,	100 ft/s.
Turbine and cooler:	965°F,	350 ft/s.

The velocity of the air entering the turbine is 700 ft/s. and the heat transfer to the air in the heater is 276 Btu/lb_m. All heat transfers to the atmosphere may be assumed to be negligible.

Calculate: (a) the temperature of the air at entry to the turbine;

(b) the heat transfer from the air in the cooler;

(c) the net work output of the plant;

(d) the efficiency.

Assume that the enthalpy of air is a function of temperature only and that the specific heat at constant pressure $c_p = 0\cdot24$ Btu/lb_m °F (see problem 7.7).

10.6 In a reversed heat engine, the work done on the engine is 55,000 ft lb_f and the heat transfer to the engine from the low-temperature region is 210 Btu. Evaluate the heat transfer to the high-temperature region and the coefficient of performance as a refrigerator and as a heat pump.

10.7 The coefficient of performance of a heat pump is 5 when the power supplied to drive it is 50 horse-power.

(a) Evaluate the magnitudes of the heat transfer rate to and from the working fluid.

(b) The heat transfer from the engine is used to heat the water flowing through the radiators of a building. Evaluate the mass flow rate of the heated water given that its temperature increases from 120°F to 160°F in flowing through the heat pump. Assume the water velocity to be negligible.

10.8 Find the coefficient of performance and the heat transfer rate in the condenser of a refrigerator (in Btu/h) which has a capacity of 0·9 tons of refrigeration per hp. [One ton of refrigeration is equivalent to the production of one ton of ice at 32°F from water at 32°F in 24 hours. The latent heat of fuson of ice at 32°F is 143·3 Btu/lb$_m$.]

10.9 In a refrigerating plant (Fig. 10.5) the states of the working fluid (Freon 12) between the various components are as follows:

Evaporator and compressor: wet vapour at a temperature of 5°F

Compressor and condenser: dry saturated vapour at a temperature of 86°F.

Condenser and expansion valve: saturated liquid at a temperature of 86°F.

Expansion valve and evaporator: wet vapour at a temperature of 5°F.

The heat transfer rate from the Freon in the condenser is 3080 Btu/h and the power required to compress the Freon is 0·25 horse-power. All heat transfers to the atmosphere and fluid velocities, may be assumed to be negligible.

Sketch the cycle on an enthalpy-pressure diagram and calculate:

(a) the mass flow rate of the Freon in lb/min;

(b) the heat transfer rate to the Freon from the cold region;

(c) the enthalpy of the Freon after the expansion valve;

(d) the enthalpy and dryness fraction of the Freon at entry to the compressor;

(e) the coefficient of performance.

Use the following properties of Freon 12.

Pressure psia	Saturation Temperature °F	Enthalpy: Btu/lb$_m$ (datum − 40°F)	
		Saturated liquid	Saturated vapour
26·5	5	9·3	78·9
107·9	86	27·7	87·4

10.10 A heat engine is used to drive a heat pump. The heat transfers from the heat engine and from the heat pump are used to heat the water circulating through the radiators of a building. The efficiency of the heat engine is 27 per cent and the coefficient of performance of the heat pump is 4. Evaluate the ratio of the heat transfer to the circulating water to the heat transfer to the heat engine.

CHAPTER 11

REVERSIBILITY

INTRODUCTION

In this chapter we introduce the idea of the *reversible engine* and show that its efficiency in given circumstances is the highest possible. This makes it important to see how reversibility can be achieved, by identifying and eliminating its opposite: irreversibility. A number of practical processes are shown by reference to the Second Law to involve irreversibility, including friction, unresisted expansion, heat transfer with a finite temperature difference, and combustion. As far as possible therefore they must be avoided in engines. This will be illustrated by discussing the engine cycle suggested by Carnot.

Symbols

C_{hp}	Coefficient of performance of a heat pump.	t	Temperature.
F	Force.	w	Net work done by (on) a heat engine.
g	Gravitational acceleration.	w_x	External work.
g_0	Constant in Newton's Second Law.	η	Efficiency of a heat engine, thermal efficiency
m	Mass.	*Subscripts*	
p	Pressure.		
Q	Heat transfer.	C	Cold reservoir.
q	Heat transfer.	H	Hot reservoir
q_1	Heat transfer between system (heat engine) and hot reservoir.	I	Irreversible.
		R	Reversible.
		1, 2, . . .	States of the working fluid.
q_2	Heat transfer between system (heat engine) and cold reservoir.		

REVERSIBILITY AND ENGINE EFFICIENCY

The reversible engine

Suppose that a reciprocating steam "engine" is driven backwards. It will act like the reciprocating compressor of a refrigerator. Similarly a turbine, when driven backwards, will act like a rotary compressor, albeit inefficiently. "Inefficiently" in this connexion means that much more work will be necessary to drive one pound of steam from the low pressure to the high pressure than could be done by the same pound of steam when flowing in the normal direction. It is however possible to *imagine* a heat engine, i.e., a complete power plant, all components of which would work *just as well* backwards as forwards.

Such a heat engine will be called a *reversible engine*. As definition we state:

A heat engine is reversible if, for operation between two heat reservoirs of fixed, but different, temperatures, its efficiency when operating directly is equal to the reciprocal coefficient of performance when operating as a heat pump.

i.e.
$$\eta_R = \frac{1}{C_{hp,R}} \qquad \qquad \dots \ (11.1)$$

Fig. 11.1 illustrates the definition. E_R is the engine when producing power. $Ǝ_R{}^*$ is the engine working as a heat pump.

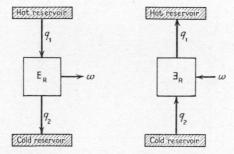

Reversible engine   Reversible engine working
working directly   as a heat pump

Fig. 11.1

An engine E_I which does not satisfy the relation (11.1) will be termed irreversible. It will be shown that for these

$$\eta_I < \frac{1}{C_{hp,I}} \qquad \qquad \dots \ (11.2)$$

Comparison of reversible and irreversible engine efficiency

Suppose that we have an irreversible engine E_I and a reversible one E_R, Fig. 11.2a, which have efficiencies, when working between the same two reservoirs of different but fixed temperatures of η_I and η_R. We wish to establish which is the greater.

Let the engines be connected in the manner shown in Fig. 11.2b, so that the heat transfer from the hot reservoir to E_I is identical with that transferred by $Ǝ_R$ (E_R reversed) to the hot reservoir. *Suppose* that E_I is more efficient than E_R:

$$\eta_I > \eta_R \qquad \qquad \dots \ (11.3)$$

---

* Symbols E and Ǝ represent respectively a direct heat engine and a reversed heat engine. Subscripts R and I mean reversible and irreversible respectively. Thus E_R = a reversible direct heat engine, $Ǝ_I$ = an irreversible reversed heat engine, i.e., an irreversible refrigerator or heat pump. Note the distinction between the terms reversed and reversible.

Then, from the definitions of efficiency, coefficient of performance and a reversible heat engine, we have

$$\frac{w_I}{q_1} > \frac{w_R}{q_1} \qquad \ldots \text{(11.4)}$$

i.e. $$w_I > w_R \qquad \ldots \text{(11.5)}$$

Now Fig. 11.2b shows that the net work output is $w_I - w_R$, which we now know to be positive; secondly, examination of the dotted system boundary shows that the $E_I - \mathfrak{H}_R$ combination exchanges heat with but one reservoir, i.e., it is an E.100.

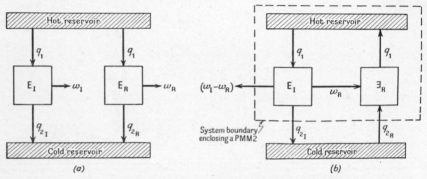

Fig. 11.2   Showing that no engine can be more efficient than a reversible engine.

But this is impossible according to the Second Law of Thermodynamics. Therefore our hypothesis (11.3) must be incorrect. Therefore

$$\eta_I \leqslant \eta_R \qquad \ldots \text{(11.6)}$$

We wish to refine this important result somewhat. Consider Fig. 11.3 in which now E_I acts as a heat pump ($\mathfrak{H}_I$) while E_R operates directly. We see that the net work output $w_R - w_I$ is given by

$$w_R - w_I = \eta_R q_1 - \frac{q_1}{C_{hp,I}}$$

$$= q_1 \left(\frac{1}{C_{hp,R}} - \frac{1}{C_{hp,I}} \right) \qquad \ldots \text{(11.7)}$$

But from the Second Law this quantity cannot be positive, for, if it were, the $\mathfrak{H}_I - E_R$ combination would be an E.100, i.e., it would be producing positive work while exchanging heat with a single reservoir. It follows that

$$\frac{1}{C_{hp,R}} - \frac{1}{C_{hp,I}} \leqslant 0$$

$$C_{hp,I} \leqslant C_{hp,R} \qquad \ldots \text{(11.8)}$$

Finally, using the definition of a reversible engine, eq. (11.1), and the definition of an irreversible engine, namely

$$\eta_{\mathrm{I}} \neq \frac{1}{C_{\mathrm{hp,I}}} \qquad \qquad \cdots \;\; (11.9)$$

equations (11.6) and (11.8) lead to the three results:—

(a) $$\eta_{\mathrm{I}} < \eta_{\mathrm{R}} \qquad \qquad \cdots \;\; (11.10)$$

(b) $$C_{\mathrm{hp,I}} < C_{\mathrm{hp,R}} \qquad \qquad \cdots \;\; (11.11)$$

(c) $$\eta_{\mathrm{I}} < \frac{1}{C_{\mathrm{hp,I}}} \qquad \qquad \cdots \;\; (11.12)$$

In words, these run:—
(a) The efficiency of a reversible engine exceeds that of an irreversible engine operating between the same two heat reservoirs. (b) The coefficient of performance (as either heat pump or refrigerator) of a reversible engine exceeds that of an irreversible engine operating between the same two heat reservoirs. (c) The efficiency of an irreversible engine is less than the reciprocal of its coefficient of performance when operating as a heat pump.

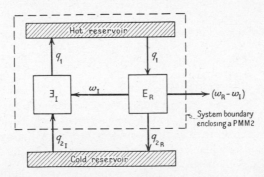

Fig. 11.3   Showing that the coefficient of performance of a reversed heat engine cannot be greater than that of a reversed reversible heat engine.

Discussion. 1. The first of these results is of the greatest importance, and we will pursue its implications below. These are both theoretical and practical in nature; the former because the result leads to the absolute temperature scale and to entropy; the latter because we now have a clue as to how engines should be built for high efficiency—they should be reversible.

2. It should be noted that it was essential to the proof that the engines communicated with the same pair of reservoirs which were uniform, but different, in temperature; for otherwise changes would have taken place within the hot reservoir, events within the system boundary would not have been cyclic, and so the Second Law could not have been applied.

REVERSIBLE PROCESSES

So far the term reversible has only been applied to heat engines and, by inference, to the cyclic processes which they perform. If a heat engine is known to be irreversible, it is important to examine which features render it so. For this, an extension of meaning is made to non-cyclic processes as follows:—

A process is reversible if means can be found to restore the system and all elements of its surroundings to their respective initial states.

Discussion. 1. This definition clearly includes the processes carried out by reversible heat engines: heat engines operate cyclically in any case so the system is easily restored to its initial state; and if the engine is reversible the effects on the surroundings of the heat transfers q_1 and q_2 and the work transfer w_1 are exactly cancelled when the same transfers take place in the opposite direction. An irreversible engine on the other hand requires, for example, a larger work quantity to restore q_1 to the hot reservoir when operating reversed than is developed when q_1 flows to the engine when operating directly; as a result the low-temperature reservoir does not return all the heat supplied to it, and permanent changes are left in the surroundings.

2. We only require that "means can be found" to restore the initial states, but do not demand that these states shall be restored automatically.

3. Any process which is not reversible is *irreversible*. This is an extension of the definition. The way to decide whether a process is reversible or irreversible is to apply the only natural law at our disposal which concerns direction: the Second Law of Thermodynamics. This will be done below.

Examples of reversible processes

We now consider a number of processes which are important in engineering and which may be regarded as reversible. It will be seen that in practice departures from reversibility always occur to a limited extent, but often these imperfections are small. The examples are illustrated in Fig. 11.4 *a* to *e*.

(*a*) *Frictionless motion of solids.* A block accelerates down a smooth plane under the influence of gravitational and other conservative forces. The process is reversible because, if at the base of the plane the block were led along a smooth runway and up another inclined plane, it would eventually come to rest, reverse direction, and return to its original state. Then the system (block) and all elements of its surroundings would be restored.

(*b*) *Extension of a spring.* The appropriately varying force F slowly extends a spring until a weak catch is sprung. Then relaxation of F does not cause the process to be reversed, for the catch prevents this. Nevertheless the process is reversible because *means can be found* to restore the initial state, namely lowering the catch and infinitesimal relaxation of F. The work involved in moving the catch is neglected.

(*c*) *Slow adiabatic expansion of a gas.* The gas in the cylinder expands without heat transfer against a frictionless piston which is acted on by the external force F. The process is reversible because an infinitesimal increase in F will suffice to cause the system and its surroundings to trace out each step in the process in the reversed order.

(d) *Slow isothermal compression of steam.* The force F slowly pushes the leak-proof frictionless piston inward, thus causing the steam in the cylinder to condense. The steam transfers heat to the walls of the cylinder. Since

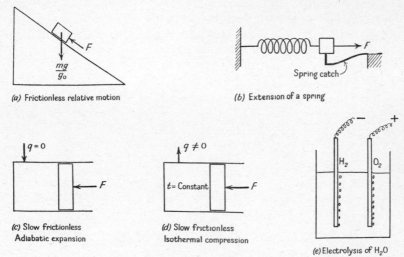

(a) Frictionless relative motion

(b) Extension of a spring

(c) Slow frictionless Adiabatic expansion

(d) Slow frictionless Isothermal compression

(e) Electrolysis of H_2O

Fig. 11.4 Reversible process.

the process is very slow, this heat transfer necessitates only an infinitesimally higher temperature in the steam than in its surroundings. The process is reversible because by reducing the force F by a negligible amount, the direction of movement reverses, the steam temperature drops infinitesimally below its previous value, the direction of heat transfer reverses, and the condensate re-evaporates. Thus the process is traced out in reverse and the initial states of system and surroundings are restored.

(e) *Electrolysis of water.* A potential difference of 1·47 volts exists between the plates of a cell containing water rendered electrically conducting by dissolved potassium hydroxide. A small current passes and bubbles of hydrogen appear at the negative electrode and bubbles of oxygen at the positive electrode. If the potential difference is slightly reduced, the process stops but does not go backwards: the bubbles of gas do not start travelling downwards to the plates and disappear there. Nevertheless the process is reversible (apart from the motion of the bubbles) because *means can be devised* by which the hydrogen and oxygen are recombined to form water and produce electrical power. Such a device is known as a *fuel cell*, and requires special electrodes. The principle is the same as that of the lead-acid accumulator but the technique is more difficult. So far it has only proved possible to recover in re-combination about 65% of the work expended in electrolysis (see bibliography).

IRREVERSIBLE PROCESSES

In this section the main types of irreversibility which occur in engines will be discussed; their irreversible nature will be proved by reference to the Second Law. The procedure of proof will be the same in each case, namely:—

(i) Describe the process, P, noting in particular its end-states and the heat and work quantities.

(ii) Assume that the process is reversible, i.e., that a reverse process, ꟼ, exists, in which the *magnitudes* of the heat and work, and of the changes of properties, are the same, but their *directions* are reversed.

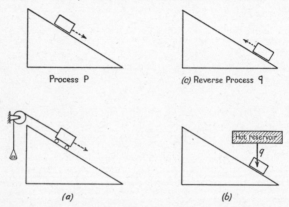

Fig. 11.5 Supposed processes used in proving that
solid friction is irreversible.

(iii) Devise a mechanism making use of ꟼ as part of a cyclic process which amounts to a heat engine of 100% efficiency.

(iv) Invoke the Second Law to prove that the hypothesis (ii) was incorrect.

The purpose of the proofs is two-fold. Firstly, they demonstrate that the irreversible natures of the various processes are not a miscellany of unconnected facts, but are all manifestations of a single law. Secondly, they show not merely that the processes will not of themselves go backwards, but that nothing that the wit of man can devise can succeed in undoing their effects. That is to say that it is no good leaving friction in a machine, for example, and then hoping to nullify its effect by a friction-cancelling device: the friction *must* be eliminated if the machine is to give the highest performance.

Solid friction

An example of friction between solids in relative motion will be considered. Fig. 11.5 illustrates this.

(i) In the process P the block slides slowly down the rough inclined plane. Both are good conductors of heat but there is no heat or other interaction with their surroundings. Both block and plane increase in temperature during the process.

(ii) Assume that a mechanism can be devised to execute the reverse process ꟼ, the end-states of which are such that the block rises up the plane to its previous starting position, both block and plane decrease in temperature, and there are no net heat or work interactions with the surroundings, i.e., the effects of P and ꟼ completely cancel in the block, in the plane and in their surroundings.

(iii) Cause the system comprising the block and the plane to execute the following cycle:—

(a) The block starts at the top of the incline. It is placed on rollers and attached by a rope and pulley to a suitably chosen weight (Fig. 11.5a). The block then rolls down, so raising the weight.

(b) Heat transfer occurs between the system and a reservoir at a higher temperature, and raises the temperature of the system to that which would have been reached if the block had slid down under friction (Fig. 11.5b).

(c) The process ꟼ is then carried out (Fig. 11.5c), with the result that the block returns to its starting point and the temperatures fall to their initial value. The cycle has then been completed.

(iv) The net effect of the cyclic process is that a weight has been raised and a corresponding amount of heat withdrawn from a single reservoir. The system is therefore a heat engine of 100% efficiency. But this is impossible according to the Second Law of Thermodynamics. Processes (a) and (b) can certainly be carried out. It follows that it is the reverse process ꟼ which is impossible. Therefore the process P is irreversible.

Q.E.D.

Discussion. The conclusion is valid for all forms of solid friction such as that between brake block and drum, between piston rings and cylinder wall, and between a shaft and its bearing. All types of solid friction must be reduced to the practical minimum if an engine is to achieve maximum efficiency. This is done by the use of lubricants and by keeping bearing loads and rubbing velocities as low as possible.

Fluid friction

The existence and causes of fluid friction have been mentioned in Chapter 3 (p. 53). As an example consider the long thermally-insulated steam pipe shown in Fig. 11.6.

(i) The steam flows steadily from point 1 to point 2. The enthalpy remains constant but the pressure falls. There are no heat or external work interactions with the surroundings, although there is in general a small net flow work. This is the process P.

(ii) Assume that a mechanism can be devised to execute the reverse process ꟼ, such that the steam flows steadily from state 2 to state 1 with no external work or heat interactions with the surroundings.

(iii) Cause the steam to execute a cyclic process by means of the following steps:—

(a) Instead of the process P, the steam flows through an adiabatic turbine, performing shaft work. Its enthalpy decreases, but the initial and final pressures and velocities are as in P.

(*b*) The steam then passes through a heater in communication with a single reservoir to restore its temperature, and therefore its enthalpy, to the values prevailing at state 2.

(*c*) Apply process ꝗ to return the steam to its initial state 1. This completes the cycle, which may be repeated indefinitely.

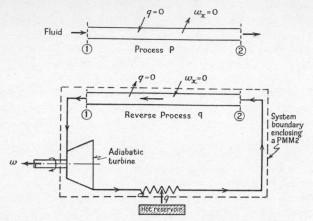

Fig. 11.6   Demonstrating that fluid friction is irreversible.

(iv) The net effect of the process is to exchange heat with a single reservoir and convert it all into shaft work. The circuit therefore comprises a heat engine of 100% efficiency. But this is impossible according to the Second Law. We deduce that the reverse process ꝗ is impossible, and so that P is irreversible.   Q.E.D.

Discussion. It follows that the frictional flow of fluids must be reduced to the practicable minimum in engines. This is accomplished in practice by keeping flow velocities low, by using smooth pipes of the largest permissible diameter, and by avoiding any unnecessary length of pipe.

Unresisted expansion

At the end of the working stroke of a petrol or diesel engine, the gases in the cylinder are at a pressure greater than atmospheric (e.g., 3 atm abs.). The exhaust valve then opens and the gas rushes into the exhaust pipe eventually emerging into the atmosphere at atmospheric pressure and relatively low velocity. This is illustrated in Fig. 11.7 and will be used as an example of an unresisted expansion process.

(i) In the process P, gas expands from state 1 in the cylinder to state 2 where it is partly outside the cylinder. Work is done on the atmosphere. The internal energy, pressure and temperature of the gas are reduced. Heat transfer and mixing of gas and air will be neglected.

(ii) Assume that a process ꝗ can be devised the net effect of which is to restore the gas to its initial state and position without heat transfer and with only an amount of external work equal to that done on the atmosphere in P.

(iii) Cause the gas to execute a cyclic process by the following steps:—

(a) Fit a piston in the (lengthened) exhaust pipe which allows the gas to expand slowly from state 1 to the atmospheric pressure. The piston is connected to a mechanism so that its movement causes weights to be raised. The internal energy and temperature of the gas meanwhile fall below those corresponding to state 2.

(b) Transfer heat to the gas in the exhaust pipe from a single sufficiently hot reservoir so that its temperature and internal energy rise to the values of state 2, meanwhile keeping the pressure constant. The gas expands still further in this process and so raises more weights. It will be found that the work done on the atmosphere during (a) and (b) is the same as in process P.

(c) Apply process ꟼ to restore the gases from the exhaust pipe to the cylinder at state 1. The cycle has now been completed.

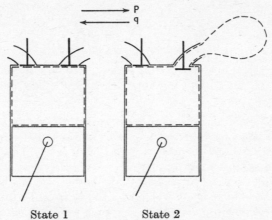

State 1 State 2

Fig. 11.7 Diagram used in proving that unresisted expansion is irreversible.

(iv) The net effect of the cyclic process has been to raise weights and exchange heat with a single reservoir. We have therefore designed an E.100. But this is impossible. Therefore P is irreversible.   Q.E.D.

Discussion. This means that as far as possible all gas expansions should be "resisted", and is one reason for the popularity of exhaust-gas turbines in diesel engine practice. Another device for reducing the irreversibility of the sudden opening of exhaust valves is to keep the flow fast but concentrated into orderly pressure waves which, with proper exhaust-pipe tuning, assist in scavenging and so reduce or eliminate the power consumption of the scavenging blower.

Heat transfer with a finite temperature difference

When high-pressure steam first enters the cylinder of a reciprocating steam engine it is at a higher temperature than the cylinder walls, which have just been in contact with expanded steam at a lower temperature.

Some of the entering steam therefore condenses on the walls, to which heat is transferred. This will serve as an example of the irreversibility of heat transfer with a finite temperature difference, Fig. 11.8.

(i) In the process P, m lb_m of steam condense on the walls of the cylinder, the temperature of which rises from t_1 to t_2. The quantity of heat, q, is transferred from steam to walls. The steam pressure falls from p_1 to p_2. The accompanying motion of the piston is immaterial to the problem and will be ignored for simplicity.

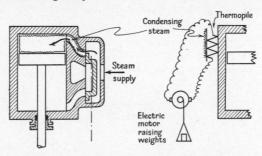

Fig. 11.8   Diagram used in proving that heat transfer with a finite temperature difference is irreversible.

(ii) Assume the process ꟼ exists, which has as its only net effects the fall in wall temperature from t_2 to t_1, a heat transfer from wall to steam of q, and the consequent re-evaporation of m lb_m of steam, the pressure of which rises from p_2 to p_1.

(iii) (a) Replace the process P by another one in which the steam condenses at constant volume on the surface of a thermopile (assembly of thermocouples), the cold junctions of which are in contact with the cylinder walls. The thermopile drives a small electric motor which raises weights. When m lb_m of steam have condensed, the circuit is disconnected. It is found that the cylinder walls have risen from t_1 to t_2', where $t_2' < t_2$.

(b) Transfer heat to the walls from a single reservoir to cause their temperature to rise from t_2' to t_2.

(c) Apply process ꟼ to re-evaporate the condensate and lower the cylinder wall temperature from t_2 to t_1. This completes the cycle, steam and walls being in their initial states.

(iv) The net effect of the cycle has been to raise weights and exchange heat with a single reservoir, which the Second Law states is impossible. The only doubtfully possible step in (iii) was ꟼ, which must be impossible. It follows that P is irreversible.   Q.E.D.

Discussion. 1. In the reciprocating steam engine the ill-effects of the process just considered are sometimes mitigated by adopting the *Uniflow* principle, in which the steam exhausts through ports near the end of the piston stroke but enters at the ends of the (double-acting) cylinder. The entry ends of the cylinder therefore tend to stay at a higher temperature than the middle (exhaust) part of the cylinder. One of the advantages of the steam turbine is that its blades stay in regions of constant temperature so that alternate condensation and re-evaporation does not occur.

2. The necessity to avoid heat transfer with finite temperature differences as far as possible has far-reaching effects in power-plant engineering. It governs the design of boiler plant and dictates the use of feed-water heating by bled steam; it is one reason for the use of the counter-flow arrangement in heat exchange plant; and it plays a part in the tendency to use re-heating and inter-cooling in gas-turbine prime movers.

3. Of course it is impracticable to avoid this form of irreversibility entirely because the smaller the temperature difference across, say, a boiler tube, the lower the *rate* of heat transfer in $Btu/ft^2 h$, and so the larger the boiler *size* for a given duty. Design has to be a compromise in which economic factors play a large part: large size means high capital costs; large temperature differences mean low efficiency and so high running costs; these have to be balanced, and the optimum arrangement will depend on the purpose and required life of the plant.

4. The irreversibility of heat transfer with finite temperature differences forms the core of an alternative statement of the Second Law due to Clausius:—

It is impossible for a system working in a cycle to have as its sole effect the transfer of heat from a system at a low temperature to a system at a higher temperature.

We have just proved this postulate by reference to Planck's statement of the Second Law. It is just as easy to derive the latter starting from Clausius's statement.

5. In general there are at least as many possible statements of the Second Law as there are irreversible processes. We could if we wished state the law as "Friction is irreversible"; then all the rest would follow.

Combustion

Nearly all power plants employ the combustion of fuel in some way. True heat engines often use the combustion products of fuel and air as their heat source; while internal-combustion engines use the product gases as a working fluid. As an example which will serve to show the irreversibility of these processes, we will consider the steady-flow adiabatic gas burner shown in Fig. 11.9.

(i) In the process P, streams of hydrogen and oxygen at atmospheric temperature and pressure enter the combustion chamber, where they react in a flame. A steady stream of steam (the combustion product) leaves the chamber at high temperature but still at atmospheric pressure. For simplicity suppose there is no excess hydrogen or oxygen. The combustion chamber is thermally insulated so there is no heat transfer to the surroundings. There is no shaft work.

(ii) Assume that a device exists which can execute the reverse process ꟼ, i.e., without heat transfer or shaft work the hot products can be steadily reconverted into the cold oxygen and hydrogen streams.

(iii) Then imagine the following cyclic process:—

(a) Atmospheric streams of hydrogen and oxygen are supplied to a fuel cell. There they re-combine to form water, while electrical power is produced which can be used for raising weights. Probably the water produced will be at a higher temperature than the gases supplied.

(b) The water is now passed to a boiler and engages in heat transfer with a single heat reservoir, emerging as steam at atmospheric pressure and at the temperature of the steam leaving the combustion chamber in P.

(c) Then apply ꟼ so as to turn the steam back into hydrogen and oxygen at the initial temperature. This completes the cycle.

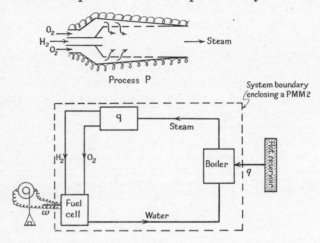

Fig. 11.9   Demonstrating that combustion is irreversible.

(iv) The net effect of the cyclic process is to raise weights and withdraw heat from a single reservoir. The circuit therefore is a perpetual motion machine of the second kind, which the Second Law states to be impossible. Hence P must be irreversible.   Q.E.D.

Discussion. 1. Generalising the above result, we may conclude that all combustion processes are irreversible, whatever the fuel and whether carried out in steady flow or at constant volume. They should therefore be avoided if we want to extract the maximum work from our limited fuel supplies.

2. Unfortunately this is easier said than done. For even the relatively simple hydrogen-oxygen reaction has only been carried out in a fuel cell on a laboratory scale at the time of writing (1958). The engineering problems involved in carrying out, for example, the coal-air reaction in this way are immense. Nevertheless it should never be forgotten that the use of combustion to obtain power is a second-best, which yields only about one third of the power from each ton of fuel which the Second Law would permit us to obtain. The same is true of the nuclear reactions currently used in atomic power stations, although the fraction is there still smaller.

Other irreversible processes

The above examples by no means exhaust the irreversible processes of importance in engineering. A list of other such processes is appended. The reader is invited to test his grasp of the foregoing method of argument by demonstrating their irreversibility with reference to the Second Law. They are:–

(a) Flow of electric current through a resistance. (Flows through inductances and capacities on the other hand are reversible.)

(b) The flow of a river over a waterfall.

(c) Unresisted expansion of an elastic structure.

(d) Driving a nail with a hammer (whether the nail penetrates the wood or not).

(e) Plastic deformation of a material.

(f) Magnetisation of a material exhibiting hysteresis.

(g) "Hydraulic jump" in the flow of water in a channel.

(h) The mixing of two unlike fluids. (To prove the irreversibility of this it is necessary to postulate membranes which are permeable to one fluid but not to the other; these membranes are then used as pistons. Such membranes exist for some pairs of fluids.)

THE CARNOT CYCLE

Now that we have seen what must be avoided in heat engine designs, an ideal engine will be considered which embodies these lessons. It was devised by Carnot at the early date of 1824. Although never realised completely, modern steam and closed-cycle gas turbine power plants approach it as nearly as is considered economically practicable.

Description of the Carnot cycle and of a machine for performing it

Fig. 11.10 illustrates a cylinder closed by a piston. There are no valves. The cylinder barrel and the piston are thermally non-conducting, but the end opposite the piston is thin and a good conductor. Vertically below the sketch of the cylinder is an indicator diagram, which, in this case, is simultaneously a p-v property diagram for the working fluid in the cylinder. This we shall suppose to be steam, although Carnot thought of a permanent gas. Two heat reservoirs H and C can be caused to communicate with the cylinder head.

Starting with the piston in the inmost position 1, let the contents of the cylinder be saturated water at the temperature of the hot reservoir, t_H. H is caused to communicate with the cylinder head and the piston is allowed to move outwards slowly. The latter is connected to a mechanism which raises weights. Friction is supposed to be absent. Since the motion is slow, heat transfer, q_1, from H to the fluid occurs with only an infinitesimal temperature difference, so the fluid executes an *isothermal expansion* to point 2, say. In this case, though not with the permanent gas used by Carnot, the expansion is also at constant pressure. We will suppose the expansion to end when all the water has just evaporated. State point 2 is therefore on the saturated steam line of the p-v diagram.

Now H is removed from the cylinder head, but the piston continues to move slowly outwards. The steam now performs an *adiabatic and reversible expansion* until the steam temperature falls to the temperature of the cooler reservoir t_C. The pressure will also be lower, and some of the steam will, as it happens, have condensed (point 3).

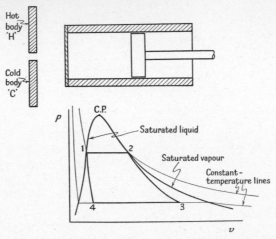

Fig. 11.10   Carnot cycle with H_2O as the working fluid.

At this stage C is caused to communicate with the cylinder head and the direction of the piston movement is reversed. Heat transfer, q_2, from the steam to C occurs with an infinitesimal temperature difference, and the steam slowly condenses *isothermally*.

Before condensation is completed, however, C is removed. The steam state is now represented by point 4, which has been so chosen that the continuation inwards of the piston motion causes a *reversible adiabatic compression* which leaves the steam exactly in state 1.

The steam has therefore performed a cyclic process. All the parts of the process were reversible; indeed they could in this case be simply reversed. The whole cycle is therefore reversible. We note that heat was transferred to the steam by H at t_H, and from the steam by C at t_C. In addition the finite area of the indicator diagram and the sense of rotation show that a finite work quantity, w, has been delivered.

The Carnot engine is therefore a reversible heat engine which can in principle be equally well used as a direct heat engine to produce power or in reverse to act as a heat pump. Since it is reversible its efficiency when working directly as a heat engine $\left(\eta_R = \dfrac{w}{q_1} \right)$ will be equal to the reciprocal of its coefficient of performance when working reversed as a heat pump $\left(C_{hp,R} = \dfrac{q_1}{w} \right)$.

Remarks on the practicability of the Carnot cycle. 1. The realisation of a Carnot engine depends partly on keeping the motion slow in order that the pressure should be uniform everywhere (this is not difficult) and that the working fluid should be uniform in temperature. This would result in a very large engine of very small power since the latter depends not only on the work per stroke but also on the strokes per minute. Economic considerations prohibit this. However the ideal is approached in practical plants by carrying out the functions of heating and cooling in separate organs—the boiler and condenser—where the working fluid can remain in contact with the heat transfer surfaces for much longer times than it spends in the cylinder. It is significant that the sizes of the boiler and of the condenser in a steam power plant are very much greater than that of the cylinder.

2. It has also been postulated that friction between the piston, or rather its rings, and the cylinder barrel, is zero. All that can be done in practice is to reduce the irreversibility due to this cause, when expressed in terms of work, to a small fraction of the useful power output.

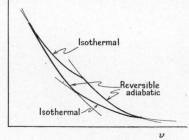

Fig. 11.11 Carnot cycle with a gas as the working fluid.

3. No materials have been discovered which fail to conduct heat entirely; moreover those which are known to be poor conductors will not stand high stress. If therefore heat transfer to cylinder and piston are to be eliminated, the time spent by the working fluid in the cylinder must be kept small. This is another reason for performing the necessary heat transfers in separate organs, as was realised by the early steam-engine builders (Savory, 1698, and Newcomen, 1705, in the case of the boiler; Watt, 1763, in the case of the condenser) well before Carnot was born (1796).

4. An additional engineering requirement for realising Carnot's cycle is correct timing. For example if C is removed too late, the adiabatic compression will cause the steam to arrive at the inward dead centre at a temperature lower than t_H. Then an irreversible transfer of heat will occur. In an engine with a separate boiler and condenser this difficulty appears in a different form: the timing is carried out by means of valves which open and shut to control conditions in the cylinder. This is true of internal-combustion engines also and is not the easiest part of the engine-designer's task. Usually the design must be a compromise, for an engine must operate under varying loads: the valve timing that is correct under one condition will not give the best performance under another.

5. Steam has been discussed in the above example, because there the isothermal processes are at constant pressure, the control of which may be somewhat easier to visualise. The condensable nature of the fluid is however in no way essential to the argument. Using a permanent gas as the working fluid, as Carnot suggested, the indicator (and p-v) diagram would be as shown in Fig. 11.11. Even with steam, it may be added, there is no need for any of the "corners" of the diagram to be situated on

the saturation line. Indeed no engineer would care to contemplate what might actually happen at the end of the compression stroke 4–1 when the piston is supposed to come to rest having just sufficient room in the cylinder for a cushion of water.

INTERNAL AND EXTERNAL REVERSIBILITY

Carnot's conception of a reversible engine cycle is a most important one, which has had a profound effect on power-plant practice. It is necessary however to emphasise that the realisation of this ideal, difficult though it may be, is not the end even of the thermodynamic aspects of power plant design. At least two points need to made here.

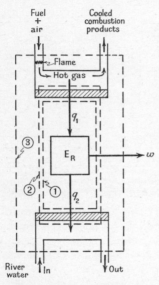

Fig. 11.12   Internal and external reversibility.

1. Heat reservoirs at high temperatures are rarely found in nature. They usually have to be made by burning fuel. The combination of a Carnot engine with a fuel-burning appliance is not, *treated as a whole*, a reversible plant. We should always prefer therefore a reliable fuel cell to such a Carnot engine.

2. In practical circumstances it is often impermissible to raise the temperature of the working fluid to the temperature of the heat source, usually because the containing walls would burst or melt. Even though the working fluid may pass through a reversible cycle therefore, we are still left with irreversibility due to heat transfer with finite temperature differences at the contact between the fluid and the hot reservoir. The same sort of irreversibility may occur at the boundary between the fluid and the cold reservoir (heat sink) due to the need to restrict the area across which heat transfer takes place.

These points are illustrated by Fig. 11.12, which shows a reversible engine receiving heat from combustion products and rejecting it to a river. If the system boundary 1 is considered, we have a reversible power plant. If the system boundary 2 is considered however, the system is no longer reversible since irreversibility occurs at both heat transfer surfaces. Usually the hot surface is the worse culprit, for the combustion gases may be at 3000°F, whereas the mean wall temperature has to be restricted to, say, 1200°F; as a result the fluid temperature may not exceed 1100°F.

If finally the boundary 3 is considered, firstly we no longer have a system, because matter crosses the boundary; the contents of the boundary can not now be called a heat engine. Secondly, the additional irreversibility of combustion is present.

These distinctions are sometimes denoted by use of the terms *internal and external reversibility*. The engine E_R would then be called internally reversible but **externally irreversible**.

Sometimes it is useful to make other distinctions. Thus friction and sudden expansion are termed *mechanical irreversibility*, heat transfer with a finite temperature gradient is called *thermal irreversibility*, while combustion is called *chemical irreversibility*.

BIBLIOGRAPHY

Fifth World Power Conference, *Recent Research in Great Britain on Fuel Cells*. Section ref. 119 K/4. 1956.

CHAPTER 11—PROBLEMS

11.1 (*a*) A reversible heat engine operating between a hot and a cold reservoir delivers a work output of 54 Btu. The heat transfer from the engine is 66 Btu. Evaluate the efficiency of the heat engine.

(*b*) The engine in (*a*) is reversed and operates as a heat pump between the same reservoirs. Evaluate (i) the coefficient of performance of the heat pump and (ii) the power input to the pump when the heat transfer rate to the hot reservoir is 450 Btu/min.

(*c*) If the reversed engine in (*b*) were considered to be a refrigerator what would be its coefficient of performance?

11.2 An engine operating on the Carnot cycle employs 1 lb_m of H_2O as the working fluid. The temperatures of the hot and of the cold body are 400°F and 100°F respectively. Referring to Figure 11.10, state 1 corresponds to saturated liquid, state 2 to dry saturated vapour, state 3 to wet vapour, dryness 0·754, and state 4 to wet vapour, dryness 0·236.

Evaluate the work done and the heat transfer in each process, the net work done during the cycle and the efficiency.

11.3 Instead of considering the Carnot cycle to be executed by a system in a piston-cylinder mechanism (see p. 197), it is possible to conceive of the four processes taking place in sequence in a steady-flow heat engine. In this case the working fluid flows steadily in turn through a heater (state 1 to state 2), a reversible turbine (2–3), a cooler (3–4) and a reversible compressor (4–1).

In such a Carnot engine using H_2O as the working fluid, the states of the H_2O are as given in problem 11.2. Evaluate, per lb_m of H_2O flowing, the external work done and the heat transfer during each process, the net work done by the engine and the efficiency.

11.4 An inventor claims to have designed a device which will produce shaft work continuously at a steady rate when it is supplied with a steady stream of steam.

The device consists of a well-insulated box, through the side of which projects a shaft; an essential requirement, it is stated, is that the insulation be such that it reduces the heat transfer from the device to the surroundings to negligible proportions. Steam flows steadily into the box at one point and flows steadily out at another point. The only fact divulged by the inventor is that the steam merely condenses in a coiled tube inside the box.

The claim is that when dry and saturated steam at a pressure of 20 psia is supplied steadily at the rate of 8·1 lb_m/min, it will leave at a pressure of 15 psia with a dryness of 0·98, while the shaft power developed will be 4·75 h.p.

Examine the feasibility of these claims by reference to (*a*) the First Law and (*b*) the Second Law.

11.5 By applying the Second Law of Thermodynamics demonstrate that the processes listed on page 197 are irreversible.

14

THE ABSOLUTE TEMPERATURE SCALE

INTRODUCTION

We have seen that a heat engine of 100% efficiency is an impossibility. Accepting this, the natural next question is "How high an efficiency *can* be reached?" The answer is that it depends only on the temperatures of the two heat reservoirs with which the engine must work. Generally speaking the greater the temperature difference, the higher is the attainable efficiency, although it is not the temperature *difference* alone that matters, as will be seen. Further we have seen that the best engines are reversible ones. We therefore consider the relationship between the efficiency of a reversible engine and the temperature of the hot and cold reservoirs between which it works.

That the efficiency is independent of the natures of the reversible engine or of the reservoir is easily proved.

Proof. Consider the reversible engines and reservoirs, made of differing materials, shown in Fig. 12.1. Suppose that the efficiency of engine $E_{R,A}$ exceeds that of $E_{R,B}$. Then reverse $E_{R,B}$ (i.e. $Ǝ_{R,B}$) and cause $E_{R,A}$ to drive it so that the same quantity of heat q_1 is returned to the hot reservoir H_B as is withdrawn from H_A. H_A and H_B are in good thermal contact so that no temperature differences arise between them. Then since η_A exceeds η_B, we have

$$\frac{w_A}{q_1} > \frac{w_B}{q_1} \qquad \ldots \ (12.1)$$

so
$$w_A - w_B > 0 \qquad \ldots \ (12.2)$$

Now C_A and C_B, which will also be supposed in good thermal contact, are at the temperature t_2 and so form a single cold reservoir. The combination of $E_{R,A}$ and $Ǝ_{R,B}$, together with H_A and H_B, form a system operating continuously, doing positive work, and exchanging heat with a single reservoir.* Since this is impossible according to the Second Law, our original hypothesis must have been incorrect. Therefore $E_{R,A}$ cannot be more efficient than $E_{R,B}$.

In the same way it can be shown that $E_{R,B}$ cannot be more efficient than $E_{R,A}$. It follows that the efficiencies of $E_{R,A}$ and $E_{R,B}$ must be equal, and so, in general, all reversible engines have the same efficiency when operating between two heat reservoirs of fixed but different temperatures. The efficiency does not depend on the nature of either the reservoirs or the reversible engines.

We might establish the relation between engine efficiency and temperature by experiment. Measurements of heat and work could be made on a reversible engine for many pairs of reservoir temperatures. However, as was stressed in Chapter 4, all our temperature scales are arbitrary anyway; the temperature-efficiency relation would therefore differ according to whether we were using mercury-in-glass or platinum-resistance thermometers, for example.

* N.B. The system boundary must exclude the cold reservoirs, since they are not in a steady state; heat is being withdrawn from them at the net rate $q_2' - q_2$.

In this situation therefore, why not take the bold step of *stating* what the efficiency-temperature relation shall be, that is to say of *defining* a temperature scale in terms of the efficiency of reversible engines? Then the above mentioned experiments can be used to *calibrate the thermometers*. This move was made by Kelvin (1851). It has the advantage of providing a temperature scale which is independent of the thermometric substance, as was previously pointed out to be desirable.

Kelvin's innovation of the Absolute Temperature Scale has been universally accepted, and in this chapter we discuss some of its implications. The attentive reader will however have perceived a difficulty: in discussing reversible engines it was made clear that a completely reversible

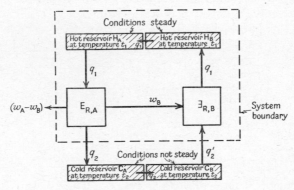

Fig. 12.1

one is only a theoretical possibility; yet now we are proposing to use them for the precise task of temperature measurement. The way in which this difficulty can be surmounted is indicated in the section on the Clausius-Clapeyron relation (p. 208).

Finally some examples will be given of the use of the Absolute Temperature in determining the maximum efficiencies and coefficients of performance of heat engines and heat pumps.

Symbols

C_{hp} Coefficient of performance of a heat pump.

h Specific enthalpy of a pure substance.

p Pressure.

q Heat transfer.

T Absolute temperature (Kelvin's proposal).

t Temperature.

v Specific volume.

w Net work done by a system (heat engine).

η Efficiency of a heat engine, thermal efficiency.

θ Absolute temperature (Alternative to Kelvin's proposal).

Subscripts

R Reversible.

f Saturated liquid (fluid).

g Saturated vapour (gas).

fg Saturated liquid to saturated vapour.

1,2 Hot, cold reservoir

THE ABSOLUTE TEMPERATURE SCALE

Definition. The absolute temperature scale is defined by

$$\eta_R \equiv \frac{T_1 - T_2}{T_1} \qquad \ldots (12.3)$$

where η_R = efficiency of a reversible heat engine

T_1 = absolute temperature of the hotter reservoir

T_2 = absolute temperature of the colder reservoir.

Discussion

Alternative forms. It is often convenient to express the definition in terms of the heat and work quantities. Referring to Fig. 12.2, we have, from eq. (12.3) and the definition of efficiency,

$$\frac{w_R}{q_1} = \frac{T_1 - T_2}{T_1} \qquad \ldots (12.4)$$

and, from the First Law, eq. (6.2)

$$w_R = q_1 - q_2 \qquad \ldots (12.5)$$

Equations (12.4) and (12.5) can be re-arranged to give

$$\frac{w_R}{T_1 - T_2} = \frac{q_1}{T_1} = \frac{q_2}{T_2} \qquad \ldots (12.6)$$

The symmetrical form of this expression renders it convenient to use and easy to remember.

The size of the temperature unit. The expression in eq. (12.3) is a ratio. This implies that, given two reservoirs, any number can be ascribed to the temperature of one of them; then a measurement on a reversible engine will fix the number which *must* be ascribed to the second one. There is therefore a choice to be made. This expresses itself as a choice of the *size* of the temperature unit in order that we may have either 180 or 100 degrees between the absolute temperature corresponding to the freezing point and boiling point of water at atmospheric pressure.

When the former choice is made, experiment shows that the temperatures 492 and 672 must be ascribed to the two fixed points. This is conventionally expressed as:— "At atmospheric pressure water freezes at 492°F abs and boils at 672°F abs". Here "°F abs" means "degrees on the Fahrenheit absolute scale". An alternative description is °R, which stands for "degrees on the Rankine scale".

When the second choice is made, the corresponding temperatures are termed respectively 273°K or °C abs and 373°K or °C abs, where °K stands for "degrees Kelvin", and °C abs for "degrees on the Centigrade absolute scale". The relations between the four scales are probably seen most clearly by reference to Fig. 12.3. We also have the relations:

$$T \text{ in } °F \text{ abs (or } °R) = t \text{ in } °F + 460 \qquad \ldots (12.7)$$

$$T \text{ in } °C \text{ abs (or } °K) = t \text{ in } °C + 273 \qquad \ldots (12.8)$$

Relation of absolute temperature scale to those based on particular thermo-metric substances. When the relative expansion of mercury in a glass container is plotted on a scale of absolute temperature, it is found to be slightly non-linear. This means that the markings of a mercury-in-glass thermometer should be somewhat unequally spaced if the corresponding temperature intervals are to be equal; this is rarely done in practice. The maximum error in a mercury-in-glass thermometer with equally spaced markings between 32°F and 212°F is about 0·2°F and occurs at about 100°F.

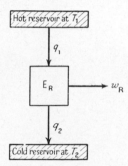

Fig. 12.2 Illustrating the definition of the absolute temperature scale.

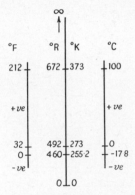

Fig. 12.3 Comparison of temperature scales.

The same is true of all other thermometric substances. Those however which are most nearly linear are thermometers using the expansion at constant pressure, or pressure rise at constant volume, of "permanent gases" such as air or hydrogen (p. 66). Indeed these substances suggest a further relation to the absolute scales as is indicated by the appearance of the numbers 492 and 273 in equations (4.3) and (4.4). This subject will be returned to in Chapter 14.

The International Scale of Temperature discussed earlier (Chapter 4) is an attempt to provide a range of thermometric substances which, by means of piecewise linear scales, will provide easy experimental techniques for measuring the temperature of a system on the absolute scale.

It will be noticed that negative temperatures have not been indicated on the absolute scales of Fig. 12.3. This is because, as will be proved below, no system at such temperatures can possibly exist.

On the possibility of other definitions of the absolute temperature. Emboldened by the apparent success of Kelvin's innovation, the reader may inquire whether other definitions would not do just as well. The answer is that other definitions could be used, and have been suggested. Eq. (12.3) has found favour however because of its simple form and because of its close relation to that of the gas thermometers. Not all definitions will do however. The permissibility of eq. (12.3) will now be demonstrated.

Consider the reservoirs and reversible heat engines shown in Fig. 12.4. The combined work of the two engines is given from eq. (12.4) by

$$w_{12} + w_{23} = \frac{T_1 - T_2}{T_1} q_1 + \frac{T_2 - T_3}{T_2} q_2$$

$$= \frac{T_1 - T_2}{T_1} q_1 + \frac{T_2 - T_3}{T_2} \cdot \frac{T_2}{T_1} q_1$$

$$= \frac{T_1 - T_3}{T_1} q_1 \qquad \ldots \quad (12.9)$$

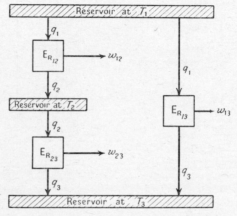

Fig. 12.4   Engine arrangements for testing the self-consistency of the definition of the absolute temperature scale.

The last expression is that which could be given by eq. (12.4) for a reversible engine working between reservoirs at temperatures T_1 and T_3, as it should be. The definition (12.3) is therefore self-consistent.

Consider however an alternative definition

$$\eta_R \equiv T_1 - T_2 \qquad \ldots \quad (12.10)$$

This would lead to

$$w_{12} + w_{23} = (T_1 - T_2)q_1 + (T_2 - T_3)q_2$$

$$= (T_1 - T_2)q_1 + (T_2 - T_3)(q_1 - w_{12})$$

$$= \{(T_1 - T_2) + (T_2 - T_3)(1 - T_1 - T_2)\}q_1 \quad \ldots \quad (12.11)$$

from which T_2 cannot be made to disappear as it ought. Definition (12.10) is therefore self-contradictory and would not be satisfactory.

The reader may care to check that the alternative definition of an absolute temperature θ

$$\eta_R \equiv \frac{\ln^{-1} \theta_1 - \ln^{-1} \theta_2}{\ln^{-1} \theta_1} \qquad \ldots \quad (12.12)$$

would be self-consistent. It is not used.

THE ABSOLUTE ZERO OF TEMPERATURE

The impossibility of negative absolute temperatures

It is impossible for a system to exist which has a negative temperature on the absolute scale.

This statement is proved as follows. If such a system can exist it may be used as the cold reservoir of a reversible heat engine. The efficiency of this engine is given by eq. (12.3) in which T_1 is a positive number representing the

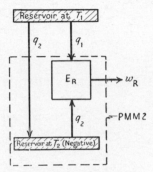

Fig. 12.5 Showing the impossibilities of negative absolute temperatures.

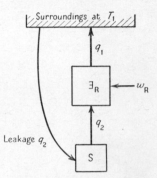

Fig. 12.6 An attempt to reduce system S to absolute zero.

temperature of any convenient hot reservoir, while T_2 is a negative number representing the temperature of the supposed system. In Fig. 12.5, which represents the arrangement, the direction of q_2 is the reverse of normal, in accordance with the implications of eq. (12.6).

Now it is certainly possible to allow a heat transfer by conduction from the system at T_1 to the system at T_2 equal to the heat transfer q_2 which is withdrawn by the engine. There is therefore no net heat transfer between the cold reservoir and its surroundings.

Consider now a system boundary enclosing the reversible engine and the cold reservoir. This is in communication with a single reservoir, and produces work continuously. According to the Second Law, this is impossible. It follows that our hypothesis was incorrect: a system at a negative absolute temperature is as impossible as a perpetual motion machine of the second kind.

The attainment of zero temperature

It is impossible, in the absence of a perfect heat insulator, to reduce a finite system to the absolute zero of temperature.

This may be proved as follows. Consider Fig. 12.6, which shows an attempt to reduce the temperature T_S of the system S to absolute zero by means of a reversible heat pump. In the absence of a perfect heat insulator, a certain heat transfer q_2 per unit time is bound to occur to S by conduction from surroundings at a higher temperature, say T_1.

Suppose a steady state can be reached such that S is at the absolute zero of temperature. Then, from eq. (12.4), the work input w_R, to the engine is given by

$$\frac{w_R}{q_2} = \frac{T_1 - T_s}{T_s}$$

But T_s is to be zero

$$\therefore \qquad w_R = \frac{T_1 q_2}{0} = \infty \qquad \ldots \ (12.14)$$

But an infinite supply of power is impossible to achieve. Therefore we shall never reduce a finite system to the absolute zero unless a perfect heat insulator can be devised. This is not of importance to engineers, but the properties of matter at very low temperatures are so interesting that it is a matter of regret to physicists.

MEASURING THE ABSOLUTE TEMPERATURE: THE CLAUSIUS-CLAPEYRON RELATION

In this section it is intended to show that, even though reversible engines cannot be constructed in practice, it is possible to use the definition

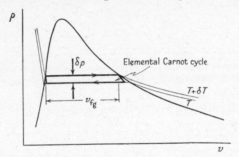

Fig. 12.7   Illustrating the proof of the
Clausius-Clapeyron relation.

of eq. (12.3) to determine the absolute temperature, by means of measurements of pressure, volume and heat transfer.

We may imagine a Carnot engine operating with steam between two reservoirs which differ in temperature by a small magnitude δT. We are free to ascribe to this *difference* any value we like. The p-v diagram for the steam will be as in Fig. 12.7. The work done in a single cycle by unit mass of steam is given by the area of the diagram and is clearly

$$w_R = \delta p \cdot v_{fg}* \qquad \ldots \ (12.15)$$

The heat transfer during the isothermal (and constant-pressure) heating is given for unit mass by

$$q_1 = h_{fg} \qquad \ldots \ (12.16)$$

* Provided that the pressure-volume relationships of steam in the reversible adiabatic parts of the cycle are not represented by horizontal lines, which may be proved by quite crude experiments.

the efficiency is therefore given by

$$\eta_R = \frac{w_R}{q_1} = \frac{v_{fg} \cdot \delta p}{h_{fg}} \qquad \cdots \quad (12.17)$$

But this is also given by the definition (12.3). We therefore deduce

$$\frac{\delta T}{T} = \frac{v_{fg} \cdot \delta p}{h_{fg}}$$

or

$$T = \frac{h_{fg}}{v_{fg}} \cdot \frac{\delta T}{\delta p} \qquad \cdots \quad (12.18)$$

Now h_{fg} can be determined by a heat transfer measurement; v_{fg} is measured by way of the dimensions of the container; and the difference of saturation pressure corresponding to (what we agree shall be called) a unit difference of absolute temperature, i.e. $\delta p/\delta T$, can be established by conventional techniques. Thus all the quantities on the right-hand side of eq. (12.18) can be measured; so the absolute temperature can be determined without recourse, except in imagination, to a reversible engine.

Eq. (12.18) is known as the *Clausius-Clapeyron Relation*, after its formulators. It is used in building up the data contained in, for example, Steam Tables, from physical measurements.

EXAMPLE

Problem. Use eq. (12.18) to check the self-consistency of the Steam Tables given in Appendix B.

Solution. In the saturated steam tables we find:—

$t°F$	p psia	v_f ft^3/lb$_m$	v_g ft^3/lb$_m$	v_{fg} ft^3/lb$_m$	h_{fg} Btu/lb$_m$.
212	14·696	0·01672	26·80	26·78	970·3
210	14·123	0·01670	27·82	27·80	971·6

Taking mean values of v_{fg} and h_{fg} over the temperature interval between 210°F and 212°F, we deduce, from eq. (12.18)

$$T = \frac{970 \cdot 95}{27 \cdot 29} \times \frac{2 \times 778 \cdot 26}{0 \cdot 573 \times 144}$$

$$= 671 \cdot 1 = 460 + 211 \cdot 1$$

which is almost exactly the arithmetic mean temperature of the two temperatures considered. We conclude that the table is self-consistent in this region.

In order to get this good check, five-figure pressure values were used, and needed. Determining the absolute temperature by means of the Clausius-Clapeyron relation therefore requires extremely accurate instrumentation. In Chapter 14, where the Ideal Gases are discussed, an experimentally easier way of determining T will be indicated.

EXAMPLES RELATING TO ATTAINABLE EFFICIENCY AND COEFFICIENT OF PERFORMANCE

We now use the above results to establish the limits of performance of heat engines and heat pumps in cases of engineering interest. When temperatures are mentioned these are supposed to be measured on thermometers calibrated with reference to the absolute scale of temperature, since these are the standard instruments now universally used. Between the first definition of the absolute temperature scale, however, and the existence of these thermometers, an immense amount of experimental work has had to be performed by physicists. Present day engineers owe them much.

EXAMPLE 1

Problem. A steam power plant operates between a heat source at 1000°F (the maximum permissible temperature of the boiler tubes) and a heat sink at 55°F (cooling water from a river). What is the maximum attainable efficiency of the plant?

Solution. The maximum efficiency attainable will be that of a reversible engine operating between the given temperature limits.

$$T_1 = 1000 + 460 = 1460°F \text{ abs}$$

$$T_2 = \quad 55 + 460 = \quad 515°F \text{ abs}$$

$$\therefore \quad \eta_R = \frac{1460 - 515}{1460}$$

$$= 0.648 \text{ or } 64.8\% \qquad \dots \quad Answer$$

Note. For various reasons associated with mechanical and fluid friction, heat transfer to the surroundings, and finite temperature differences between the steam and the tubes of the boiler or the water of the river, the actual plant efficiency will be less than two-thirds of this. When evaluating the fuel consumption it is also necessary to remember that the boiler usually only transfers about 80% of the heat to the steam which could be obtained by isothermal combustion of the fuel, i.e. steady-flow combustion in which the products leave at the temperature of the ingoing fuel and air.

EXAMPLE 2

Problem. A heat pump for domestic heating works between a heat sink at 32°F and the water in the radiator system at 180°F. What is the minimum electrical power consumption to provide a heat output of 80,000 Btu/h?

Solution. The minimum power consumption will be achieved when the heat pump is reversible.

$$T_1 = 180 + 460 = 640°F \text{ abs}$$

$$T_2 = \quad 32 + 460 = 492°F \text{ abs}$$

$$\therefore \qquad C_{hp} = \frac{1}{\eta_R} = \frac{640}{640 - 492} = 4.32$$

$$\therefore \qquad \text{Minimum work input} = \frac{80{,}000}{4\cdot32} \text{ Btu/h}$$

$$= \frac{80{,}000}{4\cdot32 \times 3412} \text{ kw}$$

$$= 5\cdot42 \text{ kw} \qquad \dots \text{ } Answer$$

Note. This is of course only $1/4\cdot32$ times the electricity requirement which would be required by the use of heating by electrical resistances. That heat pumps are still (1958) little used is due firstly to the fact that considerably lower coefficients of performance are obtained in practice (e.g. about 2 for the above case) and to the large capital expense that is required, not only in providing the heat pump itself, but also in providing thermal contact between the working fluid and a suitable low temperature heat reservoir. (Rivers run through few back-gardens; the earth is a poor conductor; air deposits ice crystals on the heat exchange surfaces thus reducing heat transfer rates.)

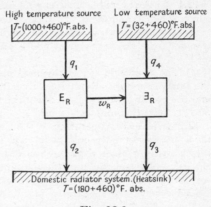

Fig. 12.8

It should not be forgotten that the electricity often has to be obtained by burning fuel in a power station, perhaps at less than 30% efficiency. The next example examines a combined installation.

EXAMPLE 3

Problem. A heat pump for the temperature range of example 2 is to be driven by a steam power-plant with a heat source temperature of 1000°F which uses the domestic radiator system as its heat sink. What is the maximum possible ratio of combined heat transfer to the 180°F sink to heat input at 1000°F?

Solution (see Fig. 12.8). We suppose engine and heat pump to be reversible. From eq. (12.6) we have:

For the engine, E_R,
$$\frac{q_2}{640} = \frac{q_1}{1460} = \frac{w_R}{820}$$

For the heat pump, $\exists_R$,
$$\frac{q_3}{640} = \frac{w_R}{148}$$

therefore
$$\frac{q_2 + q_3}{q_1} = \frac{640}{1460} + \frac{820}{1460} \times \frac{640}{148}$$

$$= 0\cdot438 + 2\cdot43$$

$$= 2\cdot878 \qquad \dots \text{ } Answer$$

Note. This means that nearly three times as much heat transfer to the building can be obtained from a ton of coal as is possible by direct combustion. This is an attractive possibility, but examination of the capital cost of the plant reduces its attractiveness. A careful study of the economics of the particular proposal is always needed before it can be seen whether a heat pump should be installed.

The above three-fold increase in output from a ton of coal is quite distinct from that mentioned in Chapter 11 as obtainable from replacing combustion by use of a fuel cell. Combining a fuel cell with a heat pump promises even greater rewards. But the difficulties will remain formidable for many years.

BIBLIOGRAPHY

Keenan, J. H., and Keyes, F. G., *Thermodynamic Properties of Steam*. Wiley & Sons and Chapman & Hall, 1936.
Keenan, J. H., *Thermodynamics*. Wiley & Sons and Chapman & Hall, 1941.

CHAPTER 12—PROBLEMS

12.1 (a) A reversible heat engine operates between reservoirs at temperatures of 300°F and 50°F. Evaluate the efficiency of the engine.

(b) The work output from the engine is 2000 ft lb$_f$. Evaluate the heat transfer from the reservoir at 300°F and the heat transfer to the reservoir at 50°F.

(c) The engine in (a) is reversed and operates as a heat pump between the same reservoirs. Evaluate the coefficient of performance of the heat pump and the power input required when the heat transfer rate from the reservoir at 50°F is 2500 Btu/min.

12.2 In an engine operating on the Carnot cycle the work output is 0·2 times the heat transfer to the cold body. The difference in the working fluid temperature when in contact with the hot and the cold body is 110°F. Evaluate the efficiency of the engine and the maximum and minimum temperatures of the working fluid.

12.3 A refrigerator operates on the reversed Carnot cycle. The temperature of the working fluid as it evaporates in the evaporator is −5°F whilst the condensing vapour in the condenser is 75°F. The heat transfer rate from the cold region to the working fluid ('refrigerating effect') is 4500 Btu/min. Evaluate the power required to drive the refrigerator.

12.4 In a steam power plant the temperature of the inner walls of the boiler tubes is 950°F. The cooling water circulating through the condenser is supplied from a river at a temperature of 55°F. What is the maximum possible efficiency of the plant?

12.5 An ice-making plant produces ice at atmospheric pressure from water at 32°F. The mean temperature of the cooling water circulating through the condenser of the refrigerating machine is 65°F. Evaluate the minimum electrical work in kWh required to produce one ton of ice. (The latent heat of fusion of ice at atmospheric pressure is 143·3 Btu/lb$_m$.)

12.6 An office block is heated by means of a heat pump. The mean air temperature within the building is 68°F when the outside mean air temperature is 25°F. The heat transfer rate to the heat pump is 100,000 Btu/h and the power required to drive the pump is 14 h.p.

(a) Evaluate the heat transfer rate to the building and the coefficient of performance of the heat pump.

(b) Evaluate the maximum possible coefficient of performance of a heat pump for these conditions and the minimum power input to the heat pump to satisfy the given heating requirements.

12.7 Exhaust steam from a process plant is to be used as a source of heat for a heat engine. The steam is available at a pressure of 20 psia with a dryness fraction of 0·6. Heat transfer from the steam to the engine causes the steam to condense to saturated liquid at 20 psia. River water is available at a mean temperature of 58°F.

Evaluate the maximum possible power which could be developed by the engine when the exhaust-steam mass flow rate is 4000 lb$_m$/h.

12.8 An inventor claims to have designed a heat engine which has an efficiency of 38% when using the exhaust gas from an engine, at a temperature of 295°F, as a source of heat.

Examine the validity of this claim.

12.9 A reversible heat engine operates between two reservoirs at temperatures of 1100°F and 100°F. The engine drives a reversible refrigerator which operates between reservoirs at temperatures of 100°F and 0°F. The heat transfer to the heat engine is 2000 Btu and the net work output of the combined engine-refrigerator plant is 350 Btu.

(a) Evaluate the heat transfer to the refrigerant and the net heat transfer to the reservoir at 100°F.

(b) Reconsider (a) given that the efficiency of the heat engine and the coefficient of performance of the refrigerator are each 40% of their respective maximum possible values.

CHAPTER 13

ENTROPY

INTRODUCTION

We now know quantitatively the maximum work output of systems which work cyclically, i.e. of heat engines. But cycles are made up of individual non-cyclic processes, each of which has to be analysed quantitatively; moreover many important engineering processes are not cyclic at all, for example those undergone by the air and the fuel in the "open-cycle" gas turbine. It is therefore necessary to see whether the definition of the absolute temperature scale can be used to answer such questions as, "What is the maximum work obtainable from a given process?" In doing this a new quantitative test for reversibility will be developed.

Symbols

g	Gravitational acceleration.	w_p	Shaft work input to a feed pump.
g_0	Constant in Newton's Second Law.	w_x	Shaft work delivered by a turbine.
h	Specific enthalpy of a pure substance.	X, Y	Arbitrary independent properties.
m	Mass.		
p	Pressure.	x	Dryness, dryness fraction.
Q	Heat transfer.	z	Elevation above an arbitrary datum.
q	Heat transfer.		
S	Entropy of a system	η	Efficiency of a heat engine, thermal efficiency.
s	Specific entropy of a pure substance.	η_{isen}	Isentropic efficiency.
T	Absolute temperature.	$\eta_{Rankine}$	Efficiency of a heat engine working on the Rankine cycle.
u	Specific internal energy of a pure substance.		
V	Velocity.	η_{ratio}	Efficiency ratio.
v	Specific volume.	ρ	Density.
W	Net work done by a system (heat engine).	*Subscripts*	
		f	Saturated liquid (fluid).
W_x	External work. Shaft work delivered by a turbine.	g	Saturated vapour (gas).
		fg	Saturated liquid to saturated vapour.
W_p	Shaft work input to a feed pump.	R	Reversible.
		1, 2, ...	States of the working fluid.

A turbine example

To make the task clear, the steam turbine illustrated in Fig. 13.1*a* will be considered. This receives a steady supply of steam of fixed state 1, and exhausts the steam at a state 2. Sufficient (two) conditions at state 1 are specified but only the pressure p_2 at state 2 is known. The turbine is adiabatic and the kinetic and gravitational energy terms are negligible. How great a shaft work output W_x is obtainable per lb_m of steam?

The Steady Flow Energy Equation, eq. (8.22) leads immediately to

$$0 - W_x = h_2 - h_1 \qquad \qquad \dots \text{(13.1)}$$

Here h_1 is known but we need another piece of information about state 2 before h_2, and so W_x, can be evaluated. Can this information be deduced from the Second Law?

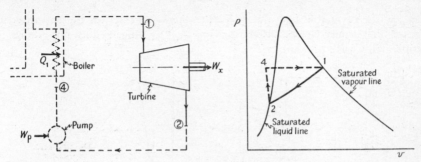

Fig. 13.1

(a) Steam turbine with imaginary boiler and pump making a cyclic process possible, supposing the turbine exhaust to be water.

(b) Illustrating the cyclic process undergone by the steam, supposing the turbine exhaust to be water.

The following argument makes it certain that the Second Law has at least something to say about state 2:—Suppose this state is that of saturated water at p_2. Then we could connect a feed pump at the turbine outlet, pump the water into a boiler, supply heat there, and so provide the turbine with its steady stream of steam at state 1.

The p-v diagram of Fig. 13.1b illustrates the cyclic path followed by the steam if this is done. Examination of the boiler-turbine-pump system shows however that we have constructed a heat engine of 100% efficiency: for the feed pump power is certainly very small, so the net work transfer is outward. The Second Law therefore requires that the dryness fraction of the exhausted steam cannot be as low as zero. How low can it be?

This question can be answered by re-constructing the imaginary heat engine: a condenser is placed between the turbine exhaust and the feed pump inlet, Fig. 13.2a, in which the steam leaving the turbine is condensed to saturated water before being pumped back into the boiler. The cyclic path followed by the steam is shown in Fig. 13.2b. It is reasonable to suppose that the turbine work output is greatest when the turbine, and all other engine components, work reversibly (this point is established on p. 222 below). The Steady Flow Energy Equation applied to the reversible adiabatic turbine gives

$$-w_{x,R} = h_2 - h_1^* \qquad \qquad \dots \text{(13.2)}$$

* Here we write the turbine work as $w_{x,R}$ (and not as $W_{x,R}$) to conform with the convention used earlier in Chapter 10 when discussing engines.

Further, from the definition of the absolute temperature scale, we know that the heat transfers q_1 and q_2 are related to the temperatures T_1 and T_2 prevailing in the boiler and condenser respectively by

$$\frac{q_1}{T_1} = \frac{q_2}{T_2} \qquad \dots \text{ (13.3)}$$

Now q_1 is given by the S.F.E.E. applied to the boiler plus feed pump as

$$q_1 + w_{p,R} = h_1 - h_3 \qquad \dots \text{ (13.4)}$$

$w_{p,R}$ is the reversible feed pump work; like h_1 and h_3 (on the saturated water line) it may be evaluated: it is $(p_1 - p_2)v_f$, since v_f does not change appreciably with pressure.

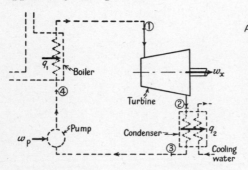

Fig. 13.2

(a) Steam turbine with imaginary boiler, pump and condenser making a cyclic process possible; turbine exhaust is wet steam.

(b) Illustrating the cyclic process undergone by the steam; turbine exhaust is wet steam.

Applying the S.F.E.E. to the condenser, we obtain

$$-q_2 = h_3 - h_2$$

Our problem can now be solved; for by combining this equation with eq. (13.3) and eq. (13.4) we obtain the unknown h_2 as

$$h_2 = h_3 + \frac{T_2}{T_1}(h_1 - h_3 - w_{p,R}) \qquad \dots \text{ (13.5)}$$

Inserting this in eq. (13.2), the maximum possible turbine shaft work when receiving steam of state 1 and exhausting at pressure p_2 is

$$w_{x,R} = h_1 - h_3 - \frac{T_2}{T_1}(h_1 - h_3 - w_{p,R}) \qquad \dots \text{ (13.6)}$$

This gives us a standard with which to compare the actual performance of the turbine.

Discussion

The above argument was rather clumsy. For the very simple case of steady flow through a turbine, it was necessary to construct our imaginary complete steam power plant and argue directly from the definition of the absolute temperature scale. The problem was made relatively simple by the fact that the reversible feed pump term was easily evaluated with sufficient accuracy because water is almost incompressible. Most engineering problems of this type are more difficult; we therefore need a simpler method of calculation.

An analogy with the First Law. It will be remembered that, in Chapter 6, the First Law of Thermodynamics was stated in terms of the heat and work in a cyclic process. In order to make it applicable to non-cyclic processes, we had to invent a new property: energy. This could then be tabulated for particular substances, with great advantage in ease and speed of calculation. Is it possible to use the same approach in the present case? Can we invent a new property in order to apply the Second Law to non-cyclic processes?

A possible line of attack. One characteristic of a property is that its change is zero in a cyclic process (p. 81), so we must look for an entity the change of which is zero in the steam turbine example. Eq. (13.3) is suggestive: if we return to the earlier convention regarding the sign of heat, indicated by putting $Q_1 \equiv q_1$ and $Q_2 \equiv -q_2$, eq. (13.3) becomes

$$\frac{Q_1}{T_1} + \frac{Q_2}{T_2} = 0 \qquad \ldots \quad (13.7)$$

Since Q_1 and Q_2 are the only heat transfers to the steam in the imaginary cyclic process, which it will be remembered was assumed to be *reversible*, we can write for this case

$$\oint \frac{dQ_R}{T} = 0 \qquad \ldots \quad (13.8)$$

where $\oint$ means the summation around the cycle, dQ_R is an element of the reversible heat transfer to the steam, and T is the absolute temperature of the steam as it receives the heat transfer dQ_R.

Here and below we especially emphasise that the heat transfer occurs during a *reversible* process by means of the subscript R. Previously, when using the symbol Q for heat transfer, it was not necessary to distinguish between heat transfers in reversible and irreversible processes. In this Chapter, however, the distinction is important; Q will represent the heat transfer in a general process (reversible or irreversible) and Q_R the heat transfer in a reversible process when the distinction is necessary.

Eq. (13.8) shows that $\oint dQ_R/T$ has a zero sum *for this particular case*, and so might serve in general as our required property. Clearly however the situation is somewhat more difficult than in the case of energy and the First Law, because it is going to be necessary to make sure whether reversible processes are in question or not.

Summary of the remainder of the chapter. It will be shown below in general terms that the magnitude $\int dQ_R/T$ is indeed *always* a property it will be given the name *entropy*. The argument is somewhat abstract,

15

but is important and not difficult; it should be studied carefully. Thereafter we shall show how entropy can be used in engineering calculations, and how its relation to the other properties of systems can be established.

ENTROPY

Definition. **Entropy, S, is a property of a system, such that its increase, $S_2 - S_1$, as the system changes from state 1 to state 2, is given by**

$$S_2 - S_1 \equiv \int_1^2 \frac{\mathrm{d}Q_R}{T} \qquad \dots \quad (13.9)$$

Notes. 1. This will be proved below. The argument is in three steps, and the intermediate results are also important.

2. Because S is a property, the value of the integral is independent of the path of the change of state, and depends only on the end-states 1 and 2. It is the latter feature which will be demonstrated.

3. When pronounced, the first syllable of the word carries the stress, viz. éntropy.

4. In differential form eq. (13.9) runs

$$\mathrm{d}S = \frac{\mathrm{d}Q_R}{T}$$

Proof that entropy is a property. Step 1: The Clausius Inequality

Statement. When any system undergoes a cyclic process the integral around the cycle of $\mathrm{d}Q/T$ is less than or equal to zero. In symbols

$$\oint \frac{\mathrm{d}Q}{T} \leqslant 0 \qquad \dots \quad (13.10)$$

Here $\mathrm{d}Q$ is an infinitesimal heat transfer, while T is the absolute temperature of the part of the system at which the heat transfer $\mathrm{d}Q$ occurs.

Re-constructing the surroundings of the system. Consider the system illustrated in Fig. 13.3. Replace the actual surroundings of the system by a single heat reservoir at absolute temperature T_0 and a reversible heat engine E_R; this can make no difference as far as the system is concerned. The system will, in general, do work on the surroundings: let the element of this work simultaneous with $\mathrm{d}Q$ be $\mathrm{d}W$. Let the corresponding element of work done by the heat engine be $\mathrm{d}W_R$. The heat engine is small and performs many cycles while the system performs one.

Argument. Applying the First Law to the system as it completes its cyclic process, we have

$$\oint (\mathrm{d}Q - \mathrm{d}W) = 0 \qquad \dots \quad (13.11)$$

Applying the Second Law to the cyclic process of the combined system within the dotted boundary of Fig. 13.3, we have

$$\oint (\mathrm{d}W + \mathrm{d}W_R) \leqslant 0 \qquad \dots \quad (13.12)$$

for otherwise this combined system would be a perpetual motion machine of the second kind.

Invoking the definition of the absolute temperature scale, (eq. 12.3), we have, for the reversible engine,

$$\frac{dW_R}{T_0 - T} = \frac{dQ}{T} \qquad \cdots \quad (13.13)$$

Conclusion. Eliminating dW and dW_R from equations (13.11), (13.12) and (13.13), we have

$$\oint \left\{ dQ + \frac{(T_0 - T)}{T} dQ \right\} \leqslant 0$$

i.e.

$$T_0 \oint \frac{dQ}{T} \leqslant 0$$

i.e.

$$\oint \frac{dQ}{T} \leqslant 0 \qquad \cdots \quad (13.14)$$

Q.E.D

Statement (13.14) is known as the *Clausius Inequality*.

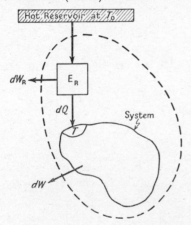

Fig. 13.3 Illustrating the proof of the Clausius inequality.

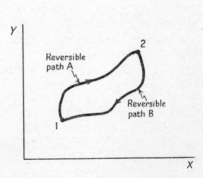

Fig. 13.4 An arbitrary reversible cyclic process.

Proof that entropy is a property—Step 2

Statement. For any system which undergoes an internally reversible cycle, the integral of dQ_R/T is zero. We write this symbolically as

$$\oint \frac{dQ_R}{T} = 0 \qquad \cdots \quad (13.15)$$

Argument. Let the system execute a cyclic process, starting at state 1, changing to state 2 via the reversible path A, and returning to state 1 via the different reversible path B. Fig. 13.4 represents this process as a plot of any property Y against any other independent property X.

Then from the Clausius Inequality, eq. (13.10), we have:

$$\text{along 1A2B1,} \qquad \oint \frac{dQ_R}{T} \leqslant 0 \qquad \ldots \quad (13.16)$$

Since the process is reversible we may reverse it and cause the system to retrace its path precisely. Let the element of heat transfer corresponding to the system boundary temperature T be dQ'_R for this reversed process. Then from eq. (13.10) we have:

$$\text{along 1B2A1,} \qquad \oint \frac{dQ'_R}{T} \leqslant 0 \qquad \ldots \quad (13.17)$$

But since the second cycle is simply the first one with the direction reversed, we have

$$\text{along 1B2A1,} \qquad dQ'_R = -dQ_R \qquad \text{along 1A2B1} \quad \ldots \quad (13.18)$$

Therefore statement (13.17) becomes

$$\text{along 1B2A1} \qquad -\oint \frac{dQ_R}{T} \leqslant 0$$

$$\text{or} \qquad \oint \frac{dQ_R}{T} \geqslant 0 \qquad \ldots \quad (13.19)$$

Conclusion. Comparing (13.16) and (13.19), we see that they can only both be true simultaneously if

$$\oint \frac{dQ_R}{T} = 0 \qquad \ldots \quad (13.20)$$

$$\text{Q.E.D.}$$

Proof that entropy is a property. Step 3.

Statement. The integral of dQ_R/T, when a system executes any reversible process between fixed end-states, is independent of the path of the process. Symbolically,

$$\text{for arbitrary paths A and B,} \qquad \int_{1 \atop A}^{2} \frac{dQ_R}{T} = \int_{1 \atop B}^{2} \frac{dQ_R}{T}$$

Argument. Let the system execute the reversible cyclic process, illustrated in Fig. 13.5, from 1 via path A to 2 and back via path C to 1. Then from eq. (13.20) we have

$$\int_{1 \atop A}^{2} \frac{dQ_R}{T} + \int_{2 \atop C}^{1} \frac{dQ_R}{T} = 0 \qquad \ldots \quad (13.21)$$

Similarly for the reversible cyclic process 1B2C1, we have from eq. (13.20)

$$\int_{1 \atop B}^{2} \frac{dQ_R}{T} + \int_{1 \atop C}^{1} \frac{dQ_R}{T} = 0 \qquad \ldots \quad (13.22)$$

Conclusion. Subtracting eq. (13.22) from eq. (13.21) we obtain

$$\int_{1}^{2} \frac{dQ_R}{T} = \int_{1}^{2} \frac{dQ_R}{T} \qquad \dots \quad (13.23)$$
$$\text{A} \qquad\qquad \text{B}$$

Q.E.D.

Final remarks. We have now proved the result foreshadowed on p. 218; for in eq. (13.23) the paths A and B are arbitrary. This means:

(i) that

$\int_{1}^{2} \dfrac{dQ_R}{T}$ has the same value for *any* reversible path between 1 and 2 ... (13.24)

Hence from the definition of entropy, eq. (13.9) we may write statement (13.24) as:

(ii) $(S_2 - S_1)$ has the same value for *any* reversible path between 1 and 2. It follows therefore that *entropy is a property.*

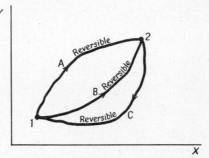

Fig. 13.5 Arbitrary reversible cyclic processes.

Discussion of entropy

Tabulation of entropy. Since entropy is a property it can, for pure substances, be tabulated as a function of two other independent properties. How its magnitude is established will be described later. For the moment it suffices to state that values of the property are now available in the scientific literature for a large number of important substances. Appendix B, for example, contains entropy values for water and steam, tabulated in the same way as enthalpy and specific volume.

Like energy, entropy has only been defined as a difference; it is therefore necessary to specify its value arbitrarily in some state. In the tables of Appendix B, entropy is taken as zero for saturated water at 32°F. Often however tables will be found for which entropy is zero at the absolute zero of temperature.

Entropy is an *extensive* property (see p. 154), for, if the mass of the system is doubled, twice the heat quantities are necessary to bring about the same changes in the system state. We therefore introduce the symbol s, standing for the entropy of unit mass of material, or specific entropy.

The units of S in this book are Btu/°F abs. The units of s are Btu/lb$_m$°F abs. As it happens, a change of the units of s to Chu/lb$_m$°K or to cal/g°K produces no change in its numerical value, because mass and temperature units are hidden in the heat units used. Of course ft lb$_f$/lb$_m$°Fabs. could also be used for s; then a change to, for example a metric, unit system would cause changes in the numerical value of s.

Since entropy is extensive, its value in a region comprising two phases can be adequately described by tabulating its values for the saturated states. Thus for steam, s is given in Table III for the saturated water and saturated steam states, viz. s_f and s_g. The entropy s of wet steam of dryness x is then evaluated, for a given pressure, from

$$s = (1 - x)s_f + xs_g \qquad \qquad \dots \quad (13.25)$$

Reversible adiabatic processes. Many engineering processes occur with negligible heat transfer: the flow of steam or gas through a turbine is an example. The convenient standard process with which these adiabatic processes may be compared is the reversible adiabatic process. Since by definition, $dQ = 0$ here, and the suffix R is appropriate, the entropy change is zero in such processes. Thus, from eq. (13.9), for a reversible adiabatic process

$$dQ_R = 0: \qquad \Delta S = 0 \qquad \qquad \dots \quad (13.26)$$

A process in which the entropy remains constant is termed an *isentropic* process. All reversible adiabatic processes are therefore isentropic. However it does not follow that all isentropic processes are either reversible or adiabatic.

THE USE OF ENTROPY

Entropy has been defined and tabulated in order to make engineering calculations easier. This Chapter began with a discussion of a steam turbine example: we will shortly show how entropy can be used in this case. First however it is desirable to prove rigorously that a reversible adiabatic expansion is the one that gives the greatest work of all adiabatic expansions from a fixed initial state to a fixed final pressure. As usual, the proof is based on the Second Law and so involves the construction of an imaginary heat engine.

Proof about the superiority of reversible processes

Statement. Of all the possible *adiabatic* processes which can be executed by a system starting at a fixed initial state and ending at a fixed final *pressure*, the reversible one gives the maximum external work.

Proof. Suppose that a process P exists which gives an external work quantity, W_x, greater than the $W_{x,R}$ given by the reversible process P_R. Then allow the system to execute a cyclic process, comprising:—
  (a) The process P.
  (b) A heat transfer at constant pressure bringing the system to the state at the end of process P_R.
  (c) The process P_R reversed, i.e. q_R.
This is illustrated by Fig. 13·6, for the case in which the processes occur sequentially in steady flow.

Examination of the dotted boundary shows that a finite work transfer $W_x - W_{x,R}$ occurs in the cycle and that heat is exchanged with a single reservoir. But this is impossible according to the Second Law. It follows that W_x cannot exceed $W_{x,R}$.

It is easy to see that if P is reversible, $W_x = W_{x,R}$, whereas if P is irreversible, $W_x < W_{x,R}$.

Comments. This proof was necessary since previously we had only demonstrated the superiority of reversible *cycles*. A similar proof can be deduced for the case where it is the final *volume* that is specified: then the heating at (*b*) must take place at constant volume. It has been assumed that the kinetic and gravitational potential energies are negligible. Modifications to account for these should be obvious.

EXAMPLE ON THE MAXIMUM WORK FROM AN ADIABATIC TURBINE

Problem. Dry saturated steam at 100 psia flows steadily into an adiabatic turbine which exhausts to a condenser at 5 psia. What is the maximum possible shaft work per lb_m of steam, if the kinetic energies at inlet and exit can be neglected?

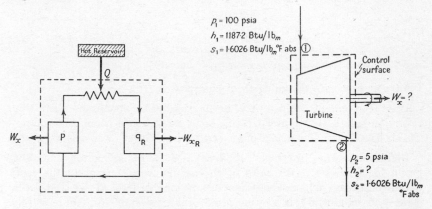

Fig. 13.6 Demonstrating that reversible adiabatic steady-flow processes do more work than irreversible adiabatic ones.

Fig. 13.7 Calculating the maximum shaft work of an adiabatic turbine.

Solution. Fig. 13.7 illustrates the situation. On it is written the information obtained by inserting the data in Steam Tables, and the unknowns. The first task is to evaluate h_2, from which W_x can be evaluated via eq. (13.1). We do this by noting that the maximum-work process is a reversible one. Then since the flow is also adiabatic, the maximum-work process must be isentropic.

$$s_1 = 1{\cdot}6026$$
$$= s_2 = (1 - x_2)s_{f_2} + xs_{g_2}$$
$$= (1 - x_2)0{\cdot}2347 + x_2(1{\cdot}8441)$$

from Steam Table III (Appendix B) for a pressure of 5 psia, assuming the steam to be wet there. This must be checked later; see below.

Hence the unknown dryness at state 2, x_2, is given by

$$x_2 = \frac{1{\cdot}6026 - 0{\cdot}2347}{1{\cdot}8441 - 0{\cdot}2347}$$

$$= 0{\cdot}850$$

The fact that this value lies between 0 and 1 confirms our guess that the exhaust steam would be wet (it often is). Had we obtained a value greater than 1 it would have been necessary to go back and establish state 2 by looking in the Superheated Steam Tables (Table IV) to find by interpolation a state with $s = 1\cdot6026$ and $p = 5$ psia. Had we obtained a value of x less than zero on the other hand, it would have meant that the arithmetic was wrong!

Looking up h_f and h_g from Steam Table III at 5 psia as $130\cdot1$ and $1001\cdot0$ Btu/lb$_m$ we now obtain h_2 from eq. (9.9) as

$$h_2 = (1 - 0\cdot85)130\cdot1 + (0\cdot85)(1131\cdot1)$$

$$= 981\cdot0$$

Hence from eq. (13.1),

$$W_{x,R} = h_1 - h_2 = 1187\cdot2 - 981\cdot0$$

$$= 206\cdot2 \text{ Btu/lb}_m \qquad \qquad \dots \text{ Answer}$$

Comment. This procedure is frequently necessary in steam power plant calculations. It is important both theoretically and practically. It should be practised until its execution becomes mechanical.

Isentropic processes as standards of comparison

It is convenient to compare actual adiabatic machines with their reversible adiabatic counterparts in order to measure their performance. This is usually done by means of an *isentropic efficiency* or an *efficiency ratio*.

Definition. **The isentropic efficiency, η_{isen}, of an adiabatic work-producing machine is the ratio of the actual work output to the work output of a reversible adiabatic machine taking in fluid at the same initial state and exhausting it at the same final pressure (or, more rarely, volume). Symbolically**

$$\eta_{\text{isen}} \equiv \frac{W_x}{W_{x,R}} \qquad \qquad \dots \quad (13.27)$$

EXAMPLE

Problem. An actual turbine taking in dry saturated steam at 100 psia and exhausting at 5 psia produces only 165 Btu/lb$_m$ of steam as shaft work. What is its isentropic efficiency?

Solution. Since the maximum possible shaft work is $206\cdot2$ Btu/lb$_m$ (see last example), we have

$$\eta_{\text{isen}} = \frac{165}{206\cdot2} = 0\cdot80 = 80\% \qquad \qquad \dots \quad \text{Answer}$$

This is of the right order for rotary machinery. A reciprocating steam engine would give in practice an isentropic efficiency nearer 50%.

Similar measures of performance are used for work absorbing machinery such as compressors. This matter is outside the scope of the present book.

The Rankine cycle. In steam power-plant practice, it is common to make the same comparison in a somewhat less direct fashion as a ratio of efficiencies. First the (thermal) efficiency, eq. (10.3), of a complete hypothetical heat engine employing the work-producing machine is calculated from

$$\eta = \frac{W_x}{h_1 - h_f} \qquad \qquad \dots \quad (13.28)$$

where h_1 is the enthalpy of the steam entering the machine, and h_{t_2} is the enthalpy of saturated water at the pressure of the exhaust steam. It will be seen that by applying the Steady-Flow Energy Equation, eq. (8.22), to the boiler and feed pump and neglecting the small feed-pump work term, the denominator is equal to the heat transfer to the steam in the boiler. (See Fig. 13.2: for this case $h_3 = h_{t_2}$.) This heat transfer is necessary to complete the cycle after the steam has been condensed. Then the same expression is evaluated for the reversible work-producing machine.

The *Rankine cycle efficiency*, η_{Rankine}, is defined as

$$\eta_{\text{Rankine}} \equiv \frac{W_{x_R}}{h_1 - h_{t_2}} \qquad \dots \quad (13.29)$$

The efficiency ratio is then defined as

$$\eta_{\text{ratio}} = \frac{\eta}{\eta_{\text{Rankine}}} \qquad \dots \quad (13.30)$$

Comparison of eq. (13.30) with eq. (13.27) shows that in this case the efficiency ratio of the cycle is identical with the isentropic efficiency of the turbine (or reciprocating engine). This is not so for heat engines in general, however; it happens to be true in this case because the small feed-pump work term has been neglected.

Sometimes the feed-pump term is taken account of in defining η and η_{Rankine}. There is little advantage in this.

A quantitative test for irreversibility in adiabatic systems

Returning to more abstract matters, we now prove (i) that *the entropy increase in an irreversible process is always greater than the integral of* $\mathrm{d}Q/T$, and (*ii*) *that the entropy of an adiabatic system can only increase.* Symbolically

(i) $\qquad\qquad S_2 - S_1 > \int_1^2 \dfrac{\mathrm{d}Q}{T}$ for any irreversible process

and

(ii) $\qquad\qquad S_2 - S_1 > 0$ for an adiabatic irreversible process.

These propositions can be used as somewhat more convenient tests of irreversibility, or for that matter tests of possibility, than those employed earlier. These tests are also quantitative.

Proofs. (i) Suppose that a system executes the cyclic process represented by Fig. 13.8 where the outward path A is irreversible with heat transfer Q, and the return path B is reversible with heat transfer Q_R. For example a mass of water might be evaporated by stirring ($Q = 0$) and then returned to its original state by slow heat transfer.

From the Clausius Inequality, we have

$$\int_{1 \atop \text{A}}^2 \frac{\mathrm{d}Q}{T} + \int_{2 \atop \text{B}}^1 \frac{\mathrm{d}Q_R}{T} < 0 \qquad \dots \quad (13.31)$$

The $<$ sign is appropriate because the cycle is irreversible, involving as it does the irreversible process A.

Introducing entropy by way of its definition, eq. (13.9),

$$S_2 - S_1 = \int_1^2 \frac{dQ_R}{T} \text{ independently of the path,}$$

we have for the reversible process B between states 2 and 1,

$$S_1 - S_2 = \int_2^1 \frac{dQ_R}{T}$$
$$\quad\quad\quad\quad B$$

Eq. (13.31) reduces to

$$S_2 - S_1 > \int_1^2 \frac{dQ}{T}$$
$$\quad\quad\quad A$$

and hence since the path A is arbitrary

$$S_2 - S_1 > \int_1^2 \frac{dQ}{T} \text{ for } \textit{any irreversible} \text{ path between 1 and 2,}$$

$$\quad\quad\quad\quad\quad\quad\quad\quad\quad\quad\quad\quad \ldots \quad (13.32)$$

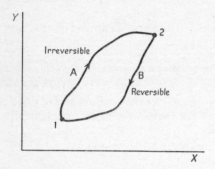

Fig. 13.8   An irreversible cyclic
process.

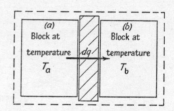

Fig. 13.9   Heat transfer with
a finite temperature
difference.

(ii) For any adiabatic process, $dQ = 0$. Therefore

$$\int_1^2 \frac{dQ}{T} = 0$$

so that, from statement (13.32), we have that for any irreversible adiabatic process:

$$S_2 - S_1 > 0 \quad\quad\quad\quad\quad\quad \ldots \quad (13.33)$$

This means that, if the adiabatic system undergoes irreversible processes, its entropy increases. If the process is reversible, we already know that the entropy remains constant. Hence only increases are possible in adiabatic processes.   Q.E.D.

The differential forms of statement (13.32) and of the definition of entropy, eq. (13.9), are often required (see Chapter 16). By combining them we may write

$$dS \geqslant \frac{dQ}{T} \qquad \dots \text{(13.34)}$$

or

$$dQ \leqslant T\,dS \qquad \dots \text{(13.35)}$$

Heat transfer with a finite temperature difference. Fig. 13.9 illustrates heat conduction between two systems a and b at temperatures of T_a and T_b. The dotted boundary encloses the composite system (a + b) which does not exchange heat with its surroundings. We can apply statement (13.35), in turn, to the component systems a and b while the small heat quantity dq^* is transferred between them. Since each component system is at a uniform temperature, and because there is an infinitesimal temperature difference at each system (block) boundary, each heat transfer is reversible. The equality sign in statement (13.34) is therefore appropriate; thus we have:

For system a,
$$dS_a = -\frac{dq}{T_a}$$

For system b,
$$dS_b = \frac{dq}{T_b}$$

Hence the entropy increase, dS, for the combined system (a + b) is given by

$$dS = dS_a + dS_b$$

$$= dq\left(\frac{1}{T_b} - \frac{1}{T_a}\right)$$

$$= dq\left(\frac{T_a - T_b}{T_a T_b}\right) \qquad \dots \text{(13.36)}$$

The right-hand side of eq. (13.36) is clearly positive if T_a exceeds T_b; so heat transfer between systems at different temperatures is irreversible. If T_a equals T_b the entropy increase is zero showing that the process is then reversible. If T_b exceeds T_a, dS is still positive, because then dq changes sign; the process is again irreversible.

Of course the heat transfer dq in general causes changes in the temperatures of both systems. Eq. (13.36) may therefore only be applied to very small heat transfers. For larger heat transfers the dependences of T_a and T_b on dq must be inserted and the total entropy increase evaluated by *integration*.

All these conclusions accord with those obtained in a more roundabout fashion in Chapter 11; entropy therefore provides a convenient testing procedure, which may be used in much more complex situations than the above, for example in examining the (sometimes extravagant) claims of the inventor of a plant which acts simultaneously as engine, heat pump, and chemical process.

* End note 7.

DETERMINATION OF ENTROPY

Although eq. (13.9) suffices as a definition of entropy, its restriction to reversible processes appears to leave us without a way of calculating the entropy change of an irreversible process: in the present section a general procedure will be provided. Eq. (13.9) is also not a convenient experimental starting-point for the determination of the entropy of systems: by relating entropy to other properties of systems, the entropy can be determined without direct experiment. This will also be dealt with.

General method of calculating entropy change in an irreversible process

The Problem. Given a system, its initial state 1, its final state 2, and an irreversible process from 1 to 2, find the entropy increase $S_2 - S_1$.

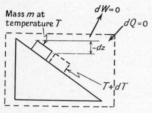

Fig. 13.10

(a) Irreversible process: friction between block and plane.

(b) Reversible process with the same end states.

Argument. We know two things about entropy:— (a) that it is a property; (b) its definition, eq. (13.9), in terms of a *reversible* process. We use the fact (a) to argue that $S_2 - S_1$ is independent of the path of the process from 1 to 2. Having established the end-states therefore we can forget about the fact that the given process was irreversible.

If the system has its properties tabulated, our task is at an end; for all we have to do is to look up in the tables the entropy values corresponding to the given states 1 and 2 and take their difference. If not however, in order to employ fact (b), we must find a reversible path from 1 to 2 (any one will do). The difference $S_2 - S_1$ can then be found by integrating $\int_1^2 dQ_R/T$ along the path selected.

Conclusion. It is therefore always possible to calculate the entropy provided sufficient information about the other properties of the system is available to enable an alternative, reversible, path to be imagined.

The procedure will now be exemplified, firstly for a "mechanical" system, secondly for a pure substance.

Entropy increase of a block and inclined plane with friction

Problem. The first example is illustrated in Fig. 13.10. The thermally conducting block of mass m lb_m falls a vertical distance $-dz$ ft in a gravitational field of acceleration g ft/s^2 in sliding down the rough conducting plane. There is no change in kinetic energy, but the block and plane rise in (uniform) temperature from T to $T + \mathrm{d}T$ °F abs. What is the entropy increase of the system comprising block plus plane?

Argument. Replace the actual process by a reversible one between the same end-states, namely:—

(*a*) Lubricate the plane and allow the block to fall $-\mathrm{d}z$ ft vertically without friction, simultaneously raising an external weight. The system does work given by

$$\mathrm{d}W = -m\,\frac{g}{g_0}\,\mathrm{d}z \text{ ft lb}_f$$

(*b*) Restore the internal energy of the system to the value corresponding to that at the end of the actual process by a reversible heat transfer $\mathrm{d}Q_R$ from an external reservoir. Since in the actual process there is no heat transfer, no work and therefore no increase in internal energy, then the combined effect of the reversible steps (*a*) and (*b*) must, by the First Law, eq. (6.5), give

$$\mathrm{d}Q_R - \left(-\frac{mg}{g_0}\,\mathrm{d}z\right) = 0$$

or

$$\mathrm{d}Q_R = -\frac{mg\,\mathrm{d}z}{g_0}$$

Conclusion. Now compute the entropy increase for the reversible process (a) + (b) from eq. (13.9). In (a) it is zero. In (b) it is

$$\mathrm{d}S = \frac{\mathrm{d}Q_R}{T} = -\frac{mg\,.\,\mathrm{d}z}{g_0\,.\,T} \text{ ft lb}_f/\text{°F abs} \qquad \dots \quad (13.37)$$

in which it has to be remembered that $\mathrm{d}z$ is a negative quantity, so that $\mathrm{d}S$ is positive.

It should be noted that the entropy increase, $\mathrm{d}S$, is *not* simply $\dfrac{\mathrm{d}Q}{T}$ for the actual process; for in this adiabatic process $\dfrac{\mathrm{d}Q}{T} = 0$. *The entropy increase can be calculated via reversible processes only.*

The entropy increase in a large fall can be computed by integrating eq. (13.37). If however the temperature changes are very small, it is sufficient to write

$$\Delta S = \frac{-m\,.\,g\,.\,\Delta z}{g_0\,.\,T} \text{ ft lb}_f/\text{°F abs} \qquad \dots \quad (13.38)$$

where $-\Delta z$ is the large vertical fall of the block, and T is the mean block temperature during the process.

The entropy increase of a pure substance

We now shift the emphasis from the particular process undergone by the system, which we have seen is only important in that it specifies end-states, to the relation of the entropy of a pure substance to the other properties. We will derive two relations, which are of fundamental importance in the study of the thermodynamics of substances.

The T ds relations. For any infinitesimal process undergone by unit mass of a pure substance in the absence of gravity, motion, electricity, magnetism and capillarity, the First Law of Thermodynamics eq. (7.5) gives

$$dQ = du + dW \qquad \ldots (13.39)$$

If in addition the process is reversible, we have

$$dQ_R = du + p \, dv \qquad \ldots (13.40)$$

since the only reversible work which such a system is capable of is fully resisted displacement work (p. 37).

From the definition of entropy, we have

$$dQ_R = T \, ds \qquad \ldots (13.41)$$

Combining eq. (13.40) and eq. (13.41) we have

$$T \, ds = du + p \, dv \qquad \ldots (13.42)$$

A companion relation is obtained by eliminating du from eq. (13.42) by means of the definition of enthalpy, $h = u + pv$. In differential form the definition becomes:

$$dh = du + p \, dv + v \, dp \qquad \ldots (13.43)$$

which, combined with eq. (13.42), gives

$$T \, ds = dh - v \, dp \qquad \ldots (13.44)$$

Remarks on the T ds relations. 1. Although proved by considering reversible processes in the absence of gravity, etc., these relations are concerned merely with properties. They may therefore be used to calculate the entropy change of a pure substance in any process, whether reversible or irreversible. Gravity and motion may also be present.

2. Since internal energy, pressure, volume and absolute temperature are comparatively easy to measure, equations (13.42) and (13.44) afford a means of deducing the value of entropy. Steam Tables are constructed in this way.

3. Combination of eq. (13.44) with the Steady Flow Energy Equation leads to an interesting comparison with equations derived in textbooks on fluid mechanics. Reference should also be made to the discussion in Chapter 8 on p. 133. *If the flow is reversible* we have

$$\text{S.F.E.E.:} \quad dQ_R - dW_x = d\left[h + \frac{V^2}{2g_0} + \frac{gz}{g_0} \right] \quad \ldots (13.45)$$

subtracting (13.44), we have

$$d\left[\frac{V^2}{2g_0} + \frac{gz}{g_0} \right] + dW_x = -v \, dp \qquad \ldots (13.46)$$

For the case of zero external work ($dW_x = 0$), this is the *Euler Equation* of fluid mechanics. It represents the application of Newton's Second Law of Motion to steady frictionless flow.

In integrated form eq. (13.46) becomes

$$\Delta \left[\frac{V^2}{2g_0} + \frac{gz}{g_0} \right] + W_x = - \int v \, dp \qquad \ldots \quad (13.47)$$

The integral on the right-hand side is an area on the p–v diagram representing the process (Fig. 13.11). If the process is adiabatic as well as reversible i.e. isentropic $(dS = 0)$, this area is also equal to the enthalpy *decrease* in the process; for the integrated form of eq. (13.44), with $ds = 0$, is

$$h_1 - h_2 = - \int_1^2 v \, dp \qquad \ldots \quad (13.48)$$

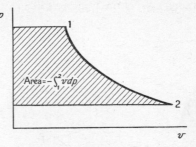

Fig. 13.11 Area representing
$$W_x + \Delta \left(\frac{V^2}{2g_0} + \frac{gz}{g_0} \right)$$
in a reversible flow process.

But there is no necessity for the flow to be adiabatic in eq. (13.46) and eq. (13.47).

If the fluid is *incompressible*, so that v is constant, eq. (13.47) may be written without the integral sign. With v replaced by $1/\rho$, where ρ is the density of the fluid, and zero shaft work, eq. (13.47) becomes the *Bernoulli* equation of fluid mechanics, namely

$$\frac{p_1}{\rho} + \frac{V_1^2}{2g_0} + \frac{gz_1}{g_0} = \frac{p_2}{\rho} + \frac{V_2^2}{2g_0} + \frac{gz_2}{g_0} \qquad \ldots \quad (13.49)$$

Once again there is no necessity for the flow to be adiabatic, but it must be frictionless, i.e. shear stresses must be absent from material boundaries across which there is relative motion.

An analogy to assist in understanding entropy. Students sometimes find the entropy concept more difficult to accept than that of, say, energy. (This is often due to lack of appreciation of the subtleties involved even in the energy concept, which is not truly to be represented by mechanical models involving "the kinetic energy of the molecules"). However the following analogy may be of some assistance:— Fig. 13.12 illustrates a mountainous terrain containing both firm ground and also loose scree. The problem is to establish the vertical distance between points A and B, $z_B - z_A$, by counting the number n of upward steps, each of 1 ft, made by the boots of a climber.

Suppose the climber mounts up the scree from A to B. He has counted the number of standard vertical steps but knows that his feet have been slipping downwards in the loose stones continuously. All he can say about his increase in altitude is

$$z_B - z_A < n_{scree} \qquad \ldots \quad (13.50)$$

where n_{scree} is the number of steps taken in the path including the scree.

In order to establish $z_B - z_A$, which has a definite value quite independently of the path of his climb, he has two possibilities:—(i) he can consult the altitude lines on his map, if available; or (ii) he can repeat the climb (or make a descent from B to A: the direction will not matter) on firm ground. Supposing that (ii) is necessary, he then finds

$$z_B - z_A = n_{firm} \qquad \ldots \quad (13.51)$$

where n_{firm} is the number of steps taken on firm ground.

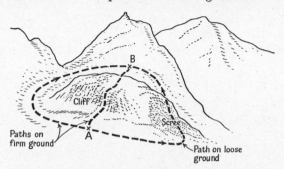

Fig. 13.12　The mountain analogy to entropy.

Provided that the climber stays on firm ground, he will always obtain the same answer from eq. (13.51): it does not matter whether he takes a gradually sloping path or climbs up the vertical cliff (experimental difficulty may suggest a preference however!).　When he climbs up the scree, on the

TABLE 13.1

	Thermodynamics	Mountain analogy
Property	S	z
Measurement method	$\int \dfrac{dQ_R}{T}$	n_{firm}
Process $\Big\{$	Reversible	Climbing on firm ground
	Irreversible	Climbing on scree
Available data	Property tables	Altitude lines on map

other hand, his values of n will differ each time; but they will all satisfy the inequality (13.50). Thus n_{firm} is a property: n_{scree} is not.

Table 13.1 should enable the thermodynamic lesson to be perceived.

Another approach.　A more conventional "explanation" of entropy is that it is a measure of *disorder*. The tendency of the entropy of an isolated system to increase can be regarded as an expression of the tendency of all things, when left to themselves, to become more mixed up and evened out. All spontaneous processes tend to produce equilibrium: heat transfer causes temperature differences to disappear; water "finds its own level". Development of this line of thought may lead either into statistical mechanics or into philosophy.

PROPERTY DIAGRAMS WITH ENTROPY AS CO-ORDINATE

Since entropy is just as much a property as pressure or internal energy, it may, like them, be used as one co-ordinate of the property diagrams of a pure substance. Two such diagrams are in common use, the other co-ordinates being respectively absolute temperature and enthalpy.

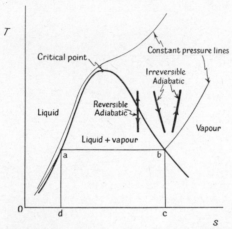

Fig. 13.13   Temperature-entropy diagram.

The temperature-entropy (T–s) diagram

Fig. 13.13 shows, to scale, the liquid- and vapour-phase regions of the temperature-entropy diagram of steam. Some lines of constant pressure are also shown.

This diagram is useful because it possesses the following features:—

1. Areas on the diagram have the dimensions of heat (or work).

2. In the mixed-phase region the constant-pressure lines are horizontal.

3. In a *reversible* process, the area under a curve is equal to the heat transfer in the corresponding process, since

$$\int dQ_R = \int T \, ds$$

For example, the heat transfer, Q_R, in a reversible isothermal process, ab, Fig. 13.13 is given by

$$Q_R = \int_a^b T \, ds$$

$$= T_a \int_a^b ds = T_a(S_b - S_a) \qquad \text{in this case}$$

$T_a(S_b - S_a)$ is, of course, the area abcd on the T–s diagram (Fig. 13.13).

16

4. *Isentropic* processes are vertical straight lines.

5. In a *reversible cycle* the area enclosed by the curve representing the process is equal to the net heat transfer to the fluid and so, from the First Law, is also equal to the net work.

6. The *efficiency of the reversible cycle* is given, if the cycle is clockwise and so represents a work-producing process, by the ratio of the area enclosed by the curve to the area beneath the upper part of the curve.

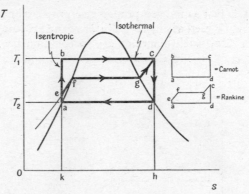

Fig. 13.14   Comparison of Rankine and Carnot cycles.

7. If the substance executes a *Carnot cycle*, its path on the T–s diagram is a rectangle. For example, Fig. 13.14 shows a Carnot cycle *abcd* with steam as the working fluid. It consists of two isothermal processes (horizontal lines *bc*, *da*) and two isentropic processes (vertical lines *ab*, *cd*). (Compare Chapter 11, p. 197.) In this case, in which all processes are reversible, the area ratio mentioned in note 6 is easily evaluated, giving the efficiency

$$\eta = \frac{\text{area abcda}}{\text{area kbchk}}$$

From geometry, the area ratio is equal to the ratio of the heights of these two rectangles, i.e. to $(T_1 - T_2)/T_1$. This is in accordance with the Absolute Temperature Scale definition, as it must be.

8. An *irreversible adiabatic* process is represented by a line tending to the right (Fig. 13.13). For the entropy increases in such a process.

The Rankine cycle on the T–s diagram. Fig. 13.14 also shows a second reversible cycle (*aefgcda*) with the same temperature limits as the Carnot cycle; this is the Rankine cycle as can be confirmed by comparison with the earlier mention of the cycle on p. 224. *cd* is the expansion in the turbine; *da* is the condensation in the condenser; *ae* is the compression of the condensate in the feed pump; and *efgc* is the constant pressure heating in the boiler. In the case illustrated the steam becomes superheated.

It is evident that, though rejecting the same heat quantity as does the Carnot engine (equal areas beneath *ad*), the work done by the Rankine engine is less (smaller area enclosed by the curve). The Rankine cycle efficiency for given temperature limits is therefore less than that of the Carnot cycle, even though both are reversible as far as the steam is concerned. How does this apparent contradiction of the result on p. 202 come about?

The answer is that the Rankine cycle engine does not take in the whole heat quantity at the highest temperature: the cycle is therefore *internally reversible*, but involves *external, thermal irreversibility* because the temperature of the H_2O during the heating process efgc is less than T_1, the supposed temperature of the hot body from which the heat transfer occurs (see p. 200).

The Rankine cycle is regarded as a more satisfactory standard of comparison for steam power machinery than the Carnot cycle (see p. 224), just because of this feature. It is "fairer" to the engine or turbine not to attribute to it the irreversibility associated with the way the boiler and feed arrangements are operated.

Consideration of Fig. 13.14 shows that the Rankine cycle will approach that of the Carnot cycle more nearly if the superheat temperature rise is reduced. There are several reasons why superheat is nevertheless regarded with favour and one is that, with fixed upper temperature, the pressure of the steam will rise to values which are difficult to deal with structurally if the superheat is reduced; another is that, without superheat, the steam is wet throughout the expansion, which leads to excessive wall-condensation in a reciprocating engine and to erosion of the blades in a turbine.

Further discussion of these matters, together with measures to raise the efficiency of practical steam power plant to that of the Carnot cycle, may be found in advanced texts on the subject.

The enthalpy-entropy ($h-s$) diagram

Fig. 13.15 shows to scale a diagram of the properties of the steam plotted with enthalpy as ordinate and entropy as abscissa. This is known as the *Mollier Diagram* for steam. Large-scale charts are available and are widely used because of the importance of enthalpy in calculations on steady-flow plant and of the isentropic process as a standard of comparison for practical adiabatic expansions and compressions.

Some lines of constant pressure and temperature are plotted on Fig. 13.15, together with lines of constant dryness fraction. The pressure and temperature lines naturally coincide in the two-phase region.

The slope of a line of constant pressure may be calculated from eq. (13.44) by putting $dp = 0$. We obtain

$$\left(\frac{dh}{ds}\right)_p = T \qquad \qquad \ldots \quad (13.52)$$

These lines therefore have constant slope, equal to the absolute temperature corresponding to p, i.e. they are straight in the two-phase (L + V) region. They gradually steepen as they advance into the vapour (V, superheat) region.

Use of the h–s diagram to determine the final state in an isentropic expansion. The Mollier diagram is particularly useful to steam power engineers because it enables the calculation described on p. 223 to be replaced by a simple graphical construction, which is usually of sufficient accuracy. On Fig. 13.15 an isentropic expansion from state 1 is represented by a straight line dropped vertically downwards. Its intersection 2 with the given exhaust pressure line p_2 is immediately found: this fixes state 2

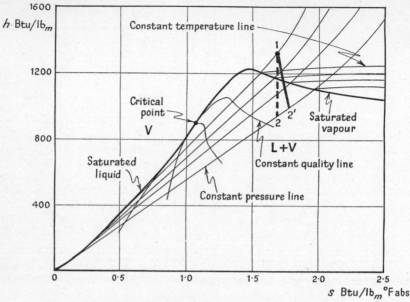

Fig. 13.15   Enthalpy-entropy diagram for steam.

(in particular, h_2) without reference to steam tables. The desired magnitude $W_{X,R}$ is equal to $(h_1 - h_2)$, according to eq. (13.1), i.e. to the vertical distance between 1 and 2, measured on the enthalpy scale.

Fig. 13.15 also shows as a full line a typical actual expansion between state 1 and pressure p_2. Its lower end-point 2' is bound, because of the upward slope of the p_2 line, to be higher than 2. The actual shaft work W_X in this adiabatic process (with assumed zero kinetic energy), which equals the vertical distance of 2' below 1, is therefore less than $W_{X,R}$, as we should expect.

BIBLIOGRAPHY

Mooney, D. A., *Mechanical Engineering Thermodynamics*. Prentice-Hall, Inc., and Bailey Bros., 1953.

Keenan, J. H., *Thermodynamics*. Wiley & Sons and Chapman & Hall, 1941.

CHAPTER 13—PROBLEMS

13.1 (a) A fluid system at a temperature of 140°F and a pressure of 14 psia undergoes a reversible process during which the temperature of the system remains constant. Given that the heat transfer to the fluid during the process is 120 Btu, evaluate the increase in entropy.

(b) The system in (a) has a mass of $2 \cdot 31$ lb$_m$. Evaluate the increase in the specific entropy of the system.

(c) A second fluid system, identical to that in (a) undergoes an irreversible isothermal process from the same initial state to the same final state as in (a). The heat transfer to the fluid in this irreversible process is 80 Btu. Evaluate the increase in the specific entropy of the fluid.

13.2 Using the Steam Tables given in Appendix B, write down the magnitude and units for each of the following:

(a) Specific entropy of dry and saturated steam at a temperature of 300°F.

(b) Specific entropy of saturated water at a pressure of 1 psia.

(c) Specific entropy of steam at a pressure of 100 psia, dryness $0 \cdot 9$.

(d) Specific entropy of steam at a pressure of 60 psia and a temperature of 1200°F.

13.3 (a) A system consists of a mixture of $0 \cdot 1$ lb$_m$ of saturated water and $0 \cdot 7$ lb$_m$ of saturated steam in equilibrium at 50 psia. Evaluate the dryness fraction, the temperature and the specific entropy of the mixture.

(b) Steam at a temperature of 400°F has a specific entropy of $1 \cdot 6100$ Btu/lb$_m$ °F abs. Evaluate the pressure, the specific volume and the specific internal energy of the steam.

(c) Steam at a temperature of 400°F has a specific entropy of $1 \cdot 4100$ Btu/lb$_m$ °F abs. Evaluate the pressure, the specific volume and the specific internal energy of the steam.

13.4 Using the Steam Tables given in Appendix B, sketch approximately to scale the boundaries of the liquid and vapour phase regions of H_2O on charts with the following coordinates:

(a) T–s (b) h–s.

On sketch (a) show a few lines of constant p and constant x, and on sketch (b) a few lines of constant p and constant T.

13.5 Reconsider problem 9.4 to obtain the entropy of the mixture.

13.6 One pound of saturated water at a pressure of 120 psia is contained in a cylinder fitted with a frictionless leakproof piston. The water undergoes a reversible (fully resisted) constant-pressure process, as the piston moves slowly outwards, causing the contents of the cylinder to be converted to dry and saturated steam. The heat transfer during the process is $877 \cdot 9$ Btu. The initial and final volume of the contents of the cylinder are $0 \cdot 01789$ ft³/lb$_m$ and $3 \cdot 728$ ft³/lb$_m$.

Evaluate the increases in entropy and in internal energy of the contents of the cylinder and compare the values calculated with those given in the Steam Tables (Appendix B).

13.7 Steam at a temperature of 400°F and a dryness $0 \cdot 9$ undergoes a reversible constant-temperature process to a pressure 40 psia.

(a) Use the Steam Tables (Appendix B) to evaluate the increase in the entropy of the steam and hence, via the definition of entropy, the heat transfer per pound of steam during the process.

(b) Use the Steam Tables to evaluate the increase in internal energy and the increase in enthalpy of the steam.

(c) Using the results of (a) and (b), and assuming the process to take place in a piston-cylinder mechanism, determine the work done, per pound of steam, during the process. Plot the path of the process to scale on a p–v state diagram, evaluate $\int p \, dv$ and compare with the calculated value for the work done.

(d) Using the results of (a) and (b) and assuming the process to take place in steady flow, with negligible changes in the kinetic and potential energies, determine the external work done, per pound of steam, during the process and compare it with $-\int v \, dp$.

13.8 $0 \cdot 1$ ft^3 of steam at a pressure of 100 psia and a dryness of $0 \cdot 95$ is contained in a cylinder closed by a frictionless piston. The steam undergoes a fully resisted expansion to a final, pressure of 20 psia, according to $pV =$ constant, where p is the steam pressure and V the corresponding steam volume.

Evaluate (a) the initial and final temperatures
         (b) the work done
         (c) the increase in entropy
         (d) the heat transfer.

13.9 Steam is compressed reversibly and adiabatically from a pressure of 20 psia, dryness $0 \cdot 9$, to a pressure of 200 psia.

Determine: (a) the final temperature:
          (b) the increase in specific internal energy;
          (c) the increase in specific enthalpy.

Using these results state:
          (d) the minimum work required to compress one pound of steam adiabatically from a pressure of 20 psia, dryness $0 \cdot 9$, to a pressure of 200 psia;
          (e) the minimum shaft work required if the compression were carried out adiabatically in steady flow, changes in the kinetic and potential energies being negligible.

13.10 1 lb$_m$ of steam at a pressure of 80 psia and a temperature of 400°F is contained in a cylinder. The steam undergoes an irreversible expansion process to a final pressure of 20 psia; the initial and final entropies of the steam are equal.

(a) Given that the work done is 80 per cent of that for a reversible adiabatic process between the same end states determine the magnitude and sign of the heat transfer during the process.

(b) In a second process between the same initial state and the same final pressure the steam does an equal amount of work to that in the first irreversible process. The second process is adiabatic. Evaluate the increase in entropy in the second process.

13.11 (a) Steam at a pressure of 450 psia and a temperature of 600°F flows steadily into a turbine and leaves at a pressure of 120 psia and a temperature of 400°F. The flow is adiabatic and changes in kinetic energy and in elevation are negligible. Evaluate the external work done per pound of steam flowing.

(b) Steam at a pressure of 450 psia and a temperature of 600°F flows steadily into a turbine and leaves at a pressure of 120 psia. The flow is adiabatic and changes in kinetic energy and in elevation are negligible. Evaluate the maximum external work which could be done by the steam.

(c) Show the expansion processes (a) and (b) on a sketch of the enthalpy-entropy diagram and evaluate the isentropic efficiency of the turbine in (a).

13.12 Check that the entropy changes in the reversible adiabatic expansion and compression processes in problem 11.2 are zero.

13.13 A steady-flow heat engine using H_2O as the working fluid operates on the Carnot cycle between the pressure limits of 200 psia and 15 psia. The working fluid changes from saturated liquid to dry saturated steam during the isothermal heating process at the higher pressure.

(a) Calculate the heat transfer and the shaft work for each process.

(b) Compare the net shaft work done and the net heat transfer during the cycle.

(c) Evaluate the cycle efficiency ($=w/q_1$) and compare it with the value obtained from the definition of the Absolute Temperature Scale.

13.14 Recalculate problem 13.13 assuming the engine to be operating on the Rankine cycle.

13.15 (a) Making use of eq. (13.47), show that for the steady, reversible flow of an incompressible fluid in which changes in kinetic energy and in elevation are negligible, the external work done is given by

$$W_x = v(p_1 - p_2)$$

where v is the specific volume of the incompressible fluid and p_1, p_2 are the initial and final pressures of the fluid.

(b) Assuming water to be an incompressible fluid for which $v = 0.0167$ ft³/lb$_m$, evaluate the shaft work required in a reversible feed pump taking in water from a condenser at a pressure of 1 psia and delivering it to a boiler steaming at 400 psia.

13.16 A steady flow of steam from a boiler enters an adiabatic turbine at a pressure of 400 psia and a temperature of 700°F and discharges into a condenser at a pressure of 1 psia. The condensed steam from the condenser enters the feed-pump as saturated liquid at a pressure of 1 psia and is returned to the boiler at a pressure of 400 psia. The isentropic efficiencies of the turbine and of the pump are 70 per cent and 50 per cent respectively. The turbine and the pump may be assumed to be adiabatic and changes in kinetic energy and in elevation are negligible.

(a) Evaluate the dryness fraction of the steam leaving the turbine and the shaft work done by the steam in the turbine per pound of steam flowing.

(b) Evaluate the work done on the water in the feed pump. Use the results from problem 13.15.

(c) Evaluate the efficiency and the efficiency ratio with and without allowance for the feed pump work.

13.17 A vapour-compression refrigerator (Fig. 10.5) uses methyl-chloride as the working fluid. The fluid flows steadily into the compressor at a pressure of 20.7 psia and is delivered to the condenser as dry and saturated vapour at a pressure of 100.6 psia. The fluid leaves the condenser as saturated liquid at a pressure of 100.6 psia and after expansion in the throttle valve to a pressure of 20.7 psia it flows through the evaporator and thence back into the compressor again. The compression process may be assumed to be reversible and adiabatic and the throttling process to be adiabatic. Changes in kinetic energy and in elevation are negligible.

(a) Evaluate the dryness fraction of the fluid entering the compressor and hence the shaft work done per pound of refrigerant.

(b) Evaluate the dryness fraction of the fluid after the throttling process.

(c) Evaluate the heat transfer to the refrigerant (per lb$_m$) in the evaporator.

(d) Evaluate the coefficient of performance of the refrigerator and compare it with the maximum possible value for the given temperature limits.

Use the following data for methyl-chloride:—

Pressure psia	Saturation temperature °F	Enthalpy Btu/lb$_m$		Entropy Btu/lb$_m$°F abs	
		Saturated liquid	Saturated vapour	Saturated liquid	Saturated vapour
20.7	4	15.9	196.8	0.036	0.426
100.6	90	48.2	206.1	0.100	0.387

13.18 (*a*) Steam at a pressure of 180 psia and a temperature of 400°F flows steadily into a horizontal nozzle with a velocity of 300 ft/s. The steam leaves the nozzle at a pressure of 50 psia. Given that the flow process is reversible and adiabatic evaluate the dryness fraction and the velocity of the steam leaving the nozzle.

(*b*) A second nozzle receives steam in the same condition and expands it to the same final pressure as in (*a*). The flow process is adiabatic but in this case, due to friction, the increase in the kinetic energy of the steam is 90 per cent of that in nozzle (*a*) (i.e. the *nozzle efficiency* is 90 per cent). Evaluate the velocity and the dryness fraction of the steam leaving the nozzle. Evaluate also the increase in specific entropy of the steam.

(*c*) Compare the exit areas of the two nozzles.

13.19 A heat engine operates steadily on the following cycle. Saturated water at a temperature of 400°F is pumped into the boiler and leaves as dry saturated steam at a temperature of 400°F. After adiabatic expansion through a turbine to a pressure of 14·7 psia the dryness fraction is 0·90. The exhaust steam from the turbine passes to a condenser and is partially condensed, leaving at a pressure of 14·7 psia with a dryness fraction of 0·15. The wet steam leaving the condenser is then compressed adiabatically in the feed pump before re-entering the boiler as saturated water at a temperature of 400°F.

(*a*) Determine the entropy values around the cycle.

(*b*) State whether the turbine and pump processes are reversible or irreversible: give reasons.

(*c*) Evaluate the heat transfer per pound of steam in each component, and determine the efficiency of the heat engine.

(*d*) Determine the value of $\oint \dfrac{\mathrm{d}Q}{T}$.

(*e*) What would have been the value of $\oint \dfrac{\mathrm{d}Q}{T}$ and of the efficiency if the turbine and pump had each been reversible with the same states at entry to and exit from the boiler and the same condenser pressure.

13.20 (*a*) Making use of eq. (13.44) show that for a substance for which $h = f(t)$ and c_p is constant, the increase in entropy between initial and final states 1 and 2 is given by

$$s_2 - s_1 = c_p \ln \frac{T_2}{T_1} - \int_1^2 \frac{v}{T}\,\mathrm{d}p.$$

Hence show that in a constant-pressure process the increase in entropy is given by

$$s_2 - s_1 = c_p \ln \frac{T_2}{T_1}$$

(*b*) An open insulated vessel is divided into two parts by a vertical non-conducting partition. On one side of the partition are 5 lb_m of water at a temperature of 100°F whilst on the other side are 10 lb_m at a temperature of 160°F. When the partition is removed the two masses of water mix and after a time conditions are uniform throughout the vessel. Assuming zero heat transfer to the atmosphere, and taking the specific heat of water at constant pressure to be 1 $\mathrm{Btu/lb}_m$ °F, evaluate the increase in entropy of the system comprising the 15 lb_m of water.

(*c*) An open insulated vessel contains 9 lb_m of water at a temperature of 68°F. 1 lb_m of ice at a temperature of 25°F is added to the water and after a time the temperature of the contents of the vessel becomes uniform. Assuming the heat transfer to the atmosphere to be zero, determine the increase in entropy of the system comprising the final contents of the vessel. Take the specific heat at constant pressure of ice to be 0.5 Btu/lb$_m$ °F and the latent heat of fusion of ice at atmospheric pressure to be 143.3 Btu/lb$_m$.

(d) A carbon-steel tool of mass 0.5 lb$_m$, at a temperature of 700°F is plunged suddenly into an insulated vessel containing 10 lb$_m$ of oil at a temperature of 65°F. After a time the temperature of the contents of the vessel becomes uniform. Assuming the heat transfer to the atmosphere to be zero, and that none of the oil evaporates, evaluate the increase in entropy of the final contents of the vessel. Take the specific heats at constant pressure of the oil and of the carbon steel to be 0.45 Btu/lb$_m$ °F and 0.115 Btu/lb$_m$ °F respectively.

13.21 By comparing the entropy increase with $\int \dfrac{dQ}{T}$ show that the following processes are irreversible:

(a) the expansion process in problem 13.11(a);
(b) the expansion process in problem 13.18(b);
(c) the mixing process in problem 13.20(b);
(d) the mixing process in problem 13.20(c);
(e) the quenching process in problem 13.20(d).

CHAPTER 14

IDEAL GASES

INTRODUCTION

So far we have been concerned to apply the First and Second Laws of Thermodynamics to systems in general and, more particularly to pure substances. Steam has been chosen as the chief example of the latter, partly because of its engineering importance, and partly because it exhibits most of the peculiarities and irregularities which are likely to be encountered. When knowledge of the properties of the fluids has been required, they have been extracted from results of experimental research embodied in tables and charts.

Since many other fluids are of engineering importance, it is fortunate that some of them, over restricted but practically interesting ranges of conditions, exhibit regularities in their properties which enable tabulation of these properties to be dispensed with: it is possible to derive simple algebraic relations between their properties which have sufficient accuracy for many purposes. This makes calculation much simpler: algebra replaces arithmetic over a large part of the calculation, with corresponding increase in speed and generality.

Every fluid permits such algebraic approximation when its temperature is sufficiently high above its critical temperature, or its pressure is very much below its critical pressure; these are the conditions mentioned on p. 150, where it was noted that isotherms tend to become rectangular hyperbolae on a p–v diagram and horizontal straight lines on diagrams with internal energy or enthalpy as ordinate. The important fluids are those for which these conditions are satisfied by moderate temperatures and pressures. Examples are the so-called "permanent" gases: oxygen, hydrogen, nitrogen, air, and carbon dioxide; even so, liquid air is a common substance in laboratories, while solid carbon dioxide ("dry ice") is carried by every ice-cream vendor.

The algebraic approximations to real gas behaviour are called *Ideal Gases*. In the present Chapter, two ideal gases are considered, namely, the *Semi-Perfect Gas* and the *Perfect Gas*. We discuss the features which a real gas must possess to approximate to an Ideal Gas, and demonstrate an important fact about the effect of temperature on such a gas: it is shown that thermometers using them indicate the *absolute temperature*. Thereafter formulae will be derived which enable First and Second Law analyses of processes executed by Ideal Gases to be made.

Symbols

C_v Specific heat at constant volume (mole basis).

c_v Specific heat at constant volume (pound mass basis).

$\bar{c}_v$ Mean specific heat at constant volume.

C_p Specific heat at constant pressure (mole basis).

c_p	Specific heat at constant pressure (pound mass basis).	$\mathscr{R}$	Universal Gas Constant.
$\bar{c}_p$	Mean specific heat at constant pressure	s	Specific entropy.
		T	Absolute temperature.
g	Gravitational acceleration.	t	Temperature.
g_0	Constant in Newton's Second Law.	u	Specific internal energy.
		V	System volume. Velocity.
h	Specific enthalpy.	V_{mol}	Molecular volume.
M	Molecular weight.	v	Specific volume.
m	Mass.	W	Net work done by a system.
$\dot{m}$	Mass flow rate.	W_x	External work.
n	Number of moles. Constant in $pv^n =$ a constant.	z	Height of a mercury column (example 2, p. 266).
p	Pressure.	γ	Ratio of specific heats,
Q	Heat transfer.		c_p/c_v, C_p/C_v.
R	Gas Constant.		

EXPERIMENTAL FACTS ABOUT "PERMANENT" GASES

Boyle's Law

Soon after the first means of pumping gases and preventing leakage became available, Boyle (in 1662) discovered that an approximately (he thought exactly) reciprocal relationship existed between the pressure and the volume of a fixed mass of "permanent" gas when expanded or compressed at constant temperature. We write this symbolically as

$$pv = \text{constant, at constant temperature}$$
$$= f(t), \text{ very closely.} \qquad \ldots \quad (14.1)$$

where $f(t)$ indicates "some function of temperature". The lower case t is used, since we shall suppose for the present that we have no means of knowing temperature on the absolute scale. Boyle's Law will be shown below to assist in removing this ignorance.

Joule's Law

The constant-u experiment. In an attempt to establish the dependence of the internal energy of "permanent" gases on their density, Joule (in 1845) carried out an experiment similar to that discussed on p. 50 under the heading "Unresisted Expansion". Fig. 14.1 illustrates the apparatus which consists of two vessels, A and B, immersed in a water bath; the vessels are inter-connected through a cock which is closed initially. At first, container A holds gas but B is evacuated. The cock is suddenly opened and gas rushes into B, equalising the pressures. If the mean temperature of the gas changes in this process, a heat transfer will occur between the surrounding water bath and the gas; this will be reflected in a change in the water temperature.

Joule found no change in water temperature, signifying no detectable heat transfer. Since the experiment is one of constant internal energy for the gas ($Q = 0$, $W = 0$ $\therefore$ $\Delta u = Q - W = 0$), we may conclude

$$u = f(t), \text{ within experimental accuracy} \qquad \ldots \quad (14.2)$$

That is to say that u depends only on the temperature of the gas and not on its pressure or specific volume (both p and v change considerably in the above experiment). Here $f(t)$ means "some function of temperature", not, of course, the same function as that in eq. (14.1). Eq. (14.2) is sometimes known as *Joule's Law*.

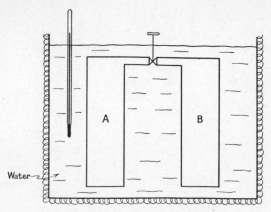

Fig. 14.1   Joule's experiment.

The constant-h experiment. Not satisfied with the above negative result, Joule and Thomson (later Lord Kelvin) in 1852 devised a steady-flow experiment for the same purpose. Since pv was known to depend only on temperature from Boyle's Law and since $h = u + pv$, a constant-h

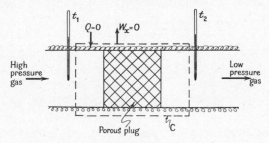

Fig. 14.2   The Joule-Thomson experiment.

experiment would serve their purpose as well as one at constant u, and would moreover be far more sensitive. Fig. 14.2 shows the apparatus. A porous plug of cotton wool is placed in a pipe. A "permanent" gas, say air, is forced steadily along the pipe and suffers a large decrease of pressure at the plug. The pipe is insulated thermally, and the steady temperatures of the gas upstream and downstream of the plug are measured; the kinetic energy of the gas is negligible both upstream and downstream. For these conditions, the enthalpy of the gas is the same upstream and downstream of the plug, as may be seen by applying the Steady Flow Energy Equation, eq. (8.22), to the control surface C, Fig. 14.2.

In these experiments small but definite temperature changes were measured, e.g. a decrease of about 0·5°F per atmosphere pressure difference for air, and an increase of about 0·05°F per atmosphere pressure difference for hydrogen, both gases being at about 32°F.

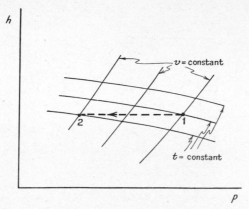

Fig. 14.3   Enthalpy-pressure diagram for a gas.

These results indicate a small dependence of enthalpy and internal energy on pressure (or specific volume) in addition to the major dependence on temperature. Nevertheless, for many purposes it suffices to ignore the pressure dependence and to quote the result as

$$h = f(t), \text{ very closely,} \qquad \text{... (14.3)}$$

and

$$u = f(t), \text{ very closely.} \qquad \text{... (14.4)}$$

Expressed graphically these equations imply that on an h–p or a u–v diagram, the isotherms are very nearly horizontal lines. Fig. 14.3 illustrates the former case and shows how a slight temperature decrease can arise in the constant-enthalpy porous-plug experiment.

THE SEMI-PERFECT GAS

Definition of the semi-perfect gas

It is natural, in view of the good approximations with which eq. (14.1), eq. (14.3) and eq. (14.4) describe the behaviour of real gases, to investigate the properties of an Ideal Gas which obeys them exactly. The characteristics of the Ideal Gas can then be used to represent very closely those of real gases. We adopt the following definition, and then proceed to examine how the pressure and volume of such a gas must depend on its temperature.

A semi-perfect gas is one which obeys exactly the equations

$$pv = f(t) \qquad \text{... (14.5)}$$

$$u = f(t) \qquad \text{... (14.6)}$$

The p–v–T relation of such a gas will be established in two steps. In the first we show that the pressure of the gas is proportional to the *absolute* temperature, T, when the volume is kept constant. In the second we show that the expression pv/T is a constant under all conditions.

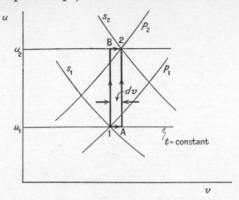

Fig. 14.4   Internal energy-volume diagram for a gas.

The p–v–T relation of a semi-perfect gas

The p–T relation in constant volume heating. Eq. (14.5) and eq. (14.6) contain the properties p, v, u and t. The only general relation which we possess relating these is equation (13.42), $T \, \mathrm{d}s = \mathrm{d}u + p \, \mathrm{d}v$
which we put in the form

$$\mathrm{d}s = \frac{1}{T}\,\mathrm{d}u + \frac{p}{T}\,\mathrm{d}v \qquad \ldots \ (14.7)$$

and then integrate, to give

$$s_2 - s_1 = \int_1^2 \frac{1}{T}\,\mathrm{d}u + \int_1^2 \frac{p}{T}\,\mathrm{d}v \qquad \ldots \ (14.8)$$

Now consider the u–v diagram for the gas shown in Fig. 14.4. The isotherms on this diagram are horizontal lines, since $u = f(t)$. Consider the states marked 1 and 2 and two paths connecting them, one via A and the other via B. The abscissae of 1 and 2 differ by the infinitesimal amount $\mathrm{d}v$, but the difference of ordinate $(u_2 - u_1)$, is finite.

Considering the right-hand side of eq. (14.8), and invoking eq. (14.6), we note that the first integral is independent of the path of integration, i.e. has a definite value, since u depends only on t and so on T. But since entropy is a property, $s_2 - s_1$ is certainly also independent of the path of integration. It follows that the second integral on the right hand side is independent of the path.

Examining this conclusion more closely, we see that it implies that the value of p/T along the line 1A is the same as that along the line B2. But the levels of 1 and 2 were arbitrarily chosen. It follows that p/T must be constant along a line of constant volume. We express this symbolically as

$$\frac{p}{T} = f(v) \qquad \ldots \ (14.9)$$

Comments. 1. It will have been noted that eq. (14.5) has not yet been invoked. Yet already we have the important result that a gas of which the internal energy depends upon temperature alone will, if used in a *constant-volume* gas thermometer, register the *absolute temperature.* Thus if a 1 degree temperature rise produces a $P\%$ increase in gas pressure at constant volume, the temperature on the absolute scale with the chosen size of degree is $100/P$ degrees absolute.

2. To be satisfactory in this respect, the gas does not have to obey eq. (14.6) under all conditions, but merely under the conditions prevailing in the constant-volume gas thermometer.*

3. It is equally possible, though less useful, to prove that a gas obeying eq. (14.9) must obey eq. (14.6), i.e. to prove the converse of the above.

4. If an actual gas deviates from eq. (14.6) by a known amount, the magnitude of its deviation from eq. (14.9) can also be calculated.

Deduction of the "Ideal Gas Rule". The second step of the argument involves the combination of eq. (14.5) and eq. (14.9) to give

$$\frac{pv}{T} = \text{const.} = R, \text{ say} \qquad \ldots \quad (14.10)$$

This is directly obvious, since what other p–v–T relation could satisfy both equations? For formality's sake, however, a proof is appended:—

Substituting eq. (14.9) in eq. (14.5), we have

$$vTf(v) = f(T) \qquad \ldots \quad (14.11)$$

remembering that $f(\ )$ merely means "some function of . . . ", and that therefore t and T are interchangeable in $f(\ )$. Since v and T are independent properties, eq. (14.11) can only be true if

$$vf(v) = \text{const} = \frac{1}{T}\, f(T)$$

Hence, from eq. (14.5)

$$\frac{pv}{T} = \text{const}$$

Q.E.D.

Eq. (14.10) is sometimes written in another form, namely as a relation between the mass m of a gas and the volume V which it occupies.

Since $V = mv$ we have, from eq. (14.10)

$$pV = mRT \qquad \ldots \quad (14.12)$$

The Gas Constant R

Eq. (14.10) is known as the *Ideal Gas Rule*. The constant R is called the *Gas Constant*. It has a different value for each gas. For a number of technically important gases at low pressures, values of R are given in Table 14.1.

* End note 8.

R may also be expressed in other units. Its value then changes in accordance with the usual rules relating the various unit systems. Common alternative units used in Engineering Thermodynamics are $Btu/lb_m°F$ abs and $Chu/lb_m°C$ abs.

TABLE 14.1. *Gas Constant R ft $lb_f/lb_m°F$ abs.*

Gas	Air	O_2	N_2 (atmospheric)	N_2	H_2	CO	CO_2	H_2O
R	53·3	48·3	54·8	55·2	766·6	55·2	35·1	85·8

Two gases included in Table 14.1 call for comment:—

(i) *Atmospheric nitrogen* is the name given to the components of air which are not oxygen. It consists of pure nitrogen together with about 1·8% by mass of argon and traces of carbon dioxide and other gases.

(ii) Steam has been included because *at low pressures* it obeys eq. (14.10) quite closely, even at temperatures well below that of the critical point.

Since real gases do not obey eq. (14.5) and eq. (14.6) exactly, they also exhibit departures from eq. (14.10). The order of magnitude of these departures is indicated by the values of pv/RT for air shown in Table 14.2; the R value is that given in Table 14.1.

TABLE 14.2. $\dfrac{pv}{RT}$ *for air*

p atm → $t°F$ ↓	0	10	100
32	1	0·9945	0·9699
392	1	1·0031	1·0364

It is evident that at low pressures the error involved in using eq. (14.10) will often be negligible.

The Universal Gas Constant $\mathscr{R}$

Thermodynamics is not concerned with the microscopic structure of materials. However, we here introduce concepts which are only explicable in terms of the molecular nature of gases.

Molecular weight. The molecular weight, M, of a substance is defined by

$$M = \frac{\text{(mass of one molecule of the substance)}}{\frac{1}{32} \times \text{(mass of one molecule of oxygen)}} \quad \dots \quad (14.13)$$

The masses of the molecules may be determined or compared experimentally. The values of M for common gases given in Table 14.3 are the results of such experiments.

In Table 14.3 it is seen that, in addition to pure gases, values are given for gases such as air which are mixtures of different kinds of molecules. The significance of these is explained in Chapter 15, p. 283.

TABLE 14.3. *Molecular weights of gases*

Gas	Air	O_2	N_2 (atmospheric)	N_2	H_2	CO	CO_2	H_2O
M	28·97	32·00	28·17	28·02	2·016	28·01	44·01	18·016

To explain why 1/32 times the mass of an oxygen molecule is used in defining M, we first note that originally the mass of one hydrogen atom was taken as the reference. This made the molecular weight of hydrogen (M_{H_2}) equal to 2 and it was thought that all the other molecular weights were also whole numbers. The molecular weight of oxygen (M_{O_2}), for example, was thought to be 32. More careful experiments then showed that the molecular weights were not exactly whole numbers, for a reason connected with the composition of molecules and atoms from even smaller particles. Since oxygen enters into more chemical combinations than hydrogen, it was decided to make $M_{O_2} = 32$ exactly, so that M_{H_2} became 2·016 and the other substances took the values shown in Table 14.3. It will be seen, however, that they are still very nearly equal to whole numbers.

The mole. In this book we have used the pound mass as the unit of mass. Frequently, however, the analysis is simplified by the use of another unit of mass, the mole, defined as follows:—

A mole is a quantity of substance whose mass is numerically equal to its molecular weight.

Then for a gas of molecular weight M we have

One pound mole (lb mole) $\equiv M \ lb_m$ of the gas

One gramme mole (g mole) $\equiv M \ g_m$ of the gas

and so on for any other mass units. The definition therefore ascribes units, lb mole/lb_m for example, to molecular weight.

The introduction of a different mass unit for each material appears a retrograde step, similar to using both "troy weight" and avoirdupois"[*]. The molal units however lead to great simplification in chemical calculations (see Chapter 16), because of their relation to the molecular constitution of matter which has just been indicated.

[*] Troy weight is used for gold and has 12 ounces per lb_m, as compared with avoirdupois which is used for other substances and has 16 ounces per lb_m.

17

The Universal Gas Constant $\mathscr{R}$. The molecular weight has been introduced in the present chapter because of an experimental fact about gases which obey the Ideal Gas Rule. It is found that the product of the Gas Constant and the molecular weight of such gases is independent of the nature of the gas.

Symbolically

$$RM = \text{constant}$$

$$\equiv \mathscr{R}, \text{ for } all \text{ gases} \qquad \ldots \quad (14.14)$$

$\mathscr{R}$ is known as the *Universal Gas Constant* and is *defined* by eq. (14.14).

The numerical value of $\mathscr{R}$ depends on the units used. For example, in the lb_m, lb_f, ft, °F set of units

$$\mathscr{R} = 1545{\cdot}4 \text{ ft lb}_f/\text{lb mole °F abs for } all \text{ Ideal Gases.}$$

Then, for a particular Ideal Gas, eq. (14.14) gives

$$R = \frac{1545{\cdot}4}{M} \text{ ft lb}_f/\text{lb}_m \text{°F abs}$$

Table 14.4 gives the values of $\mathscr{R}$ for various sets of units together with the corresponding units of R.

TABLE 14.4

If R is in	$\mathscr{R}$ is
ft lb_f/lb_m°F abs	1545·4 ft lb_f/lb mole°F abs
Btu/lb_m°F abs	1·986 Btu/lb. mole°F abs
ft lb_f/lb_m°K	2781·7 ft lb_f/lb mole°K
Chu/lb_m°F abs	1·986 Chu/lb mole°K
cal/g_m°K	1·986 cal/g_m mole°K

The Ideal Gas Rule in molal units. The Ideal Gas Rule has been stated as

$$pv = RT \qquad \ldots \quad (14.10)$$

or

$$pV = mRT \qquad \ldots \quad (14.12)$$

These equations may be written in terms of the mole as follows. Let V_{mol} be the volume occupied by one mole of a gas of molecular weight M. Then eq. (14.13) becomes

$$pV_{\text{mol}} = MRT$$

Substituting from eq. (14.14) we have

$$pV_{\text{mol}} = \mathscr{R}T \qquad \ldots \quad (14.15)$$

or if a mass of n moles occupies a volume V then

$$pV = n\mathscr{R}T \qquad \ldots \quad (14.16)$$

Remarks on $\mathscr{R}$ and M.

1. *Avogadro's Hypothesis.* The experimental fact $RM = \mathscr{R}$, stated in eq. (14.14) was first suspected by Avogadro in 1811, who expressed his hypothesis as:— "Equal volumes of gases at equal pressures and temperatures contain equal numbers of molecules".

That this statement is consistent with eq. (14.14) may be shown by substituting from eq. (14.14) in eq. (14.12). Thus

$$m = \frac{pV}{RT} = M\,\frac{pV}{\mathscr{R}T}$$

so that

$$\frac{m}{M} = \frac{pV}{\mathscr{R}T} \qquad \qquad \ldots \ (14.17)$$

If now a number of gases occupy equal volumes V at equal pressures p and temperatures T, and $\mathscr{R}$ is a universal constant, then from eq. (14.17)

$$\frac{m}{M} = \text{constant, for all gases} \qquad \ldots \ (14.18)$$

Eq. (14.18) means that the masses of equal volumes of all gases at equal pressures and temperatures are proportional to the masses of their molecules. The numbers of molecules in each equal volume must therefore be equal.

In addition, eq. (14.18) also means that equal volumes of gases at equal pressures and temperatures contain equal numbers of moles. This follows from eq. (14.16), (14.12) and (14.14) since

$$n = \frac{pV}{\mathscr{R}T} = \frac{mR}{\mathscr{R}} = \frac{mR}{MR} = \frac{m}{M}$$

The two interpretations of eq. (14.18) link together the mole concept and Avogadro's Hypothesis.

Avogadro's Hypothesis is obeyed by real gases to the same extent as is the Ideal Gas Rule.

2. *Molecular volume.* From eq. (14.15) and the information contained in Table 14.4 it follows that

1 lb mole of any Ideal Gas occupies 359 ft^3

when $p = 14 \cdot 7$ psia and $t = 32°$F.

or

1 g mole of any Ideal Gas occupies 22,416 cm^3

when $p = 1$ atm., and $t = 0°$C.

The two volumes are sometimes known as the *pound molecular volume* and the *gram molecular volume* respectively.

Charles' Law

A consequence of the Ideal Gas Rule is that at a fixed pressure, the specific volume of a gas obeying the Rule increases linearly with absolute temperature. This fact is often confused with Charles' Law, discovered in 1787, which may be expressed as:— "The specific volume of a "permanent" gas at constant pressure increases (approximately) linearly with the temperature measured on a uniformly divided mercury-in-glass thermometer."

Charles' Law was propounded well before the establishment of the First and Second Laws of Thermodynamics and the definition of the Absolute Temperature scale. Temperature therefore had to be defined in

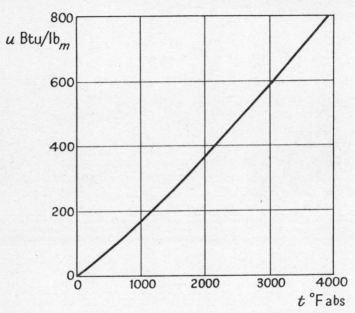

Fig. 14.5   Internal energy-temperature diagram for air at low pressure.

terms of a particular thermometric substance. Of course the gas itself could be used as the thermometric substance, in which case the "law" would reduce to a mere definition of a temperature scale, the only advantage of which would lie in the fact that *any* "permanent" gas could be used in the thermometer.

Charles' Law in itself tells us nothing about the absolute temperature. It is only the deductions from Boyle's and Joule's Laws, given above, that enable us to deduce that a temperature scale using an Ideal Gas as thermometric substance happens to measure the absolute temperature directly.

The specific heats of gases obeying the Ideal Gas Rule

We have seen that many gases obey eq. (14.3) and eq. (14.4) very closely. It follows that property diagrams with internal energy or enthalpy as ordinate and temperature as abscissa reduce to single curves, as illustrated by Figs. 14.5 and 14.6 which are drawn to scale for air.

Recalling the definition of c_v and c_p introduced in equations (7.6) and (7.7), we see that they may be re-written for a gas obeying eq. (14.10) by dropping the conditions that v and p should respectively be kept constant in the differentiation. Thus for a semi-perfect gas

$$c_v = \frac{du}{dt} \qquad \qquad \ldots \quad (14.19)$$

$$c_p = \frac{dh}{dt} \qquad \qquad \ldots \quad (14.20)$$

c_v and c_p are the slopes of the curves illustrated by Figs. 14.5 and 14.6. Since these curves curl upwards with their slopes increasing, c_v and c_p are not constants but increase with temperature. This is the case for *all* gases.

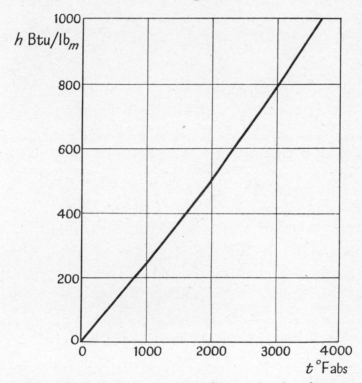

Fig. 14.6 Enthalpy-temperature diagram for air at low pressures.

Relation between c_v, c_p and R for Semi-Perfect Gases. Internal energy and enthalpy are connected by the definition, eq. (7.8)

$$h = u + pv$$

which, in view of eq. (14.10) may be written

$$h = u + RT \qquad \qquad \ldots \quad (14.21)$$

Differentiating with respect to temperature, and remembering that R is a constant we obtain

$$\frac{\mathrm{d}h}{\mathrm{d}t} = \frac{\mathrm{d}u}{\mathrm{d}t} + R\frac{\mathrm{d}T}{\mathrm{d}t}$$

i.e. $\qquad\qquad\qquad\qquad c_p = c_v + R \qquad\qquad\qquad$ ... (14.22)

provided that the temperature scale we are using, t, is equal to the absolute temperature minus a constant, as is always the case nowadays, so that $\mathrm{d}T/\mathrm{d}t$ equal unity (see p. 204).

Eq. (14.22) is an important relation which should be remembered. Of course it is necessary that consistent units should be used. Since c_p and c_v will normally be in Btu/lb$_m$°F, R must be expressed in the same units.

Sometimes it is convenient to work with the lb mole as the unit of mass. Then *molal specific heats*, C_v and C_p, are used, defined by

$$C_v \equiv Mc_v \qquad\qquad\qquad \text{... (14.23)}$$

$$C_p \equiv Mc_p \qquad\qquad\qquad \text{... (14.24)}$$

From equations (14.14) (14.22) (14.23) and (14.24), we deduce

$$C_p = C_v + \mathscr{R} \qquad\qquad\qquad \text{... (14.25)}$$

The specific heat ratio, γ. It will later be found convenient to write eq. (14.22) and eq. (14.25) in terms of the ratio of the specific heats, γ defined by

$$\gamma \equiv \frac{c_p}{c_v} = \frac{C_p}{C_v} \qquad\qquad\qquad \text{... (14.26)}$$

Substituting from eq. (14.26) in eq. (14.22) we have

$$\frac{R}{c_v} = \gamma - 1 \qquad\qquad\qquad \text{... (14.27)}$$

and

$$\frac{R}{c_p} = \frac{\gamma - 1}{\gamma} \qquad\qquad\qquad \text{... (14.28)}$$

Corresponding relations are obtained from eq. (14.25).

$$\frac{\mathscr{R}}{C_v} = \gamma - 1 \qquad\qquad\qquad \text{... (14.29)}$$

$$\frac{\mathscr{R}}{C_p} = \frac{\gamma - 1}{\gamma} \qquad\qquad\qquad \text{... (14.30)}$$

γ is a property of the gas. For real gases γ tends to decrease as the temperature rises since both c_p and c_v increase, the difference between them remaining constant.

Since R and the specific heats are positive, it is clear that γ must be greater than unity. Values for common gases at moderate and high temperatures are given in Table 14.5.

A striking feature of Table 14.5 is that at moderate temperatures all the di-atomic molecules have identical values of γ. This is because γ is related to the number of degrees of freedom of the molecule. The subject is an advanced one however, particularly when the decrease of γ at high temperatures has to be explained, and we will not discuss it here.

Sometimes the symbol k is used in place of γ.

TABLE 14.5.

Gas	Air	Atm N_2	N_2	O_2	H_2	CO	CO_2	A
γ at 60°F	1·4	1·4	1·4	1·4	1·4	1·4	1·3	1·67
γ at 2000°F	1·32	1·32	1·32	1·3	1·36	1·32	1·17	1·67
No. of atoms in molecule	≈ 2	≈ 2	2	2	2	2	3	1

Mean specific heats, $\bar{c}_V$ and $\bar{c}_p$. Formulae treating specific heats as *constants* are so convenient that we sometimes use them even though the u–t and h–t lines are curved, by defining mean specific heats valid over specified temperature interval. For any two states, 1 and 2, of the gas, the definitions are:—

$$\bar{c}_{V_{12}} \equiv \frac{\int_1^2 c_V \, dt}{t_2 - t_1} = \frac{u_2 - u_1}{t_2 - t_1} \qquad \ldots \quad (14.31)$$

$$\bar{c}_{p_{12}} \equiv \frac{\int_1^2 c_p \, dt}{t_2 - t_1} = \frac{h_2 - h_1}{t_2 - t_1} \qquad \ldots \quad (14.32)$$

Often internal energy and enthalpy data for gases will be found tabulated in this way. Then the lower temperature will have some specified standard value, t_0, such as 32°F or 0°F abs., while the upper temperature of the range will be the argument t of the table. Any desired internal energy difference, for example, is then calculated from

$$u_2 - u_1 = (u_2 - u_0) - (u_1 - u_0)$$
$$= \bar{c}_{V_{02}}(t_2 - t_0) - \bar{c}_{V_{01}}(t_1 - t_0) \qquad \ldots \quad (14.33)$$

If, and only if, the base temperature t_0 is equal to 0 this reduces to

$$u_2 - u_1 = \bar{c}_{V_{02}} t_2 - \bar{c}_{V_{01}} t_1$$

Similarly the enthalpy difference is given by

$$h_2 - h_1 = \bar{c}_{p_{02}}(t_2 - t_0) - c_{p_{01}}(t_1 - t_0) \qquad \ldots \quad (14.34)$$

The First Law of Thermodynamics for a Semi-Perfect Gas. We now illustrate the use of mean specific heats by writing the First Law, eq. (7.5), for a Semi-Perfect Gas. This, in differential form, becomes:

$$dQ = c_{\text{v}}\, dt + dW \qquad \ldots (14.35)$$

and for a larger change

$$Q = \bar{c}_{\text{v}_{12}}(t_2 - t_1) + W \qquad \ldots (14.36)$$

Likewise the Steady Flow Energy Equation eq. (8.22) becomes in differential form

$$dQ - dW_{\text{x}} = c_{\text{p}}\, dt + d\left(\frac{V^2}{2g_0} + \frac{gz}{g_0}\right) \qquad \ldots (14.37)$$

and for a finite change

$$Q - W_{\text{x}} = \bar{c}_{\text{p}_{12}}(t_2 - t_1) + \Delta\left(\frac{V^2}{2g_0} + \frac{gz}{g_0}\right) \qquad \ldots (14.38)$$

An *important point* to notice is that in eq. (14.35) and eq. (14.36) the specific heat at constant volume may be used even though, in general, the volume of the system will change; likewise in eq. (14.37) and eq. (14.38),

TABLE 14.6. c_{p} for air

T°F abs	300	400	600	800	1000	2000	3000
c_{p} Btu/lb$_m$°F	0·239	0·239	0·240	0·244	0·248	0·278	0·293

the specific heat at constant pressure is used, even though, in general, the pressure of the gas changes. This is permissible since neither the internal energy nor the enthalpy of a Semi-Perfect gas, which are expressed here in terms of c_{v} and c_{p}, are affected by changes in volume or pressure. There is, however, one useful formula which can only be used when the pressure remains constant: *for a non-flow, constant-pressure, reversible process of a Semi-Perfect Gas*, the First Law eq. (14.35) becomes

$$\begin{aligned} Q &= \bar{c}_{\text{v}_{12}}(t_2 - t_1) + p(v_2 - v_1) \\ &= \bar{c}_{\text{v}_{12}}(t_2 - t_1) + R(T_2 - T_1) \\ &= \bar{c}_{\text{p}_{12}}(t_2 - t_1) \qquad \ldots (14.39) \end{aligned}$$

Tabulation of the properties of gases obeying the Ideal Gas Rule. The variations of u and h for gases have to be established experimentally just as for less regular fluids. The results are contained in tables. However, since temperature is the only dependent variable, the information about a single substance can be tabulated in much less space. A widely used source of data is Keenan and Kaye's *Gas Tables*, an extract from which is printed in Table 14.6 above.

c_{v} can be derived from these data, via eq. (14.22), by subtracting R in the appropriate units. For air this is $53\cdot3/778 = 0\cdot0685$ Btu/lb$_m$°F abs.

An important deduction from Table 14.6 is that at moderate temperatures c_p for air is fairly constant at about 0·240 Btu/lb$_m$°F; correspondingly c_v for air is fairly constant at 0·240 − 0·0685 = 0·171 Btu/lb$_m$°F. This means that the slopes of the h–t and u–t curves are nearly constant. In this range it is usually sufficiently accurate to assume that the h–t and u–t curves are straight lines and to replace $\bar{c}_p$ by c_p and $\bar{c}_v$ by c_v. This greatly facilitates calculation.

THE PERFECT GAS

For a Semi-Perfect Gas it has been shown that $pv = RT$ and that c_p and c_v depend upon its temperature only. The characteristics of real gases are represented adequately by these relationships over a *wide range* of conditions.

The near-constancy of the specific heats of real gases over practically important temperature ranges makes it desirable to define a second Ideal Gas, the *Perfect Gas*, to include this characteristic also. The characteristics of a Perfect Gas will represent those of real gas over a *restricted range* of conditions.

Definition of a Perfect Gas. A Perfect Gas obeys exactly the equations:

(1) $$pv = RT \qquad \qquad \ldots \quad (14.10)$$

(2) $$c_p = \text{constant} \qquad \qquad \ldots \quad (14.40)$$

Here part (1), the Ideal Gas Rule, is a consequence of the definition of a Semi-Perfect Gas adopted earlier, (eq. (14.5) and eq. (14.6)), as has been proved. Specification of c_p in part (2) of the definition is arbitrary; we could equally well have stated $c_v = \text{constant}$, because of the relation (14.22).

The second part of the definition makes it possible to derive explicit algebraic expressions for the properties of a Perfect Gas, and for the heat and work quantities in various technically important processes. The remainder of the Chapter will be devoted to their derivation.

The properties of a Perfect Gas

The *internal energy* and *enthalpy* are obtained explicitly by integrating eq. (14.19) and eq. (14.20). Using the absolute temperatures, we obtain

$$u - u_0 = c_v(T - T_0) \qquad \ldots \quad (14.41)$$

$$h - h_0 = c_p(T - T_0) \qquad \ldots \quad (14.42)$$

where u_0 and h_0 are the values at some base temperature T_0. It should be noted that if u_0 is arbitrarily made equal to zero, as is permissible, then h_0 will *not* be zero, but will equal RT_0 from the definition of h, eq. (14.21).

The *entropy of a Perfect Gas* is obtained by integrating one or other of the T ds relations. Taking eq. (13.42) as our starting point, namely

$$T \, ds = du + p \, dv$$

we have

$$ds = c_v \frac{dT}{T} + \frac{p}{T}\, dv$$

$$= c_v \frac{dT}{T} + \frac{R\, dv}{v}$$

Since for the Perfect Gas c_v is constant, we have on integration*

$$s_2 - s_1 = c_v \ln\left(\frac{T_2}{T_1}\right) + R \ln\left(\frac{v_2}{v_1}\right) \qquad \dots \quad (14.43)$$

By substitution from the Ideal Gas Rule eq. (14.10), this may be written in two other ways, namely

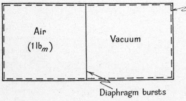

$$s_2 - s_1 = c_p \ln\left(\frac{T_2}{T_1}\right) - R \ln\left(\frac{p_2}{p_1}\right)$$
$$\dots \quad (14.44)$$

and

$$s_2 - s_1 = c_p \ln\left(\frac{v_2}{v_1}\right) + c_v \ln\left(\frac{p_2}{p_1}\right)$$

Fig 14.7 Unresisted expansion of air.
$$\dots \quad (14.45)$$

Since these three relations are readily derived, it is not recommended that they should be remembered. Which one should be used in practice depends on the problem. If temperatures and volumes are known, as in the following example, eq. (14.43) is preferable.

It may be remarked in passing that equations (14.43) to (14.45) are particular analytical instances of the fact that entropy is a property, i.e. that its value is specified, apart from a constant, when the values of two independent properties are fixed.

EXAMPLE

Problem. 1 lb$_m$ of air at 100 psia and 500°F abs expands into an evacuated insulated container so that its volume doubles (Fig. 14.7). What is the increase of entropy of the air?

Solution. A convenient system for the analysis of this problem is that enclosed by the boundary S, Fig. 14.7. For this system the work and the heat are each zero and so, by the First Law, eq. (7.5), the internal energy remains constant. Therefore, assuming the air to be a Perfect Gas, no temperature change occurs. Substituting in eq. (14.43) we have

$$s_2 - s_1 = c_v \ln\left(\frac{500}{500}\right) + R \ln\left(\frac{2}{1}\right)$$
$$= 0{\cdot}0685 \ln 2$$
$$= 0{\cdot}0475 \text{ Btu/lb}_m\text{°F abs.} \qquad \dots \quad Answer$$

Comments. 1. The pressure and temperature (apart from the latter's constancy) were immaterial to the problem.

2. We note that the entropy *increases*, as was in fact to be expected of this isolated irreversible process (see p. 225).

* Note that to integrate the equation for a Semi-Perfect Gas we would need to know how c_v varies with temperature T.

PROCESSES EXECUTED BY PERFECT GASES

In the final section of this chapter, formulae are derived which replace for Perfect Gases the references to property tables which were necessary in applications of the First and Second Laws made in earlier Chapters. None of the formulae, except perhaps that involving pv^γ, are worth remembering, and blind application of the formulae should not be employed as a substitute for the analysis of a problem in terms of system and control-volume boundaries, the interactions across them, and their relations through the First and Second Laws. In all cases it is necessary to understand the restrictions on the validity of the formulae. All of them are subject to the restriction that the gas obeys *both* parts of the Perfect Gas Definition.

The reversible adiabatic process (isentropic): $p-v-T$ relations

The importance of the reversible adiabatic process was stressed earlier (p. 222). For steam, calculation of the state at the end of an expansion starting from a given state was made via the Steam Tables. We now discuss the counterpart of this calculation for a Perfect Gas.

For a reversible adiabatic process, s does not change, so the right-hand side of, for example, eq. (14.43) can be put equal to zero:

$$c_v \ln \left(\frac{T_2}{T_1}\right) + R \ln \left(\frac{v_2}{v_1}\right) = 0$$

which may be re-written as

$$\frac{T_2}{T_1} \left(\frac{v_2}{v_1}\right)^{R/c_v} = 1 \qquad \ldots \quad (14.46)$$

Use of eq. (14.44) or eq. (14.45) leads similarly to

$$\frac{T_2}{T_1} \left(\frac{p_2}{p_1}\right)^{-R/c_p} = 1 \qquad \ldots \quad (14.47)$$

and

$$\frac{p_2}{p_1} \left(\frac{v_2}{v_1}\right)^{c_p/c_v} = 1 \qquad \ldots \quad (14.48)$$

These equations may be written in terms of the specific heat ratio, γ, by using the following γ-R relations developed for a Semi-Perfect Gas (p. 254),

$$\gamma = \frac{c_p}{c_v} \qquad \ldots \quad (14.26)$$

$$\frac{R}{c_v} = \gamma - 1 \qquad \ldots \quad (14.27)$$

$$\frac{R}{c_p} = \frac{\gamma - 1}{\gamma} \qquad \ldots \quad (14.28)$$

Equations (14.26), (14.27) and (14.28) are valid for the Perfect Gas, since it is merely a particular sort of Semi-Perfect Gas. Their special feature with regard to the Perfect Gas is that γ is constant and therefore independent of temperature; this follows from part (2) of the definition of a Perfect Gas. This is in contrast to the Semi-Perfect Gas for which γ depends upon temperature (p. 254).

Equations (14.46), (14.47) and (14.48) become respectively

$$\left(\frac{T_2}{T_1}\right) = \left(\frac{v_1}{v_2}\right)^{\gamma-1} \qquad \ldots \quad (14.49)$$

$$\left(\frac{T_2}{T_1}\right) = \left(\frac{p_2}{p_1}\right)^{(\gamma-1)/\gamma} \qquad \ldots \quad (14.50)$$

$$p_2 v_2^{\gamma} = p_1 v_1^{\gamma} \qquad \ldots \quad (14.51)$$

It should be noted that eq. (14.49), eq. (14.50) and eq. (14.51) are *not applicable* to Semi-Perfect Gases. It is not permissible to use in them a mean value of γ defined as the ratio of the mean specific heats, viz. $\bar{\gamma}_{12} \neq \bar{c}_{p_{12}}/\bar{c}_{v_{12}}$. γ has no significance for a change of state; γ has meaning at a *particular state* only.

Eq. (14.51) is most usually quoted, because it gives the equation for the curve of the expansion on the p-v diagram.

Since γ is greater than unity, reversible adiabatic processes are represented by curves on the p-v diagram which are steeper than the isotherms (pv = constant). Fig. 14.8 illustrates this. A consequence is that the gas temperature *falls* in a reversible adiabatic *expansion*, and *rises* in a reversible adiabatic *compression*.

Calculation of work done in adiabatic processes of a Perfect Gas

The First Law applied to a system comprising a pure substance in the absence of gravity, motion, etc., eq. (7.5), states

$$Q = (u_2 - u_1) + W$$

If the pure substance is a Perfect Gas and the process is adiabatic ($Q = 0$), we have

$$W = u_1 - u_2$$
$$= c_v(T_1 - T_2)$$
$$= \frac{p_1 v_1 - p_2 v_2}{\gamma - 1} \qquad \ldots \quad (14.52)$$

The most useful form of this relation, as of all those which follow, is that most nearly fitting the data of the problem.

Here W represents all the work done by the system in changing from state 1 to state 2. In *steady-flow* problems this comprises flow work and external work. Usually we are only interested in the latter, W_x. For a Perfect Gas in adiabatic steady flow, the S.F.E.E. eq. (8.22) becomes

$$W_x + \Delta\left(\frac{V^2}{2g_0} + \frac{gz}{g_0}\right) = h_1 - h_2$$
$$= c_p(T_1 - T_2)$$
$$= \frac{\gamma}{\gamma - 1}(p_1 v_1 - p_2 v_2) \qquad \ldots \quad (14.53)$$

Eq. (14.52) and eq. (14.53) hold whether the process is reversible or irreversible. To evaluate the formulae, two pieces of information must be specified for both final and initial states. If however we are told that the process is reversible, one piece of information may be omitted: for example, it suffices to know the initial state and the final pressure.

Reversible adiabatic processes. If reversibility is specified, the initial and final states are connected by the p–v–T relations, equations (14.49), (14.50) and (14.51). The appropriate ones may be substituted into eq. (14.52) and eq. (14.53) giving, among other possible expressions

$$W = \frac{p_1 v_1}{\gamma - 1}\left[1 - \left(\frac{p_2}{p_1}\right)^{(\gamma-1)/\gamma}\right]$$

$$= \frac{p_1 v_1}{\gamma - 1}\left[1 - \left(\frac{v_1}{v_2}\right)^{\gamma-1}\right] \qquad \ldots \quad (14.54)$$

and

$$W_x + \Delta\left(\frac{V^2}{2g_0} + \frac{gz}{g_0}\right) = \frac{\gamma}{\gamma - 1} p_1 v_1\left[1 - \left(\frac{p_2}{p_1}\right)^{(\gamma-1)/\gamma}\right]$$

$$= \frac{\gamma}{\gamma - 1} p_1 v_1\left[1 - \left(\frac{v_1}{v_2}\right)^{\gamma-1}\right] \qquad \ldots \quad (14.55)$$

These relations can be derived in an *alternative way*, by evaluation of the $p\,dv$ or $v\,dp$ integrals. For a reversible process we have

$$W = \int_1^2 p\,dv \qquad \ldots \quad (14.56)$$

Inserting p from eq. (14.51) this becomes

$$W = p_1 v_1{}^\gamma \int_1^2 \frac{dv}{v}$$

$$= \frac{p_1 v_1{}^\gamma}{1 - \gamma}\left[\frac{1}{v_2^{1-\gamma}} - \frac{1}{v_1^{1-\gamma}}\right]$$

$$= \frac{p_1 v_1}{\gamma - 1}\left[1 - \left(\frac{v_1}{v_2}\right)^{\gamma-1}\right] \qquad \ldots \quad (14.54)$$

as before.

For reversible steady-flow processes in general, we have from eq. (13.47)

$$W_x + \Delta\left[\frac{V^2}{2g_0} + \frac{gz}{g_0}\right] = -\int_1^2 v\,dp \qquad \ldots \quad (14.57)$$

Inserting v, from eq. (14.51) this becomes

$$W_x + \Delta\left[\frac{V^2}{2g_0} + \frac{gz}{g_0}\right] = -v_1 p_1^{1/\gamma}\int_1^2 \frac{dp}{p^{1/\gamma}}$$

$$= -\frac{v_1 p_1^{1/\gamma}}{1 - \gamma}\left[p_2^{1-(1/\gamma)} - p_1^{1-(1/\gamma)}\right]$$

$$= \frac{\gamma}{\gamma - 1} p_1 v_1\left[1 - \left(\frac{p_2}{p_1}\right)^{(\gamma-1)/\gamma}\right] \qquad \ldots \quad (14.55)$$

as before.

"Polytropic" process of a Perfect Gas: $p-v-T$ relations

The formulae for adiabatic and reversible adiabatic processes are of such convenience in engineering calculations, that we attempt to extend them to processes that are not adiabatic, and consider the family of processes that have the pressure-volume relation.

$$pv^n = \text{constant} \qquad \ldots \quad (14.58)$$

when n is any number.

These processes are termed *"polytropic"*. They are important because the pressure-volume relations of a number of technically important processes can be *approximately* represented by eq. (14.58). That is to say

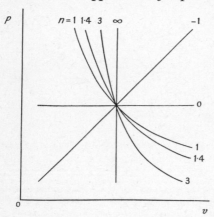

that it is possible to find a value of n which more or less fits the experimental results. It must be clearly understood however that whereas γ is a property of the gas, n is not: it depends upon the process. Fig. 14.8 illustrates the curves given by different values of n. Values close to unity are usually encountered. Of course not all practically-encountered curves belong to this family: examples of some that do not are given at the end of this section.

Fig. 14.8   Polytropic paths.

Relations connecting initial and final states in a polytropic process. To underline its similarity with eq. (14.51), eq. (14.58) will be written as

$$p_2 v_2{}^n = p_1 v_1{}^n \qquad \ldots \quad (14.59)$$

By substitution from the Ideal Gas Rule, two further relations can be derived, corresponding respectively to eq. (14.49) and eq. (14.50). They are

$$\frac{T_2}{T_1} = \left(\frac{v_1}{v_2}\right)^{n-1} \qquad \ldots \quad (14.60)$$

$$\frac{T_2}{T_1} = \left(\frac{p_2}{p_1}\right)^{(n-1)/n} \qquad \ldots \quad (14.61)$$

These relations may be used to relate the initial and final states of a polytropic process. If the process is *reversible*, eq. (14.59) can be used for evaluating work from $\int p \, dv$, or external work from $-\int v \, dp$.

Entropy change in a polytropic process. In contrast to the reversible adiabatic ($pv^\gamma = \text{constant}$) process for which the entropy is constant, the entropy of a Perfect Gas usually changes in a polytropic process. We now calculate the entropy change, making use of the general relations for the entropy of a Perfect Gas, equations (14.43), (14.44), (14.45), and of the polytropic p–v–T relations just derived. Substituting eq. (14.60) in eq. (14.43) for example, we obtain

$$s_2 - s_1 = c_{\mathrm{v}} \ln \left(\frac{T_2}{T_1} \right) + \frac{R}{n - 1} \ln \left(\frac{T_1}{T_2} \right)$$

$$= \left(\frac{1}{\gamma - 1} - \frac{1}{n - 1} \right) R \ln \left(\frac{T_2}{T_1} \right)$$

$$= \frac{(n - \gamma)}{(\gamma - 1)(n - 1)} R \ln \left(\frac{T_2}{T_1} \right) \qquad \ldots \ (14.62)$$

Relations in terms of pressure and specific volume may also be derived, namely

$$s_2 - s_1 = \frac{(n - \gamma)}{n(\gamma - 1)} R \ln \left(\frac{p_2}{p_1} \right) \qquad \ldots \ (14.63)$$

and

$$s_2 - s_1 = - \frac{(n - \gamma)}{\gamma - 1} R \ln \left(\frac{v_2}{v_1} \right) \qquad \ldots \ (14.64)$$

Examination of each of these expressions shows that the entropy change is zero when $n = \gamma$; this is in accordance with expectations.

It should be understood that, in a polytropic process, an entropy increase is not necessarily a sign that the process is irreversible, for the increase may have resulted from reversible heat exchange with the surroundings. Entropy decreases are possible if the gas is cooled.

Heat and work in polytropic processes. Application of the First Law to a system containing unit mass of a Perfect Gas in the absence of gravity, motion, etc., leads to

$$Q - W = u_2 - u_1$$

$$= c_{\mathrm{v}}(T_2 - T_1)$$

$$= \frac{p_2 v_2 - p_1 v_1}{\gamma - 1} \qquad \ldots \ (14.65)$$

If in addition the process is polytropic, we can derive further relations. For example substituting from eq. (14.59) in eq. (14.65) we obtain

$$u_2 - u_1 = Q - W = \frac{p_1 v_1}{\gamma - 1} \left[\left(\frac{p_2}{p_1} \right)^{(n-1)/n} - 1 \right]$$

$$= \frac{p_1 v_1}{\gamma - 1} \left[\left(\frac{v_1}{v_2} \right)^{n-1} - 1 \right] \qquad \ldots \ (14.66)$$

Application of the S.F.E.E. eq. (8.22) to the steady flow of unit mass of a Perfect Gas leads to

$$Q - W_{\mathrm{x}} - \Delta \left[\frac{V^2}{2g_0} + \frac{gz}{g_0} \right] = h_2 - h_1$$

$$= c_{\mathrm{p}}(T_2 - T_1)$$

$$= \frac{\gamma}{\gamma - 1} (p_2 v_2 - p_1 v_1) \quad \ldots \ (14.67)$$

If, in addition, the process is polytropic, further relations can be derived, namely

$$Q - W_x - \Delta\left[\frac{V^2}{2g_0} + \frac{gz}{g_0}\right] = \frac{\gamma}{\gamma - 1} p_1 v_1 \left[\left(\frac{p_2}{p_1}\right)^{(n-1)/n} - 1\right]$$

$$= \frac{\gamma}{\gamma - 1} p_1 v_1 \left[\left(\frac{v_1}{v_2}\right)^{n-1} - 1\right] \quad \dots \quad (14.68)$$

These equations do not permit the separate determination of the heat and work quantities. For that to be possible, either one of them must be given, or a statement about the reversibility must be made.

Still without restricting ourselves to reversible processes, the integrals of $p\,dv$, $-v\,dp$ and $T\,ds$ will now be evaluated. The resulting relations are general for polytropic processes because they relate to properties.

Integral property relations in polytropic processes. By a similar integration procedure to that applied to eq. (14.56), we find that in a $pv^n = $ constant process

$$\int_1^2 p\,dv = \frac{p_1 v_1}{n - 1}\left[1 - \left(\frac{v_1}{v_2}\right)^{n-1}\right]$$

$$= \frac{p_1 v_1}{n - 1}\left[1 - \left(\frac{p_2}{p_1}\right)^{(n-1)/n}\right] \quad \dots \quad (14.69)$$

Likewise we derive

$$-\int_1^2 v\,dp = \frac{n}{n - 1} p_1 v_1 \left[1 - \left(\frac{v_1}{v_2}\right)^{n-1}\right]$$

$$= \frac{n}{n - 1} p_1 v_1 \left[1 - \left(\frac{p_2}{p_1}\right)^{(n-1)/n}\right] \quad \dots \quad (14.70)$$

The integral of $T\,ds$ is obtained from eq. (13.42) namely

$$T\,ds = du + p\,dv$$

The integral of the first term of its right-hand side has already been evaluated in eq. (14.69); the integral of the second term is given in eq. (14.69). Combining these we are led to

$$\int_1^2 T\,ds = \frac{(\gamma - n)}{(\gamma - 1)(n - 1)} p_1 v_1 \left[1 - \left(\frac{p_2}{p_1}\right)^{(n-1)/n}\right]$$

$$= \frac{(\gamma - n)}{(\gamma - 1)(n - 1)} p_1 v_1 \left[1 - \left(\frac{v_1}{v_2}\right)^{n-1}\right]$$

$$= \frac{(\gamma - n)}{(\gamma - 1)(n - 1)} R(T_1 - T_2) \quad \dots \quad (14.71)$$

The special case of $n = 1$. Each of the integral property relations becomes indeterminate when $n = 1$. This case is that of an isothermal change of the Perfect Gas; it may be reversible or irreversible. The following relations are then valid:—

$$\int_1^2 p \, dv = p_1 v_1 \int_1^2 \frac{dv}{v}$$

$$= p_1 v_1 \ln \left(\frac{v_2}{v_1}\right)$$

$$= p_1 v_1 \ln \left(\frac{p_1}{p_2}\right) \qquad \dots \quad (14.72)$$

$$-\int_1^2 v \, dp = -p_1 v_1 \int_1^2 \frac{dp}{p}$$

$$= p_1 v_1 \ln \left(\frac{p_1}{p_2}\right)$$

$$= \int_1^2 p \, dv \qquad \dots \quad (14.73)$$

$$\int_1^2 T \, ds = u_2 - u_1 + \int_1^2 p \, dv$$

$$= \int_1^2 p \, dv \qquad \dots \quad (14.74)$$

since there is no change in temperature or internal energy. The relations can therefore be summarised by

$$\int_1^2 T \, ds = -\int_1^2 v \, dp = \int_1^2 p \, dv$$

$$= p_1 v_1 \ln \left(\frac{v_2}{v_1}\right)$$

$$= p_1 v_1 \ln \left(\frac{p_1}{p_2}\right) \qquad \dots \quad (14.74)$$

Reversible polytropic processes of a Perfect Gas. The integral property relations have been derived because of their importance when the process is *reversible*. For this case only we can write, *in general*

$$\int_1^2 p \, dv = W, \text{ in the absence of gravity, motion, etc.} \quad \dots \quad (14.75)$$

$$-\int_1^2 v \, dp = W_x + \Delta \left(\frac{V^2}{2g_0} + \frac{gz}{g_0}\right) \text{ in steady flow} \qquad \dots \quad (14.76)$$

$$\int_1^2 T \, ds = Q_R \qquad \dots \quad (14.78)$$

18

When the process is *polytropic* for a Perfect Gas, these quantities can then be evaluated from the relations just derived, namely equations (14.69) to (14.74).

EXAMPLES

This Chapter will be concluded by two examples of calculations with Perfect Gases, which illustrate the pitfalls, firstly of unthinking application of formulae, and secondly of the lack of general application of the polytropic formulae.

EXAMPLE 1

Problem. Measurements of pressure and temperature at various stages in an *adiabatic* air turbine show that the air states lie on the line

$$pv^{1.25} = \text{constant}$$

Derive a formula for the shaft work per lb_m as a function of pressure, neglecting kinetic and gravitational potential energy. γ for air $= 1.4$.

Wrong solution.

$$W_x = -\int_1^2 v \, dp \text{ and so from eq. (14.70)}$$

$$W_x = \frac{n}{n-1} p_1 v_1 \left[1 - \left(\frac{p_2}{p_1}\right)^{(n-1)/n} \right]$$

$$= 5.0 p_1 v_1 \left[1 - \left(\frac{p_2}{p_1}\right)^{1/5} \right]$$

Correct solution.

$Q = 0$ and so from eq. (14.68)

$$W_x = \frac{\gamma}{\gamma-1} p_1 v_1 \left[1 - \left(\frac{p_2}{p_1}\right)^{(n-1)/n} \right]$$

$$= 3.5 p_1 v_1 \left[1 - \left(\frac{p_2}{p_1}\right)^{1/} \right] \qquad \ldots \text{ Answer}$$

Comment. The discrepancy is a big one. The fault in the wrong solution lay in the first step. The process is not reversible, so $W_x < -\int_1^2 v \, dp$. Substitution in eq. (14.63) shows that there is an increase of entropy when p_2 is less than p_1, even though the process is adiabatic: this is an infallible sign of irreversibility.

EXAMPLE 2

Problem. Air at 1 atm pressure and 800°F abs is enclosed in a 60 inch long vertical tube. The upper end is closed and the lower end just rests in a tank of mercury (Fig. 14.9). As the air cools, (*a*) what is the *p-v* relation of the air? (*b*) How high does the mercury rise if the air cools to 500°F abs? (*c*) How much work will the air do per lb$_m$ if the mercury rises 15 inches?

Solution (*a*).

From hydrostatics:
$$p = 1 - \frac{z}{30}$$

where *p* is the air pressure in atm, *z* is the height of the mercury in the tube in inches, and 30 inches of mercury corresponds to 1 atm.

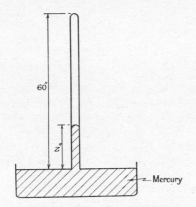

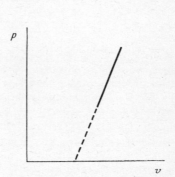

Fig. 14.9   Diagram used in the solution of Example 2.

Fig. 14.10   Pressure-volume diagram for process in Example 2.

From geometry
$$\frac{v}{v_1} = \frac{60 - z}{60}$$

when v_1 is the initial specific volume of the air.
Eliminating *z*,
$$p = \frac{2v}{v_1} - 1 \qquad \qquad \ldots \quad Answer\ (a)$$

Comment. This relation does not fit into the polytropic family. It is sketched in Fig. 14.10.

Solution (*b*).

From the Ideal Gas Rule:
$$\frac{(pv)_{500}}{(pv)_{800}} = \frac{500}{800}$$

Hence
$$\left(1 - \frac{z_{500}}{30}\right)\left(1 - \frac{z_{500}}{60}\right) = \frac{500}{800}$$

The physically meaningful solution of this quadratic equation is
$$z_{500} = 8 \cdot 25 \text{ inches} \qquad \qquad \ldots \quad Answer\ (b)$$

Solution (c). Only displacement work is done, and the process is reversible, so

$$W = \int_1^2 p \, dv = \int_0^{15} 14 \cdot 7 \times 144 \left(1 - \frac{z}{30}\right) \left(-\frac{v_1}{60} \, dz\right)$$

$$= -14 \cdot 7 \times 144 \times \frac{v_1}{60} \left[z - \frac{z^2}{60}\right]_0^{15}$$

$$= -\frac{RT_1}{60} \left[15 - \frac{(15)^2}{60}\right]$$

$$= -\frac{RT_1}{4} \times \frac{3}{4}$$

$$= -\frac{53 \cdot 3 \times 800 \times 3}{16}$$

$$= -8000 \text{ ft lb}_f/\text{lb}_m \qquad \qquad \dots \text{ Answer (c)}$$

Comment. The polytropic relations were not useful here, and we had to return to fundamentals. Since this situation arises frequently in engineering problems, the fundamental relations are the only ones which are worth remembering.

BIBLIOGRAPHY

Keenan, J. H. and Kaye, J. *Gas Tables.* J. Wiley and Sons: Chapman & Hall, 1948.

Keenan, J. H. *Thermodynamics.* J. Wiley and Sons: Chapman & Hall, 1941.

CHAPTER 14—PROBLEMS

14.1 Examine the conditions under which (a) Boyle's Law and (b) the Ideal Gas Rule may be applied to superheated steam by evaluating pv and pv/T from Table IV of the Steam Tables (Appendix B) for the following conditions:
   (i) Temperature, 300°F; pressures, 1 psia, 14·7 psia and 60 psia.
   (ii) Temperature, 700°F; pressures, 1 psia, 14·7 psia, 60 psia, 800 psia and 3000 psia.
   (iii) Temperature, 1600°F; pressures, 1 psia, 14·7 psia, 60 psia, 800 psia and 3000 psia.

14.2 Two rigid vessels, connected by a valve, are immersed in a constant-temperature bath. Initially one vessel is evacuated and the other contains steam. The valve is opened; after a time, conditions become uniform throughout the two vessels. Calculate the changes in the internal energy of the steam for the following cases:
   (i) Far from the critical point.
   Initially: steam temperature = 1600°F, pressure = 20 psia.
   Finally: steam pressure = 10 psia.
   (ii) Near the critical point.
   Initially: steam temperature = 700°F, pressure = 1200 psia.
   Finally: steam pressure = 600 psia.

14.3 Steam is expanded in adiabatic steady flow through a porous plug, the final pressure being one-half of the initial pressure. Assuming that changes in kinetic energy and in elevation are negligible, estimate the changes in the temperature of the steam for the following initial conditions:
   (i) Far from the critical point: temperature = 1600°F, pressure = 20 psia.
   (ii) Near the critical point: temperature = 700°F, pressure = 1200 psia.

14.4 Taking the value of the Universal Gas Constant $\mathscr{R}$ as 1·986 Btu/lb mole °F abs and using the values of molecular weight given in Table 14.3 (p. 249), confirm that the values of the Gas Constant R for each gas given in Table 14.1 are correct.

14.5 Each of the cylinders of a marine diesel engine has a bore of 16 in. and a clearance volume (see page 42) of 425 in³. The piston stroke is 20.8 in.

At the end of the suction stroke (i.e. with the piston in its outermost position) the pressure and temperature of the gas in the cylinder are 14 psia and 100°F respectively. On the assumption that the gas obeys the Ideal Gas Rule and that for this gas $R = 53$ ft lb$_f$/lb$_m$ °F abs, calculate the mass and the number of pound moles of the gas contained in the cylinder at the end of the suction stroke.

14.6 A boiler drum of volume 68 ft³ contains steam at a temperature of 400°F and a pressure of 20 psia. Calculate the mass of steam contained in the drum,

    (i) assuming steam to obey the Ideal Gas Rule. Use the value of R given in Table 14.1;

    (ii) using the Steam Tables (Appendix B).

Which value is correct? and why?

14.7 (a) 1·5 lb moles of an Ideal Gas of molecular weight 25 are contained in a rigid vessel of volume 60 ft³ at a temperature of 200°F. Evaluate the mass, the pressure, the specific volume and the Gas Constant of the gas.

    (b) For this condition the gas has a value of $\gamma = 1·38$. Evaluate the corresponding values of c_p and c_v.

    (c) Subsequently the gas cools to atmospheric temperature, 60°F. Evaluate the final pressure of the gas.

    (d) Assuming the gas to be perfect, evaluate the increase in internal energy, the increase in enthalpy and the magnitude and sign of the heat transfer.

14.8 Using the definition of a Perfect Gas (page 257), sketch the following property charts for such a gas.

$$\text{(i) } p, t; \text{ (ii) } h, p; \text{ (iii) } p, v; \text{ (iv) } u, v.$$

Show a few lines of constant volume in (i), and a few lines of constant temperature in (ii), (iii) and (iv).

14.9 One pound of nitrogen at a temperature of 300°F occupies a volume of 4 ft³. The nitrogen undergoes a fully resisted constant-pressure expansion, without friction, to a final volume of 7 ft³. Evaluate the final pressure, the final temperature, the work done and the heat transfer.

Assume nitrogen to be a Perfect Gas for which $c_v = 0·177$ Btu/lb$_m$ °F and $R = 55·2$ ft lb$_f$/lb$_m$ °F abs.

14.10 In a chemical plant carbon monoxide flows steadily into a turbine at a pressure of 120 psia and a temperature of 340°F; there it expands reversibly and adiabatically to a final pressure of 15 psia. Changes in velocity and elevation are negligible.

    (i) Calculate the final specific volume, the final temperature and the increase in entropy. (ii) Given that the mass flow rate is 10 lb$_m$/s, evaluate the heat transfer rate from the gas and the power delivered by the turbine.

Assume carbon monoxide to be a Perfect Gas for which $M = 28·01$, $c_v = 5447$ ft lb$_f$/lb mole °F. Take $\mathscr{R} = 1·986$ Btu/lb mole °F abs.

14.11 12 ft³ of oxygen initially at a temperature of 420°F and a pressure of 60 psia are compressed reversibly and isothermally to a final volume of 2 ft³.

Calculate the mass, the final pressure, the increase in the internal energy, the work done, the heat transfer and the change in entropy.

Assume oxygen to be a Perfect Gas for which $R = 48 \cdot 2$ ft $\mathrm{lb}_f/\mathrm{lb}_m$ °F abs.

14.12 (a) One pound of air at a pressure of 100 psia and a temperature of 200°F undergoes a reversible polytropic process which may be represented by $pv^{1 \cdot 1} = $ constant. The final pressure is 20 psia.

(i) Evaluate the final specific volume, the final temperature and the increase in entropy.

(ii) Evaluate the work done and the heat transfer.

Assume air to be a Perfect Gas for which $R = 53 \cdot 3$ ft $\mathrm{lb}_f/\mathrm{lb}_m$ °F abs and $\gamma = 1 \cdot 4$.

(b) Repeat (a) assuming the process to be irreversible and adiabatic.

14.13 The indicator diagram of a reciprocating air-compressor shows that during the compression stroke the volume of air in the cylinder is $0 \cdot 028$ ft³ when the pressure is 20 psig. Correspondingly when the pressure is 90 psig the volume is $0 \cdot 011$ ft³. The mass of air contained in the cylinder at both points is $4 \cdot 7 \times 10^{-3}$ lb_m. The barometric pressure is $30 \cdot 55$ in. Hg.

(i) Calculate the temperature of the air at each point.

(ii) On the assumption that the compression process may be represented by $pV^n = $ constant, where n is a constant, evaluate n.

(iii) Assuming the process to be reversible and polytropic, evaluate the magnitude and sign of the work and of the heat transfer.

Assume air to be a Perfect Gas for which $R = 53 \cdot 3$ ft $\mathrm{lb}_f/\mathrm{lb}_m$ °F abs and $c_p = 0 \cdot 24$ Btu/lb_m °F.

14.14 (a) Air flows steadily into a compressor at a temperature of 62°F and a pressure of 15 psia and leaves at a temperature of 476°F and a pressure of 90 psia. There is no heat transfer to or from the air as it flows through the compressor; changes in velocity and elevation are negligible. Evaluate the external work done per pound of air, assuming air to be a Perfect Gas for which $R = 53 \cdot 3$ ft $\mathrm{lb}_f/\mathrm{lb}_m$ °F abs and $\gamma = 1 \cdot 4$.

(b) Evaluate the minimum external work required to compress the air adiabatically from the same initial state to the same final pressure.

(c) Evaluate the isentropic efficiency of the compressor (see page 224).

14.15 Helium at a pressure of 12 psia and a temperature of 140°F flows steadily into a rotary compressor and leaves at a pressure of 28 psia. Changes in velocity and elevation are negligible; the compression process may be assumed to be adiabatic.

Given that the isentropic efficiency of the compressor is 73 per cent, calculate:

(a) the temperature of the helium leaving the compressor;

(b) the power required to compress 10 lb_m of helium per minute.

Assume helium to be a Perfect Gas for which $c_p = 1 \cdot 25$ Btu/lb_m °F and $M = 4$. Take $\mathscr{R} = 1 \cdot 986$ Btu/lb mole°F abs.

14.16 (a) A gas turbine develops a power of 8500 horse-power when the gas mass flow rate is 50 lb_m/s. The gas flows steadily into the nozzles of the turbine at a pressure of 60 psia and a velocity of 500 ft/s. The gas leaves the turbine at a pressure of $15 \cdot 5$ psia, a temperature of 900°F and a velocity of 900 ft/s. The expansion process may be assumed to be adiabatic.

Assume the gas to be Perfect and take $c_p = 0 \cdot 276$ Btu/lb_m °F and $R = 53 \cdot 3$ ft $\mathrm{lb}_f/\mathrm{lb}_m$ °F abs.

Calculate: (i) the temperature of the gas entering the turbine;

(ii) the flow area at entry to the turbine nozzles.

(b) The gas leaving the turbine flows into a cooler; at exit from the cooler the gas pressure is 15 psia, its temperature is 150°F and its velocity is 200 ft/s. Determine the heat transfer from the gas in the cooler.

14.17 (*a*) A cylinder, fitted with a piston, contains 0·7 ft^3 of methane (CH$_4$) at a pressure of 70 psia and a temperature of 240°F. The methane undergoes a process to a pressure of 14 psia during which it does 7400 ft lb$_f$ of work and receives 1 Btu of heat. Determine the final temperature of the methane and the increase in entropy.

(*b*) If the process between the same initial state and the same final pressure had been reversible and adiabatic, what would have been the final temperature and the work done?

(*c*) If the process between the same initial state and the same final pressure had been such that the final and initial entropies were equal, and if the heat transfer during this process had been −1·5 Btu, what would have been the final temperature and the work done?

Assume methane to be a Perfect Gas for which $c_p = 0\cdot53$ Btu/lb$_m$°F. Take $\mathscr{R} = 1\cdot986$ Btu/lb mole °F abs.

14.18 A rigid vessel of volume 10·5 ft^3 contains air at a pressure of 5 psia and a temperature of 60°F. Atmospheric air at a pressure of 15 psia and a temperature of 60°F leaks slowly into the vessel. When the pressure of the air in the vessel has risen to 10 psia the leak is stopped; it is then found that the temperature of the air in the vessel is 120°F.

Calculate: (i) the mass of air which has leaked in;

(ii) the magnitude and sign of the heat transfer through the vessel walls;

(iii) the pressure in the vessel when its contents have cooled to atmospheric temperature.

Assume air to be a Perfect Gas for which $\gamma = 1\cdot4$ and $R = 53\cdot3$ ft lb$_f$/lb$_m$ °F abs.

14.19 A well-insulated, rigid vessel contains 0·6 lb$_m$ of a Perfect Gas ($M = 20$, $c_p = 0\cdot4$ Btu/lb$_m$ °F) at a pressure of 15 psia and a temperature of 70°F. A coiled tube within the vessel is connected to a reservoir containing dry and saturated steam at a pressure of 15 psia. The steam condenses in the coil at the bottom of which it collects as saturated water at a pressure of 15 psia.

(i) Calculate the maximum pressure reached by the gas.

(ii) Calculate the quantity of steam condensed in the coil to achieve this maximum pressure.

14.20 The compression ratio r of a reciprocating internal-combustion engine is defined by the relation $r = (V_c + V_{sw})/V_c$ where V_c is the cylinder clearance volume and V_{sw} the cylinder swept volume ('the cylinder capacity'). One limitation to the value of r which may be used in a petrol engine (to avoid 'pre-ignition') is the temperature at which a petrol-air mixture is supposed to ignite spontaneously. For a typical motor fuel this temperature may be taken as 850°F.

In a particular engine the pressure and temperature of the mixture at the beginning of the compression stroke (outer dead-centre) are 14 psia and 210°F respectively and the compression process may be represented by $pV^{1\cdot34} = $ constant.

(i) Determine the maximum value of r which may be used if the above limitation is not to be exceeded.

(ii) Given that the bore and stroke of the engine are 2·6 in. and 3·7 in. and assuming the process to be fully resisted, evaluate the work done and the heat transfer during the compression process. Assume the petrol-air mixture to be a Perfect Gas with $c_p = 0\cdot24$ Btu/lb$_m$ °F and $R = 46\cdot7$ ft lb$_f$/lb$_m$ °F abs.

14.21 A nozzle is supplied with a steady stream of a Perfect Gas ($\gamma = 1\cdot4$ at a pressure of 100 psia, a temperature of 110°F, a density of $0\cdot28$ lb_m/ft^3 and a velocity of 400 ft/s.

(i) Determine the Gas Constant, R, in ft lb_f/lb_m °F and the specific heat at constant pressure, c_p, in Btu/lb_m °F.

(ii) Assuming the flow to be reversible and adiabatic determine the temperature and velocity of the gas at exit from the nozzle where the pressure is 60 psia.

(iii) If the mass flow rate is 2 lb_m/s, determine the cross sectional areas at entry to and exit from the nozzle.

14.22 (a) A Perfect Gas flows steadily into a convergent-divergent nozzle (Fig. 8.10) from a reservoir where the absolute pressure is p_1 and the absolute temperature is T_1. As the gas expands reversibly and adiabatically in the nozzle its pressure falls continuously; at any downstream section, where the area is A, the pressure is p. Derive expressions for the velocity V and the area A in terms of the mass flow rate $\dot{m}$ and p_1, T_1, p, γ and R.

(b) For fixed inlet conditions and mass flow rate plot A against p/p_1. Note that A first decreases and then increases.

(c) By differentiating the expression for A with respect to p determine the values of p/p_1 and V at the minimum value of A.

(d) A *convergent* nozzle of fixed shape and size is connected to a supply at a fixed absolute pressure p_1 and absolute temperature T_1 and a reservoir of variable pressure p_2. A Perfect Gas flows reversibly and adiabatically through the nozzle; the entry velocity is negligible. Show that the mass flow rate $\dot{m}$ is a maximum when

$$p_2/p_1 = \left(\frac{2}{\gamma + 1} \right)^{\frac{\gamma}{\gamma - 1}}$$

(N.B. The expression for $\dot{m}$ indicates that as p_2/p_1 is reduced below this 'critical' value the mass flow decreases. This does not really happen. The reason is that for $p_2/p_1 <$ critical value, the formula only applies if the nozzle becomes convergent-divergent (see above), i.e. *changes* in shape.)

14.23 A hot-air engine operates on the Carnot cycle between the temperature limits of 500°F and 100°F; all the processes take place in a piston-cylinder mechanism. The pressure and volume at the start of isothermal expansion are 100 psia and 1 ft³ respectively. The pressure after isothermal expansion is 50 psia. Assume air to be a Perfect Gas with $\gamma = 1\cdot4$ and $R = 53\cdot3$ ft lb_f/lb_m °F abs.

(i) Show the cycle on sketches of the p-v and T-s diagrams. Mark on each sketch the numerical values of the co-ordinates at each "corner" in the cycle diagram.

(ii) Evaluate the efficiency of the cycle and the work done per cycle.

(iii) Evaluate the power developed by the engine if it performs 100 cycles/min.

14.24 A cyclic process, known as the Air-Standard Diesel cycle, is often used as a standard of comparison for reciprocating oil engines. The cycle is executed by unit mass of air contained in a cylinder closed by a frictionless leakproof piston and consists of four processes in sequence, exemplified in the following.

(a) Initially, with the piston in its outermost position (outer dead-centre), the cylinder contains air at pressure p_1, temperature T_1 and specific volume v_1 (state 1).

(b) As the piston is pushed slowly inwards to its innermost position (inner dead-centre) the air is compressed reversibly and adiabatically to state 2 such that $v_1 = rv_2$ where r is the 'compression ratio' (see problem 14.20).

(c) The piston now commences its outward stroke, during the first part of which the pressure is constant and heat is transferred to the air. This ceases when the air is at state 3 where $v_3 = \lambda v_2$; λ is the 'cut-off ratio' ($\lambda < r$).

(d) As the piston continues its outward stroke to the outer dead-centre the air expands reversibly and adiabatically to state 4; $v_4 = v_1$.

(e) Finally, with the piston at the outer dead-centre (volume $= v_4$), heat transfer from the air at constant volume restores the air to its original state. The sequence may then be repeated.

Assuming air to be a Perfect Gas:

(i) Sketch the p-v and T-s state diagrams.
(ii) Derive an expression for the efficiency η of the cycle in terms of r, λ and the ratio of the specific heats of the working fluid, γ.
(iii) Evaluate η when $r = 12$, $\lambda = 1\cdot5$ and $\gamma = 1\cdot4$.
(iv) Evaluate the temperature at each state point given that $T_1 = 80°F$.
(v) Evaluate the work done per cycle.

14.25 A cyclic process, known as the Joule (constant-pressure) cycle is often used as a standard of comparison for gas-turbine engines. The cycle consists of four processes which take place in sequence in steady flow, exemplified in the following. (See Fig. 10.3).

(a) Initially, air at pressure p_1, temperature T_1 (state 1) is compressed reversibly and adiabatically in a rotary compressor to state 2; $p_2 = rp_1$ where r is the 'pressure ratio.'

(b) Heat transfer at constant pressure to the air in the heater raises the air temperature to T_3 (state 3).

(c) The air then undergoes a reversible adiabatic expansion in a turbine to state 4 such that $p_4 = p_1$.

(d) Finally, heat transfer from the air at constant pressure restores the air to its initial state before it re-enters the compressor to repeat the process.

Assuming air to be a Perfect Gas and neglecting changes in velocity and in elevation:

(i) Sketch the p-v and T-s state diagrams.
(ii) Derive an expression for the efficiency, η, of the cycle in terms of r and the ratio of the specific heats of the working fluid, γ.
(iii) Evaluate η when $r = 5$ and $\gamma = 1\cdot4$.
(iv) Derive an expression for the net shaft work per pound of air in terms of r, γ, T_1 and T_3.
(v) Evaluate the shaft work per pound of air when $T_1 = 100°F$ and $T_2 = 1400°F$. For air take $R = 53\cdot3$ ft lb_f/lb_m °F abs.
(vi) In what respects would your answers be different if the air underwent the same changes of state in a piston-cylinder apparatus?

14.26 A closed-cycle gas-turbine engine (Fig. 10.3) employs air as the working fluid. The pressure and temperature at entry to the rotary compressor are 20 psia and 100°F respectively. The pressure ratio is 5 and the temperature at entry to the turbine is 1400°F. The isentropic efficiency of the compressor is 83 per cent and that of the turbine is 87 per cent. There are no pressure losses in the heater or in the cooler and all heat transfers may be assumed to be negligible except in the heater and cooler.

Assuming air to be a Perfect Gas with $\gamma = 1\cdot4$ and $R = 53\cdot3$ ft lb_f/lb_m °F abs:

(i) Sketch the T-s state diagram.
(ii) Evaluate the temperatures at the four points in the cycle.

(iii) Evaluate the efficiency of the engine.

(iv) Evaluate the shaft work done per pound of air.

14.27 (a) 2.5 lb$_m$ of a Semi-Perfect Gas at a pressure of 15 psia and a temperature of 210°F occupy a volume of 78 ft^3.

(i) Evaluate the Gas Constant R for the gas.

(ii) Given that the specific heat at constant pressure of the gas at this state is 0.42 Btu/lb$_m$ °F, evaluate γ for this condition.

(iii) The mean specific heat at constant pressure of the gas between the temperatures of 32°F and 210°F is 0.41 Btu/lb$_m$ °F. Evaluate the specific enthalpy and the specific internal energy of the gas for the given condition.

(b) The gas undergoes a process to a final pressure of 60 psia and a final temperature of 600°F. The specific heat at constant pressure corresponding to the final state is 0.64 Btu/lb$_m$ °F; the mean specific heat at constant pressure between temperatures 32°F and 600°F is 0.51 Btu/lb$_m$ °F.

(i) Evaluate γ corresponding to the final state of the gas.

(ii) Evaluate the final specific volume, the final specific enthalpy and the final specific internal energy of the gas.

(iii) Evaluate the mean values of the specific heat at constant pressure and of the specific heat at constant volume between the temperatures 210°F and 600°F.

(c) If the process in (b) may be represented by $pV^n = $ constant find the value of n.

(d) Assuming the process to take place reversibly and polytropically in a piston-cylinder mechanism evaluate the work done and the heat transfer during the process.

(e) Assuming the process to take place adiabatically and polytropically in steady flow with negligible changes in velocity and elevation evaluate the external work done per pound of gas.

14.28 Re-calculate problem 14.27 assuming the gas to be Perfect. Take the specific heat at constant pressure as 0.40 Btu/lb$_m$ °F.

14.29 A steady flow of air enters a heater at a pressure of 60 psia, a temperature of 100°F and a velocity of 200 ft/s. The air leaves the heater at a pressure of 56 psia and a temperature of 1000°F. The flow area at exit is 29 in.^{2} and the air mass flow rate is 10 lb$_m$/s. Given that R for air equals 53.3 ft lb$_f$/lb$_m$ °F abs, evaluate the exit velocity and the heat transfer rate to the air by each of the following methods.

(i) Assuming air to be a Perfect Gas with specific heat at constant pressure $= 0.24$ Btu/lb$_m$ °F.

(ii) Assuming air to be a Semi-Perfect Gas. Use the following data:

Temperature °F	100	300	500	700	900	1100
Enthalpy Btu/lb$_m$	133·8	182·1	231·0	281·1	332·4	385·0

In this case evaluate the mean specific heat at constant pressure for the given temperature range.

14.30 Air flows steadily at the rate of 40 lb$_m$/s throughout a rotary air compressor, entering with a velocity of 300 ft/s, a pressure of 14 psia and a density of 0.074 lb$_m$/ft^3 and leaving with a velocity of 500 ft/s, a pressure of 50 psia and a density of 0.17 lb$_m$/ft^3. The compression process may be assumed to be adiabatic. Given that R for air is 53.3 ft lb$_f$/lb$_m$ °F abs evaluate the ratio of the inlet area to the outlet area and the power input using methods (i) and (ii) given in problem 14.29.

CHAPTER 15

GASEOUS MIXTURES

INTRODUCTION

In the last chapter it was stated that air, which is a mixture of oxygen, nitrogen and other gases, can be treated for many purposes as though it were a single chemical substance. We even went so far as to speak of the "molecular weight" of air, despite the fact that there is no such thing as an air molecule. This procedure will be justified in the present chapter, which is devoted to the thermodynamics of gas-phase mixtures.

The discussion will explain a number of commonly observed facts that, at first sight, do not seem to accord with statements made earlier. For example, water is known to "disappear into thin air", i.e. to vaporise, at temperatures much below the boiling-point for the prevailing pressure. Ice, too, can turn directly into vapour, even at atmospheric pressure, which is over a hundred times as great as that of the triple point.

The main reason for discussing gas-phase mixtures here, however, is that they occur in many engineering processes. Thus, in steam-power-plant practice, the cooling-water for the condenser is often cooled in its turn by coming into direct contact with air in a so-called cooling-tower; the vaporisation of a small proportion of the water into the air assists materially in lowering the temperature of the remainder. In the combustion chambers of furnaces and engines, it is essential that fuel, air and combustion products should be mixed in order for the chemical reaction to proceed; to design combustion equipment we need to calculate the properties of the mixtures. Many mechanical engineers are concerned with the design of processing plant: textile dryers, air-conditioning plant, paper-making machinery and the like; in all these fields the behaviour of mixtures of air and water vapour has to be predicted quantitatively. Such problems assume perhaps their greatest importance in chemical engineering, where the mixing, and still more the separating, of different substances are central tasks.

The main thermodynamic idea introduced in this chapter is *Dalton's Law* with the refinements made to it by Gibbs. This law enables the techniques introduced in earlier chapters to be brought to bear on mixtures, by showing how the properties of a mixture are related to the properties of its components. We shall exemplify Dalton's Law by discussing, first, mixtures of Ideal Gases and, second, mixtures of Ideal Gases with a condensable vapour. The way is then clear for the application of the First and Second Laws of Thermodynamics to systems comprising mixtures.

Representation of the thermodynamic properties of mixtures is conveniently made with the help of diagrams. We discuss three types of these. Although water and air are used as examples, the methods are general.

Symbols

c_v Specific heat at constant volume.

c_p Specific heat at constant pressure.

H Enthalpy of a pure substance.

h Specific enthalpy of a pure substance.

m Mass.

n Number of moles.

p Pressure.

R Gas Constant.

$\mathscr{R}$ Universal Gas Constant.

S Entropy of a pure substance.

s Specific entropy of a pure substance.

T Absolute temperature.

t Temperature.

U Internal energy of a pure substance.

u Specific internal energy of a pure substance.

V Volume of a pure substance.

V_{mol} Molecular volume.

v Specific volume of a pure substance.

w Mass of steam.

y Mass fraction of air in an air-H_2O mixture.

ϕ Relative humidity.

γ Ratio of specific heats, c_p/c_v

ρ Density.

ω Specific humidity.

Subscripts.

a, b, . . . n Components a, b, . . . n of a mixture. Symbols without subscripts represent mixture properties.

w Liquid water.

G Air-steam mixture.

v Water vapour

g Saturated steam.

1,2 Initial, final state of a fluid.

THE GIBBS-DALTON LAW

Dalton's Law

Consider the apparatus shown in Fig. 15.1. A rigid vessel, fitted with a thermometer and a pressure gauge is connected by means of pipes fitted with stop-cocks to storage bottles containing various pure chemical substances.

Suppose that the vessel is at first evacuated, but that thereafter each of the stop-cocks is opened for a short period in turn. As a result the vessel finally holds some oxygen, some nitrogen, some steam, and so on.

We consider the case in which the final contents of the vessel, which we will call the system, are entirely gaseous, are uniform in pressure and temperature, and are uniform and invariant in composition and chemical aggregation. This means that the gases are completely mixed, and have no tendency to react chemically with each other. The system is therefore a *pure substance* as defined in Chapter 7, page 93, even though it is not chemically pure.

The thermometer and the pressure gauge are in contact with all the components of the mixture simultaneously; their readings give respectively the temperature and pressure of the *mixture*. No thermometer can measure the "temperature" of a single component of the mixture, say the nitrogen, so this term has no meaning. In the same way, the "pressure" of an individual component cannot be measured, although the "partial pressure" of a component, defined below, is often thought of as being the same as the pressure exerted by that component.

In preceding chapters, we have been concerned with how the easily observable properties, pressure, temperature and volume, are related to the properties which feature in the First and Second Laws of Thermodynamics. It has been shown that these relations must be determined experimentally; the results of the experiments are embodied in tables, charts and, in the case of the Ideal Gases, algebraic formulae. If the

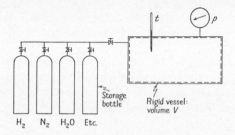

Fig. 15.1   Illustrating the mixing of pure substances.

same procedure is necessary for mixtures, the number of experiments which must be carried out becomes enormous, because of the great variety of mixtures which are of practical interest. It is therefore natural to look for a short cut, preferably one which enables us to calculate the thermodynamic properties of a mixture knowing only the properties of the components and the proportions in which they are mixed together.

Dalton's Law. Fortunately such a short cut is available. It rests on a regularity in the behaviour of gaseous mixtures first perceived and formulated by Dalton (1802), who expressed it in the phrase now known as Dalton's Law:

Any gas is as a vacuum to any other gas mixed with it.

This compact statement means that each component of a gaseous mixture acts, and has the same properties, as if it alone filled the vessel. The statement is based on experiments which show that, although departures from Dalton's Law do exist, they are usually small enough to be ignored in engineering calculations. Certainly Dalton's Law is much more closely obeyed by most substances than is the Ideal Gas Rule.

It should be remarked that Dalton's Law should only be applied to the *thermodynamic* properties of a mixture. The so-called *transport properties*, viscosity, thermal conductivity and diffusion coefficient, do not obey it.

Dalton's Law, together with Dalton's implicit assumption that each component acts as if it were at the temperature of the mixture, has been expanded into a form suitable for engineering use by Gibbs (1875), whose re-formulation of the principle is known as the *Gibbs-Dalton Law.*

The Gibbs-Dalton Law

Gibbs' formulation is in two parts. The first is concerned with the intensive property, pressure; the second with the extensive properties, internal energy, enthalpy and entropy:

1. The pressure of a gaseous mixture is the sum of the pressures which each component would exert if it alone occupied the volume of the mixture at the temperature of the mixture.

The pressure which a component would exert in these circumstances is known as the *partial pressure* of the component. It has to be measured in a separate experiment in which the mass of the component present in the mixture actually does occupy the volume by itself at the mixture temperature.

2. The internal energy, the enthalpy and the entropy of a gaseous mixture are respectively equal to the sums of the internal energies, the enthalpies and the entropies which each component of the mixture would have, if each alone occupied the volume of the mixture at the temperature of the mixture.

These component properties also must be measured, in the ways indicated in earlier chapters, by separate experiments on the appropriate masses of the isolated components.

Algebraic representation. The Gibbs-Dalton Law is expressed symbolically by the following equations, in which the subscripts a, b, ... n each refer to a particular component of the mixture. The symbol for a mixture property is left without suffix.

The assumption about temperature implicit in Dalton's Law is written as

$$t = t_a = t_b = \ldots = t_n \qquad \ldots \quad (15.1)$$

Since by Dalton's Law each component is thought of as occupying the whole volume V, we write

$$V = V_a = V_b = \ldots = V_n \qquad \ldots \quad (15.2)$$

or, in terms of the specific volumes, v,

$$mv = m_a v_a = m_b v_b = \ldots = m_n v_n \qquad \ldots \quad (15.3)$$

where the m's are the masses.

Since the mass of the mixture is equal to the sum of the masses of the components, i.e.

$$m = m_a + m_b + \ldots + m_n \qquad \ldots \quad (15.4)$$

the relation between the specific volumes can be written, from eq. (15.3) and eq. (15.4), as

$$\frac{1}{v} = \frac{1}{v_a} + \frac{1}{v_b} + \ldots + \frac{1}{v_n} \qquad \ldots \quad (15.5)$$

The reciprocal of the specific volume is the density, so eq. (15.5) can also be written as

$$\rho = \rho_a + \rho_b + \ldots + \rho_n \qquad \ldots \quad (15.6)$$

which means that the density of the mixture is equal to the sum of the densities of the components.

The *first part of the Gibbs-Dalton Law* is expressed symbolically as

$$p = p_a + p_b + \ldots + p_n \qquad \ldots \quad (15.7)$$

where p with a suffix signifies the *partial* pressure of a component.

The *second part of the Gibbs-Dalton Law* is written

$$U = U_a + U_b + \ldots + U_n$$

or
$$mu = m_a u_a + m_b u_b + \ldots + m_n u_n \qquad \ldots \quad (15.8)$$

$$H = H_a + H_b + \ldots + H_n$$

or
$$mh = m_a h_a + m_b h_b + \ldots + m_n h_n \qquad \ldots \quad (15.9)$$

and

$$S = S_a + S_b + \ldots + S_n$$

or
$$ms = m_a s_a + m_b s_b + \ldots + m_n s_n \qquad \ldots \quad (15.10)$$

Use of the Gibbs-Dalton Law. By means of the equations (15.1) to (15.10) we can predict the thermodynamic properties of a gaseous mixture from the properties of the components, provided that the composition of the mixture and, say, its volume and temperature are given. The following example illustrates the method.

EXAMPLE

Problem. A mixture consisting of 1 lb_m of air and 2 lb_m of nitrogen occupies 10 ft^3 at 80°F. Evaluate the specific volume, the pressure, the specific enthalpy, the specific internal energy and the specific entropy of the mixture, assuming air and nitrogen to be Ideal Gases for which R is 53·3 and 55·2 ft lb_f/lb_m°F abs. respectively.

Solution. Denoting air and nitrogen by subscripts a and b respectively, we have:

For 1 lb_m air: $\quad V = 10\,ft^3;\qquad t_a = 80°F.$

$$v_a = \frac{10}{1} = 10\ ft^3/lb_m$$

∴ From the Ideal Gas Rule $\quad p_a = \dfrac{53\cdot3 \times 540}{10 \times 144} = 20$ psia.

Then from tables of properties of air (Keenan and Kaye) we obtain

$$h_a = 129\cdot06\ Btu/lb_m$$
$$u_a = 92\cdot04\ Btu/lb_m$$
$$s_a = 0\cdot5797\ Btu/lb_m°F\ abs.$$

For 2 lb_m nitrogen: $\quad V = 10\,ft^3;\qquad t_b = 80°F$

$$v_b = \frac{10}{2} = 5\ ft^3/lb_m$$

correspondingly $\quad p_b = \dfrac{55\cdot2 \times 540}{5 \times 144} = 41\cdot4$ psia.

Hence from tables of properties of nitrogen (Keenan and Kaye) we have

$$h_b = 133 \cdot 9 \text{ Btu/lb}_m$$

$$u_b = 95 \cdot 7 \text{ Btu/lb}_m$$

$$s_b = 1 \cdot 563 \text{ Btu/lb}_m \text{°F abs.}$$

Then *for the 3 lb$_m$ of mixture:* $V = 10 \text{ ft}^3$; $t = 80\text{°F}$

$$v = \frac{10}{3} = 3 \cdot 33 \text{ ft}^3/\text{lb}_m \qquad \qquad \text{... } Answer$$

$$p = p_a + p_b \text{ from eq. (15.7)}$$

$$= 20 + 41 \cdot 4 = 61 \cdot 4 \text{ psia.} \qquad \text{... } Answer$$

From eq. (15.9)

$$h = \frac{1 \times 129 \cdot 06 + 2 \times 133 \cdot 9}{(1 + 2)}$$

$$= 132 \cdot 3 \text{ Btu/lb}_m \text{ mixture} \qquad \text{... } Answer$$

From eq. (15.8)

$$u = \frac{1 \times 92 \cdot 04 + 2 \times 95 \cdot 7}{(1 + 2)}$$

$$= 94 \cdot 5 \text{ Btu/lb}_m \text{ mixture} \qquad \text{... } Answer$$

From eq. (15.10)

$$s = \frac{1 \times 0 \cdot 5797 + 2 \times 1 \cdot 563}{(1 + 2)}$$

$$= 1 \cdot 235 \text{ Btu/lb}_m \text{°F abs.} \qquad \text{... } Answer$$

Remarks. 1. It should be noted that the numerical values of h, u, and s depend on the state chosen as datum. In this case, for both components, the zero of h in the tables used is 0°F abs and, since $h = u + pv$, this fixes the datum for u also; the zero of s is at a temperature of 0°F abs and a pressure of one atmosphere.

2. If the given mixture properties are pressure and, say, temperature, the equations (15.1) to (15.10) have to be solved simultaneously instead of one by one. This often involves trial and error.

The specific heats of a gaseous mixture. The specific heats at constant volume and pressure are respectively the differentials with respect to temperature of u and h (Chapter 7, pp. 100, 102). Symbolically we have

$$c_v = \left[\frac{du}{dt}\right]_v; \qquad c_p = \left[\frac{dh}{dt}\right]_p$$

Now by differentiating eq. (15.8) with respect to temperature we obtain

$$m\left[\frac{du}{dt}\right]_v = m_a\left[\frac{du_a}{dt}\right]_v + m_b\left[\frac{du_b}{dt}\right]_v + \ldots + m_n\left[\frac{du_n}{dt}\right]_v$$

It follows therefore that

$$mc_v = m_a c_{v_a} + m_b c_{v_b} + \ldots + m_n c_{v_n} \qquad \text{... (15.11)}$$

Similarly from eq. (15.9) we get

$$mc_p = m_a c_{p_a} + m_b c_{p_b} + \ldots + m_n c_{p_n} \qquad \ldots (15.12)$$

where c_{v_a}, c_{p_a}, etc. are the specific heats of the individual components when occupying the whole volume of the mixture at the temperature of the mixture.

Application of the Gibbs-Dalton Law to mixtures of Ideal Gases

The algebraic rules for the properties of gaseous mixtures become particularly simple when the components are Ideal Gases; for the properties of such gases themselves obey algebraic formulae, as seen in Chapter 14. We therefore exemplify the Gibbs-Dalton Law first by reference to Ideal Gas mixtures.

Proof that a mixture of Ideal Gases is itself an Ideal Gas. Suppose that masses m_a, m_b, ... m_n of different Ideal Gases form a homogeneous mixture at pressure p and absolute temperature T. We will investigate whether this mixture is itself an Ideal Gas, by deriving its p–v–T relation.

For the individual components, we have

$$p_a v_a = R_a T$$

$$p_b v_b = R_b T \quad \text{etc.} \qquad \ldots (15.13)$$

where R_a, R_b, etc., are the respective Gas Constants.
Combining eq. (15.13) with eq. (15.7), the pressure p of the mixture is

$$p = \frac{R_a T}{v_a} + \frac{R_b T}{v_b} + \ldots \frac{R_n T}{v_n} \qquad \ldots (15.14)$$

The v's can be eliminated from this equation by means of eq. (15.3) expressing the fact that each component occupies the same volume at temperature T. We obtain

$$p = \frac{m_a}{mv} \cdot R_a T + \frac{m_b}{mv} \cdot R_b T + \ldots + \frac{m_n}{mv} \cdot R_n T$$

$$= \frac{T}{mv} (m_a R_a + m_b R_b + \ldots m_n R_n) \qquad \ldots (15.15)$$

where m is the total mass of the mixture. If we now introduce a symbol R, defined by

$$R \equiv \frac{1}{m} (m_a R_a + m_b R_b + \ldots + m_n R_n) \qquad \ldots (15.16)$$

eq. (15.15) becomes

$$p = \frac{RT}{v}$$

or

$$pv = RT \qquad \ldots (15.17)$$

19

Now R is a constant for a mixture of given composition; for m_a/m, m_b/m etc. are constants and R_a, R_b, etc. are in fact the Gas Constants of the components. Eq. (15.17) therefore asserts that *the mixture of Ideal Gases is itself an Ideal Gas, and that R is its Gas Constant*. It will be noted that eq. (15.16) shows that R is an average, formed by "weighting" the individual R's with respect to the mass proportions of the components.

This completes the required proof. There is no need to prove separately that the internal energy of the mixture, for example, is dependent on temperature alone: this follows from the fact that the mixture obeys eq. (15.17), by reason of the arguments in Chapter 14.

The molecular weight of a mixture. The Gibbs-Dalton relations take a similar form to the above when the quantities of the components are expressed in molal units. For example, since $n_a = m_a/M_a$, $V_{mol_a} = M_a v_a$, etc., equations (15.3) and (15.4) become,

$$n V_{mol} = n_a V_{mol_a} = n_b V_{mol_b} = \ldots = n_n V_{mol_n} \quad \ldots \text{ (15.18)}$$
and
$$n = n_a + n_b + \ldots + n_n \qquad \qquad \ldots \text{ (15.19)}$$

Here n_a is the number of moles of substance a and V_{mol_a}, is its molal volume, and so on for the other pure components. n and V_{mol} for the mixture, on the other hand, must be taken as being *defined* by equations (15.18) and (15.19); for a molecule of the mixture as such does not exist.

If it is to be useful to talk about the number of moles of mixture, n, and the molecular volume of a mixture V_{mol}, these quantities must satisfy the same relations as do n_a and V_{mol_a}, etc.; we must therefore satisfy ourselves that

$$p V_{mol} = \mathscr{R} T \qquad \qquad \ldots \text{ (15.20)}$$
and
$$V = n V_{mol} \qquad \qquad \ldots \text{ (15.21)}$$

The second of these relations is easily established by inspection of eq. (15.18); for the mixture volume, V, is equal to the volume of each component at the mixture temperature, T, i.e. to $n_a V_{mol_a}$ etc. To demonstrate eq. (15.20) however we must first re-write eq. (15.15) in terms of molal quantities as

$$p = \frac{T}{mv} (n_a \mathscr{R} + n_b \mathscr{R} + \ldots n_n \mathscr{R})$$

$$= \frac{\mathscr{R} T}{mv} (n_a + n_b + \ldots n_b) \qquad \qquad \ldots \text{ (15.22)}$$

$$= \frac{n}{mv} \mathscr{R} T, \text{ from eq. (15.19)}$$

$$= \frac{\mathscr{R} T}{V_{mol}} \qquad \qquad \ldots \text{ (15.23)}$$

which is the relation eq. (15.20) which we wished to prove.

For the pure component a, we have

$$p_a v_a = \frac{\mathscr{R}_a T}{M_a} = R_a T \qquad \ldots \quad (15.24)$$

where M_a is its molecular weight. By analogy, we *define* the molecular weight of the mixture M so that

$$pv = \frac{\mathscr{R} T}{M} \qquad \ldots \quad (15.25)$$

Comparison of eq. (15.22) and eq. (15.25) then shows that

$$M = \frac{m}{n_a + n_b + \ldots + n_n} = \frac{m}{n} \qquad \ldots \quad (15.26)$$

i.e. that the molecular weight of the mixture equals the mass of the mixture divided by the number of moles of mixture, as indeed it should.

In order to relate M to the molecular weights of the individual components directly, we note that $n_a = m_a/M_a$, etc. Substituting in eq. (15.26) we obtain

$$M = \frac{m}{\dfrac{m_a}{M_a} + \dfrac{m_b}{M_b} + \ldots + \dfrac{m_n}{M_n}}$$

or more symmetrically

$$\frac{m}{M} = \frac{m_a}{M_a} + \frac{m_b}{M_b} + \ldots + \frac{m_n}{M_n} \qquad \ldots \quad (15.27)$$

To complete the parallelism between a mixture of Ideal Gases and a chemically pure Ideal Gas, the relation between M, R and $\mathscr{R}$ will be derived. Since $M_a = \mathscr{R}/R_a$, etc., substitution in eq. (15.27) gives

$$\frac{m}{M} = \frac{m_a R_a}{\mathscr{R}} + \frac{m_b R_b}{\mathscr{R}} + \ldots + \frac{m_n R_n}{\mathscr{R}} \qquad \ldots \quad (15.28)$$

Re-arranging and substituting from eq. (15.16), this becomes

$$\frac{1}{M} = \frac{1}{\mathscr{R}m} (m_a R_1 + m_b R_2 + \ldots + m_n R_n)$$

$$= \frac{R}{\mathscr{R}} \qquad \ldots \quad (15.29)$$

So
$$M = \frac{\mathscr{R}}{R} \qquad \ldots \quad (15.30)$$

in complete conformity with a chemically pure Ideal Gas.

Adiabatic mixing of Ideal Gases

In order to illustrate some special features of Ideal Gases, we now consider a mixing process. Fig. 15.2 shows the system under consideration; it comprises a rigid adiabatic container separated into compartments of various size by removable partitions. Each compartment is filled with a separate Ideal Gas, designated a, b, . . . n; the pressures and temperatures prevailing in each compartment are the same, p and T respectively.

The process consists of the removal of the partitions, which is followed by the mixing of the gases as a result of the molecular motions. At the end of the process, all the gases are uniformly mixed. We will examine whether the pressure and temperature of the system change in this adiabatic constant-volume process.

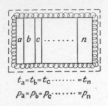

$t_a = t_b = t_c \cdots = t_n$

$p_a = p_b = p_c \cdots = p_n$

Fig. 15.2
Adiabatic, constant-volume mixing of Ideal Gases.

No heat or work cross the system boundary during the process. From the First Law therefore, the internal energy remains constant. But the internal energy of each component is a function of temperature alone because the gases are Ideal. Since the internal energy of the mixture is equal to the sum of the internal energies of the components in the mixed state, and moreover each component is to be regarded as at the mixture temperature, the only possibility is that *the final temperature is equal to the initial temperature.*

We now evaluate the final mixture pressure, p'. Let the volumes of the various compartments be V_a, V_b, . . . V_n, the masses of the components be m_a, m_b, . . . m_n, and the final partial pressures be p_a, p_b, . . . p_n. Then from the Gibbs-Dalton Law,

$$p' = p_a + p_b + \ldots + p_n \qquad \ldots \quad (15.31)$$

and from geometrical considerations the mixture volume V is given by

$$V = V_a + V_b + \ldots + V_n \qquad \ldots \quad (15.32)$$

Now the gases obey the Ideal Gas Rule. Since there is no change of temperature, and the initial pressure of each component is p, we have

$$\left. \begin{array}{r} pV_a = p_a V \\ pV_b = p_b V \\ \text{etc.} \end{array} \right\} \qquad \ldots \quad (15.33)$$

for each gas finally occupies the whole volume V. Combining eq. (15.31) and eq. (15.33), we obtain

$$p' = \frac{pV_a}{V} + \frac{pV_b}{V} + \ldots + \frac{pV_n}{V}$$

$$= \frac{p}{V} (V_a + V_b + \ldots + V_n)$$

$$= p, \qquad \ldots \quad (15.34)$$

from eq. (15.32).

This proves that the final mixture pressure is equal to the initial pressure of the components: *the pressure in the system does not change.* A corollary is that, if we had postulated constancy of pressure during the process, it would have been found that the volume does not change.

Volumetric and molal analysis of an Ideal Gas mixture. Because of the results of the last section it is permissible and useful to speak of the *volumetric analysis* of a gas mixture. For example, air is said to consist of 21% of oxygen and 79% of (atmospheric) nitrogen, *by volume*, even though both oxygen and nitrogen fill the whole volume. This means that, if 0·21 ft³ of oxygen and 0·79 ft³ of (atmospheric) nitrogen at equal temperatures and pressures are mixed in the manner indicated above, 1 ft³ of air at the same temperature and pressure will result.

It will now be demonstrated that *the volumetric analysis is identical with the molal analysis.* To fix ideas however we first introduce the following definitions:—

(*a*) The *mass analysis* of the mixture which has been considered is:—

$$\frac{100 m_a \%}{m} \text{ of gas a, by mass}$$

$$\frac{100 m_b \%}{m} \text{ of gas b, by mass}$$

$$\text{etc.}$$

(*b*) The *volumetric analysis* of the mixture is

$$\frac{100 V_a \%}{V} \text{ of gas a, by volume}$$

$$\frac{100 V_b \%}{V} \text{ of gas b, by volume}$$

$$\text{etc.}$$

(*c*) The *molal analysis* of the mixture is

$$\frac{100 n_a \%}{n} \text{ of gas a, by moles}$$

$$\frac{100 n_b \%}{n} \text{ of gas b, by moles}$$

$$\text{etc.}$$

Proof. For gas a, the Ideal Gas Rule in molal units gives

$$p_a V = n_a \mathscr{R} T \qquad \qquad \ldots \quad (15.35)$$

Eliminating p_a by means of eq. (15.33), we have

$$p V_a = n_a \mathscr{R} T \qquad \qquad \ldots \quad (15.36)$$

i.e.

$$n_a = V_a \cdot \frac{p}{\mathscr{R} T} \qquad \qquad \ldots \quad (15.37)$$

Thus the number of moles of gas a is proportional to the volume of that gas present before adiabatic mixing at constant pressure and temperature took place; for $p/\mathscr{R}T$ is a constant, equal to n/V, according to eq. (15.23). Thus

$$\frac{n_a}{n} = \frac{V_a}{V}$$

$$\frac{n_b}{n} = \frac{V_b}{V} \quad \text{and so on} \qquad \dots \quad (15.38)$$

The volumetric and molal analyses are therefore identical. It should be mentioned that for non-Ideal Gases, the volumetric analysis ceases to have any useful meaning; for mixing two such gases at constant pressure brings about a change in volume in general.

Entropy change in mixing Perfect* Gases adiabatically. In Chapter 14, p. 258, a formula, eq. (14.43), was derived for the dependence of the entropy of a Perfect Gas on the temperature and specific volume. Applying this to the specific entropy increase, Δs_a, of gas a, in the above constant-temperature mixing process, we obtain

$$\Delta s_a = R_a \ln \left(\frac{V}{V_a} \right) \qquad \dots \quad (15.39)$$

Since V is greater than V_a, we note that the entropy of this component, and so of all components, has increased. *Mixing is therefore an irreversible process.* This is easier to understand if it is realised that it is possible, in principle and sometimes in practice also, to devise a piston permeable to all except one gas, and so to extract work from the interpenetration of the gases; in the actual mixing process above we fail to extract this work.

EXAMPLE

Problem. What is the entropy increase when $0 \cdot 232$ lb$_m$ of oxygen and $0 \cdot 768$ lb$_m$ of (atmospheric) nitrogen at equal temperatures, mix adiabatically at constant pressure to form air?

Solution. If the oxygen and nitrogen are given suffixes a and b respectively, we have from Table 14.1

$$R_a = 48 \cdot 3 \text{ ft lb}_f/\text{lb}_m$$

$$R_b = 55 \cdot 2 \text{ ft lb}_f/\text{lb}_m$$

Now for constant-pressure, adiabatic mixing, the final mixture temperature is equal to the initial temperature of the components. Denoting this temperature by T, we have

$$V_a = 0 \cdot 232 \times 48 \cdot 3 \ T/p \text{ ft}^3$$

$$V_b = 0 \cdot 768 \times 55 \cdot 2 \ T/p \text{ ft}^3.$$

* N.B. Not Ideal Gases in general.

If the final mixture volume is V, then

$$\frac{V}{V_a} = \frac{0 \cdot 232 \times 48 \cdot 3 + 0 \cdot 768 \times 55 \cdot 2}{0 \cdot 232 \times 48 \cdot 3} = 4 \cdot 76$$

$$\frac{V}{V_b} = \frac{0 \cdot 232 \times 48 \cdot 3 + 0 \cdot 768 \times 55 \cdot 2}{0 \cdot 768 \times 48 \cdot 3} = 1 \cdot 263$$

The entropy increase is

$$\Delta s = 0 \cdot 232 \Delta s_a + 0 \cdot 768 \Delta s_b$$

$$= 0 \cdot 232 \times 48 \cdot 3 \ln 4 \cdot 76 + 0 \cdot 768 \times 55 \cdot 2 \ln 1 \cdot 263$$

$$= 27 \cdot 35 \text{ ft lb}_f/\text{lb}_m \text{ air } °\text{F abs}$$

$$= 0 \cdot 0352 \text{ Btu/lb}_m \text{ air } °\text{F abs} \qquad \qquad \ldots \quad Answer$$

An interesting question arises from the fact that mixing of two different gases causes an entropy increase. Suppose that the two gases are identical. Then when the partition is removed, molecular motions ensue and cause mixing so that eventually molecules which initially were in the separate compartments can be found at all parts of the vessel. Yet this time there is no entropy increase; for adding, say, 1 lb_m of oxygen to 1 lb_m of oxygen at the same pressure and temperature merely produces 2 lb_m of oxygen. Why is there an entropy increase when the gases differ in chemical properties and not when they do not?

This is known as *Gibbs' Paradox*. The answer is that when the gases are identical it is no longer possible, even in principle, to devise means to extract work from the interpenetration of the gases; for a semi-permeable piston cannot distinguish between two molecules of the same sort.[*]

MIXTURES OF AN IDEAL GAS WITH A CONDENSABLE VAPOUR

Steam-air mixtures: gaseous phase

The most important mechanical engineering example of mixtures of Ideal Gases with a condensable vapour is the steam-air system. This will be dealt with exclusively from now on, but it should be understood that the methods and results are applicable to any other combinations of appropriate substances.

Single-phase mixtures. When only the gaseous phase is present (no liquid water), the Gibbs-Dalton law is applicable without modification. A single example should suffice as illustration.

EXAMPLE

Problem. 0·01 lb_m of steam and 0·99 lb_m of air form a gaseous mixture at 1 atm pressure and 70°F. Determine (a) the partial pressures of the steam and air, (b) the specific volume of the mixture, and (c) the enthalpy of the mixture.

[*] End note 9.

Solution (a) and (b). These have to be solved simultaneously. We have

$$p = 14.7 \text{ psia} = p_{\text{steam}} + p_{\text{air}}$$

For air: $\qquad\qquad p_{\text{air}} = \dfrac{53.3 \times (460 + 70)}{144 \times v_{\text{air}}}$ psia, from the Ideal Gas Rule

For steam: $\quad p_{\text{steam}}$ is related to v_{steam} by the Superheated Steam Table. Further,

$$1 \times v = 0.01\, v_{\text{steam}} = 0.99\, v_{\text{air}}, \quad \text{from eq. (15.3)}$$

These five relations permit us to determine the five unknowns. However examination of the Superheated Steam Table (Appendix B) shows that it does not extend into the low-pressure region which will certainly be required. We therefore *assume* that at low pressures steam can be treated as an Ideal Gas, so replacing the Steam Table by

$$p_{\text{steam}} = \frac{85.8 \times (460 + 70)}{144 \times v_{\text{steam}}} \text{ psia, from the Ideal Gas Rule.}$$

where $85.8 \text{ ft lb}_f/\text{lb}_m\,°\text{F}$ abs is the Gas Constant for H_2O (see Table 14.1).

Then $\qquad\qquad \dfrac{p_{\text{steam}}}{p_{\text{air}}} = \dfrac{85.8}{53.3} \times \dfrac{v_{\text{air}}}{v_{\text{steam}}}$

$$= \frac{85.8}{53.3} \times \frac{0.01}{0.99} = 0.01628$$

Now from eq. (15.7) $p_{\text{steam}} + p_{\text{air}} = 14.7$ psia.

$\therefore \qquad\qquad\qquad p_{\text{steam}} + \dfrac{p_{\text{steam}}}{0.01628} = 14.7$

or $\qquad\qquad p_{\text{steam}} = \dfrac{0.01628}{1 + 0.01628} \times 14.7 = 0.236$ psia. ... $\qquad$ *Answer (a)*

Hence $\qquad\qquad p_{\text{air}} = 14.7 - 0.236 = 14.46$ psia. $\qquad$ ... *Answer (a)*

and so $\qquad\qquad v_{\text{steam}} = \dfrac{85.8 \times 530}{144 \times 0.236} = 1340 \text{ ft}^3/\text{lb}_m$

therefore $\qquad v = 0.01 \times 1340 = 13.40 \text{ ft}^3/\text{lb}_m$ mixture. ... *Answer (b)*

Note. Solution by means of the Steam Tables would be a trial-and-error process. The steps are as follows:

   (i) Select a value of p_{steam}.
   (ii) From the Steam Tables, at $t = 70°\text{F}$, look up the corresponding value of v_{steam}.
   (iii) Evaluate p_{air} from eq. (15.7).
   (iv) Evaluate v_{air} from the Ideal Gas Rule.
   (v) The values of v_{steam} and v_{air} have to satisfy eq. (15.3) viz. $0.01\, v_{\text{steam}} = 0.99\, v_{\text{air}}$. Select values of p_{steam} until agreement is reached.

Solution (c). The enthalpy of the mixture is given by

$$h = 0.01\, h_{\text{steam}} + 0.99\, h_{\text{air}}$$

Once again the Superheated Steam Table fails us. We therefore take, consistently with our Ideal Gas assumption that $h = f(t)$, the enthalpy to be equal to that at the saturation pressure at 70°F, namely 1092·3 Btu/lb$_m$. For air, we take $c_p = 0·240$ and choose an enthalpy base of 32°F.

Then
$$h = 0·01 \times 1092·3 + 0·99 \times 0·24(70 - 32)$$
$$= 10·92 + 9·03$$
$$= 19·95 \text{ Btu/lb}_m \text{ mixture.} \qquad \qquad \dots \quad Answer \ (c)$$

Steam-water-air mixtures

In the last example, the partial pressure of the steam (0·236 psia) was less than the saturated steam pressure (0·363 psia) which Steam Tables show to prevail at 70°F. If the calculation had shown a partial pressure in excess of 0·363 psia, as would have happened if the mass of H_2O per lb$_m$ of mixture had been appreciably greater, the assumption of the calculation, viz. that only one phase was present, would have been wrong. For the saturation pressure corresponding to the mixture temperature is the highest pressure at which the vapour can exist at that temperature.

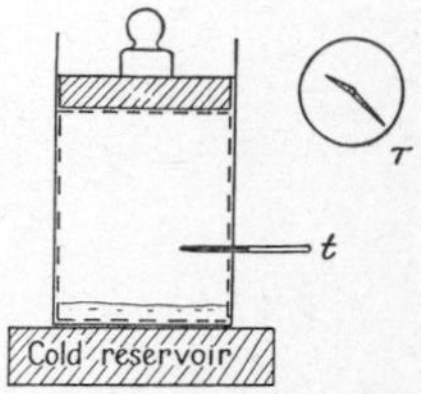

To explain this, the transition between phases will be discussed in a similar way to that employed for pure substances in Chapter 9. We consider once more a series of constant-pressure experiments, but this time suppose heat to be transferred *from* the system.

Fig. 15.3 Constant-pressure cooling of an air-H_2O mixture.

Constant-pressure cooling experiments. Fig. 15.3 illustrates the apparatus. A cylinder fitted with a frictionless leak-proof piston surmounted by a weight contains a mixture of air and steam. We suppose that initially the temperature of the system (the air and the steam) exceeds the boiling-point of water at the pressure of the system. The base of the cylinder is placed in thermal contact with a very cold body and the variation of the system temperature is observed and plotted against time.

Fig. 15.4 shows typical curves resulting from such experiments. The curve, b, corresponds to a mixture containing only a small amount of steam. To fix ideas, we suppose that the pressure within the cylinder is atmospheric. The temperature-time curve consists of two approximately straight sections; the change of slope occurs abruptly at 32°F.* In contrast to the curves obtained for a pure substance (Fig. 9.2), the slope of the curve is finite (and negative) everywhere; there are no horizontal steps and the temperature falls continuously.

If the interior of the cylinder is observed during this first experiment, it is seen that during the period of steep slope only the gaseous phase is present. At the temperature corresponding to the kink in the curve, point b_1, tiny crystals of ice begin to form on the base of the cylinder; these continue to grow in size, though at a decreasing rate, as the temperature falls further. The experiment has reproduced the conditions for the formation of *hoar frost*.

The next experiment is supposed to be carried out at the same pressure as before with a greater mass ratio of steam to air. This time curve, c, is obtained in which the kink (c_1) occurs earlier, i.e. at a higher temperature than 32°F. However, when 32°F* is reached, the curve exhibits a second kink c_2 and becomes horizontal for a period, c_2c_3; thereafter the curve bends downward once more. Observation of the interior of the cylinder

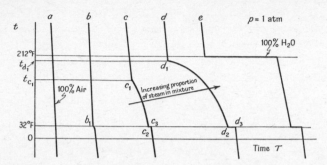

Fig. 15.4   Temperature–time curves for air-H_2O mixtures cooling at atmospheric pressure (to scale).

reveals that, at the first kink c_1, small droplets of water appear on the base; these grow in size until the second kink c_2 is reached. At 32°F, the droplets freeze, the temperature remaining unchanged during this process. The third kink c_3 occurs when all the condensed water has turned to ice; thereafter the quantity of ice increases as a result of further deposition from the gas phase and the temperature falls continuously. This experiment illustrates the formation of *dew*, which subsequently freezes.

If successive experiments are carried out with the same pressure of 1 atmosphere and increasing proportions of steam to air, the temperature at which the first kink occurs rises continuously, and the horizontal extension of the curve increases. Eventually, when the proportion of air has been reduced to zero, the curve degenerates to the form already encountered for pure H_2O; a broad step occurs at 212°F and a narrower one occurs at 32°F. At the other extreme, when there is no steam present, curve, a, is obtained. Fig. 15.4 illustrates these trends.

Further series of experiments can be carried out at other pressures. The general tendency of the temperature-time curves is the same, but the temperature of the upper kink increases as the pressure rises. When the pressure is below that of the triple point of H_2O (0·0888 psia), the upper kink does not occur, and all the changes of slope are confined to the region below 32°F; this means that no water is formed whatever the initial steam concentration, as will be understood by recalling the behaviour of pure steam at low pressures.

In studying the properties of a pure substance, in Chapter 9, a single series of experiments sufficed, pressure being the only variable. The

* Actually the temperature would be slightly below 32°F and would vary with the mixture composition. The difference may be neglected for engineering purposes.

necessity to carry out several series for steam-air mixtures is a consequence of the fact that such a mixture is not a pure substance; *three* properties are needed to fix its state, e.g. temperature, specific volume *and composition*.

The enthalpy-composition diagram. Pursuing the parallel with the procedure of Chapter 9 still further, we note that measurements of heat transfer quantities can be made during the constant-pressure cooling experiments; these yield the enthalpy changes directly. The results for a given pressure can then be plotted on a diagram with specific enthalpy of the mixture as ordinate and composition as abscissa. The composition will be characterised by a quantity y, defined as

$$y = \frac{\text{mass of air}}{\text{mass of mixture}} \qquad \ldots \quad (15.40)$$

Thus $y = 1$ denotes pure air; $y = 0$ denotes pure H_2O.

Fig. 15.5 shows such a diagram, approximately to scale, for a pressure of one atmosphere, with the enthalpy base chosen as 32°F for saturated water and for air. Inspection of the diagram shows that there are four regions: the upper one corresponds to states of purely gaseous phase (air and steam); the next lower one corresponds to mixtures in which the gaseous and liquid phases are present (air + steam + water); next comes a region comprising states involving the gaseous, liquid and solid phases simultaneously (air + steam + water + ice); the lowest region covers states in which only the gaseous and solid phases are present (air + steam + ice). Pure air states are found on the right-hand vertical border, a, where $y = 1$; pure steam, steam + water, pure water, water + ice, and pure ice occupy successively lower stretches of the left-hand vertical border, e, where $y = 0$.

Lines of constant temperature are drawn on the h-y diagram of Fig. 15.5. They consist of nearly straight lines because of the very slight dependence of the enthalpies of air, steam, water and ice on (partial) pressure. They exhibit kinks at the phase boundaries. The pattern made by these isotherms is best understood by direct inspection of the diagram and by thought about its relation to the constant-pressure cooling experiments described above. The state-point of the system undergoing such a process of course moves downward on the diagram along a vertical line. The lines a, b, c, d, e, of Figs. 15.4 and 15.5 correspond. The kinks in these lines in Fig. 15.4 occur when those in Fig. 15.5 cross the phase boundaries. Fig. 15.5 should be compared with Fig. 15.7 which shows, to scale, the h-y diagram for air-water at a pressure of one atmosphere with the enthalpy base chosen as 32°F; it will be noted that for clarity the scale of the lower part of Fig. 15.5 has been distorted.

Because composition is a third independent variable, a single h-y diagram cannot cover all possible states of the system; a family of such diagrams is needed, one for every pressure. The higher the pressure, the higher rises the lower boundary of the gas phase region. At lower pressures the size of the regions involving water decreases; these regions are altogether absent at pressures below that of the triple point.

The saturation line. For most engineering purposes, only the air-steam-water regions are important; interest is restricted to the regions adjoining the upper phase boundary. This boundary is known as the *saturation line*.

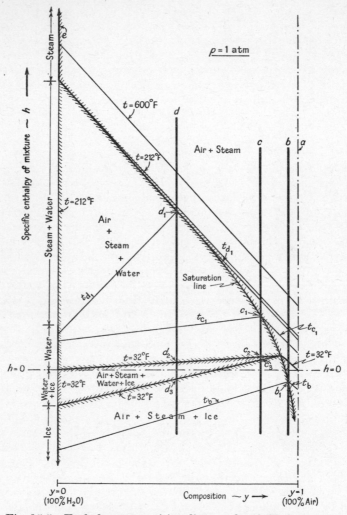

Fig. 15.5 Enthalpy-composition diagram for air-H_2O at atmospheric pressure, approximately to scale. For clarity the scale in the regions where ice is present has been distorted. This diagram should be compared with Fig. 15.7 which is drawn to scale.

States lying on it comprise air and saturated steam, i.e. the mixtures exhibit no tendency to change when brought in contact with saturated water at the same temperature and pressure.

Mixtures of air and saturated steam are known as *saturated air*. The term is to some extent misleading, for it suggests that the air *soaks up* water vapour. In reality, according to Dalton's Law, the steam ignores the presence of air altogether: it is the *space* that is saturated.

The composition of saturated air is calculated from the condition that the steam is saturated: its partial pressure is therefore that appearing in the Saturated Steam Tables opposite the prevailing temperature.

EXAMPLE.

Calculate y and h for saturated air at 70°F and 14·7 psia.

Solution. From the Gibbs·Dalton Law,

$$p_{\text{steam}} + p_{\text{air}} = 14\cdot7 \text{ psia} \qquad \text{[eq. (15.7)]}$$

$$y \cdot v_{\text{air}} = (1 - y)v_{\text{steam}} \qquad \text{[eq. (15.3)]}$$

$$h = y \cdot h_{\text{air}} + (1 - y)h_{\text{steam}} \qquad \text{[eq. (15.9)]}$$

From the Ideal Gas Rule, for air at 70°F.

$$p_{\text{air}} = \frac{53\cdot3 \times (460 + 70)}{144 \times v_{\text{air}}} \qquad \text{[eq. (14.10)]}$$

From Table II, Appendix B, for saturated steam at 70°F

$$p_{\text{steam}} = 0\cdot363 \text{ psia}$$

$$v_{\text{steam}} = 868 \text{ ft}^3/\text{lb}_m$$

$$h_{\text{steam}} = 1092\cdot3 \text{ Btu/lb}_m$$

We obtain first the partial pressure of air, as

$$p_{\text{air}} = 14\cdot7 - 0\cdot363$$

$$= 14\cdot337 \text{ psia}$$

This leads to the specific volume of air, as

$$v_{\text{air}} = \frac{53\cdot3 \times 530}{14\cdot337 \times 144}$$

$$= 13\cdot68 \text{ ft}^3/\text{lb}_m \text{ air}$$

and so to y, as

$$\frac{y}{1 - y} = \frac{868}{13\cdot68} = 63\cdot4$$

$$\therefore \qquad y = \frac{63\cdot4}{64\cdot4} = 1 - 0\cdot0155$$

$$= 0\cdot9845 \text{ lb}_m \text{ air/lb}_m \text{ mixture} \qquad \dots \quad Answer$$

Finally, taking the specific heat of air at constant pressure to be 0·240 Btu/lb_m°F, we have

$$h = 0\cdot9845 \times 0\cdot240(70 - 32) + 0\cdot0155 \times 1092\cdot3$$

$$= 8\cdot97 + 16\cdot92$$

$$= 25\cdot89 \text{ Btu/lb}_m \text{ mixture.} \qquad \dots \quad Answer$$

Constructing an h–y diagram. The example shows how an enthalpy-composition diagram can be constructed using Steam Tables, thermodynamic data for air, and the Gibbs-Dalton Law. When the saturation line and the temperature intercepts on the pure H_2O and pure air boundaries have been drawn, isotherms can be drawn as straight lines between points of equal temperature without appreciable error, because of the pressure-independence of enthalpy noted above.

It is also possible to draw on the *h-y* diagram lines of constant specific volume, constant entropy, or any other desired property.

Other graphical representations of air-steam-water properties. Because of the technical importance of the air-H_2O system, several other ways of representing the system properties graphically have been developed. Two which are frequently encountered will be mentioned.

One, due to Mollier, also has enthalpy and mass composition as co-ordinates. It differs from the *h-y* diagram however in basing both quantities on unit mass of air instead of on unit mass of mixture; the mass quantity is specially emphasised by the name "dry air". The enthalpy of the Mollier chart therefore exceeds *h* by an amount which increases with the proportion of H_2O present. The composition is characterised by the ratio (mass of H_2O)/(mass of dry air). The Mollier chart therefore represents a *projection* of the *h-y* diagram carried out in such a way that the left-hand boundary goes to infinity; the left-hand part of the diagram is necessarily left undrawn.

The second graphical representation is the so-called *psychrometric chart*, Fig. 15.6. This has temperature as abscissa and composition as ordinate, usually in the form of (mass of H_2O)/(mass of dry air). This represents a *distortion* of the *h-y* diagram which is useful for some purposes. The relation of the psychrometric chart of Fig. 15.6 to the *h-y* chart of Fig. 15.5 may be seen if the latter is imagined as being rotated clockwise through 90° and then having all its isotherms "straightened" and made vertical.

Care should always be taken to establish whether enthalpy and composition are being expressed in terms of *h* and *y* or of other units.

Special terms in use in psychrometry

Psychrometry is the study of steam-air mixtures and is particularly concerned with measurement of their properties. It is of special importance to heating-and-ventilating engineers, for the moisture (steam) content, i.e. the humidity, of the atmosphere greatly influences human comfort.

Specific humidity, ω, is the measure of moisture content used in the Mollier and psychrometric charts. Its definition is therefore

$$\omega \equiv \frac{\text{mass of } H_2O}{\text{mass of (dry) air}}$$

$$= \frac{1-y}{y} \qquad\qquad \dots \quad (15.41)$$

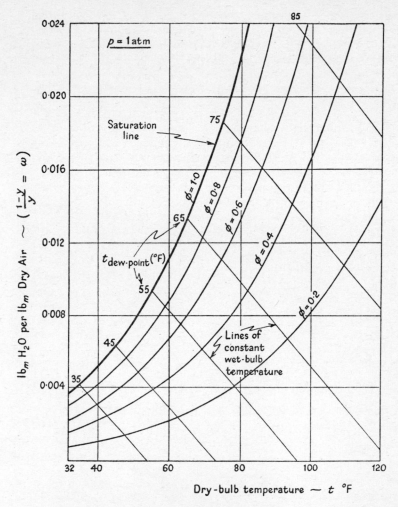

Fig. 15.6 Psychrometric chart for air-H$_2$O at 1 atm (to scale).

At the temperatures and pressures encountered in heating-and-ventilating practice, steam can be regarded as an Ideal Gas. It is therefore permissible to write

$$\omega = \frac{m_{H_2O}}{m_{air}}$$

$$= \frac{v_{air}}{v_{H_2O}} \qquad \text{from eq. (15.3)}$$

$$\approx \frac{\mathscr{R}T}{M_{air}p_{air}} \cdot \frac{M_{steam}p_{steam}}{\mathscr{R}T} \quad \text{from the Ideal Gas Rule, eq. (14.10)}$$

$$\approx \frac{p_{steam}}{p_{air}} \times \frac{18}{29} \qquad \qquad \cdots \quad (15.42)$$

the numerical factor representing the ratio of the molecular weights of steam and air.

If the specific humidity is small, the partial pressure of the air p_{air} is only slightly less than p, the pressure of the mixture. In that case eq. (15.42) becomes

$$\omega \approx 0 \cdot 622 \frac{p_{steam}}{p} \qquad \ldots \quad (15.43)$$

Relative humidity. It is convenient to compare the humidity of the air with the humidity of saturated air at the same pressure and temperature. The *relative humidity*, ϕ, is therefore defined as the ratio of the specific volume of saturated steam at the mixture temperature (v_g) to the specific volume of the steam in the mixture (v_{steam}).

$$\phi = \frac{v_g}{v_{steam}} \qquad \ldots \quad (15.44)$$

As a consequence of the definition, $\phi = 1$ for saturated air.

Since from eq. (15.3)

$$v_{steam} = \frac{v_{air}}{\omega} \qquad \ldots \quad (15.45)$$

eq. (15.44) can be written

$$\phi = \frac{\omega v_g}{v_{air}} \qquad \ldots \quad (15.46)$$

$$= \omega \frac{p_{air} v_g}{R_{air} T} \qquad \ldots \quad (15.47)$$

When steam is treated as an Ideal Gas, this reduces to

$$\phi \approx \omega \frac{R_{steam}}{R_{air}} \cdot \frac{p_{air}}{p_g}$$

$$\approx \omega \frac{29}{18} \frac{p_{air}}{p_g} \qquad \ldots \quad (15.48)$$

where p_g is the saturation pressure of the steam at the prevailing temperature.

Other definitions of ϕ.

(1) ϕ may be defined as the ratio of the mass of water vapour in a given *volume* of mixture to the mass of water vapour in an *equal volume* of *saturated* mixture, at the mixture temperature. This means that ϕ is equal to the ratio of the density of the steam in the mixture to the density of saturated steam at the mixture temperature and is therefore equivalent to the definition expressed by eq. (15.44).

(2) ϕ may be defined as the ratio of the partial pressure of the water vapour in the mixture to the saturation pressure of water vapour at the mixture temperature. If water vapour is assumed to be an Ideal Gas, this definition is equivalent to (1) above and so to that expressed by eq. (15.44).

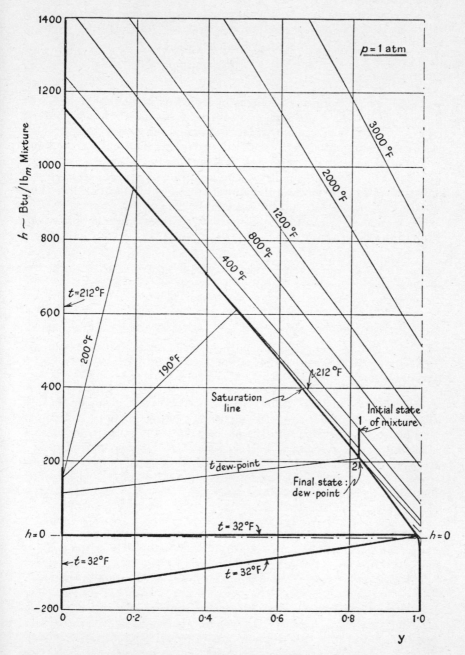

Fig 15.7 *h-y* diagram for air-H$_2$O at atmospheric pressure, to scale, showing the constant-pressure cooling of a given air-H$_2$O mixture to obtain the dew point.

(3) ϕ is sometimes defined as the ratio of the specific humidity of a given *volume* of mixture to the specific humidity of an *equal volume* of *saturated* mixture at the mixture temperature and pressure. This definition gives ϕ a slightly different magnitude from that of eq. (15.44); if the Ideal Gas assumption is made it will be $\dfrac{(p_{air})_{\text{sat. mixture}}}{(p_{air})_{\text{mixture}}}$ times as big as the value given by eq. (15.44).

Dew-point. The moisture content of a mixture is sometimes measured by just such a constant-pressure cooling process as has been described above (p. 289): the mixture is slowly cooled and the temperature at which condensation of water first occurs is noted. This temperature, at which the mixture has become saturated, is known as the dew-point; it corresponds to the temperature of the point at which a vertical through the mixture state-point on an h-y diagram crosses the saturation line (Fig. 15.7); y and ω are constant during this cooling process.

Evaluation of y or ω from a dew-point measurement follows from eq. (15.41) and eq. (15.3)

$$\omega = \frac{1-y}{y} = \frac{v_{air}}{v_g} \text{ at the dew-point}$$

$$= \frac{R_{air} T_{\text{dew-point}}}{v_g (p - p_g)} \qquad \qquad \ldots \quad (15.49)$$

where v_g and p_g are respectively the specific volume and pressure of saturated steam at the dew-point temperature, $T_{\text{dew-point}}$; p is the mixture pressure.

Dry-bulb temperature. The dry-bulb temperature of a steam-air mixture is simply the temperature of the mixture. The special term arises from the practice of measuring the moisture content of a mixture by means of a *wet-and-dry-bulb hygrometer.* This consists of two thermometers exposed to a stream of the mixture (Fig. 15.8). The bulb of one of the thermometers is kept wet by a wick dipping into water; the other is dry, and gives the (dry-bulb) temperature of the mixture.

Wet-bulb temperature. The temperature registered by the thermometer wetted by the wick is known as the *wet-bulb temperature.* This is normally lower than the dry-bulb temperature; the difference between the two is a measure of the humidity of the air.

The relation between the two temperatures is fixed by processes which lie outside thermodynamics: the so-called *rate processes* of heat transfer from the mixture stream to the wick surface, and of mass transfer (diffusion of steam) from the surface into the stream. Heat must be transferred at a rate sufficient to provide the latent heat of vaporisation of steam leaving the wick. However it is a good approximation to take the wet-bulb temperature as equal to the *adiabatic saturation temperature,* which is dealt with below (p. 303) as one of the applications of the First Law.

On the psychrometric chart, Fig. 15.6, it will be seen that the ordinate is ω and the abscissa is the dry-bulb (mixture) temperature; lines of constant ϕ and constant wet-bulb temperature are plotted on the chart. The chart may therefore be used to obtain values of ω and ϕ directly from the readings of the wet- and dry-bulb thermometers.

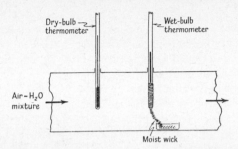

Fig. 15.8   Wet and dry bulb hygrometer.

The Orsat Gas-Analysis Apparatus. We have deferred until this point discussion of a method of determining experimentally the composition of a given Ideal Gas mixture, because the experiment is always carried out with gas which is first saturated with water vapour. There are several

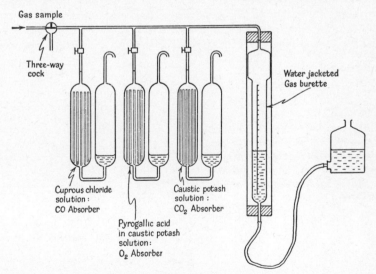

Fig. 15.9   Orsat gas analysis apparatus.

variants of the apparatus, of which the Orsat type, Fig. 15.9, is most familiar. It consists of a graduated cylinder containing the gas, a series of absorption devices which remove one component after another from the mixture, and a device for restoring the pressure of the mixture to atmospheric when measuring its volume.

In effect, the Orsat carries out the mixing process of p. 276 in reverse. If the volume of the mixture is initially V, and the volume decreases resulting from absorption of the components are V_a, V_b, etc., measured at the initial pressure and temperature of the mixture, then the volumes measured in the graduated cylinder are successively V, $V-V_a$, $V-V_a-V_b$, etc.; from these measurements the volumetric analysis of the gas is easily calculated.

The only subtlety lies in the fact that, although the mixture is saturated with steam, only the permanent gases feature in the analysis. This is often called the "dry gas analysis" for emphasis. The explanation is as follows:— The pressure of the mixture does not feature in the expressions for the volumetric analysis provided that it is constant. The partial pressures of the Ideal Gases add up to a total that is less than the mixture pressure, the deficit being the steam partial pressure. Provided that the gas remains saturated however, and the temperature is constant, the partial pressure of steam remains unchanged. The sum of the partial pressures of the Ideal Gases therefore is also constant. The presence of the water vapour consequently has no influence on the results, because as the volume decreases a proportionate amount of water condenses out.

APPLICATIONS OF THE FIRST LAW TO MIXTURES

Now that we have seen how the internal energy and other properties of mixtures are related to the properties of the components, the computation of heat and work quantities in processes undergone by mixtures is a simple matter of applying the First Law of Thermodynamics. A few examples should be sufficient illustration.

An Ideal Gas example

Problem. A rigid insulated vessel of 1 ft^3 capacity contains pure hydrogen at a pressure of 15 psia and a temperature of 50°F. It is connected to a compressed-air main in which the air is at a pressure of 40 psig (atmospheric pressure 14·8 psia) and at a temperature of 70°F. Air enters the vessel until the pressures in the main and in the vessel are equal. What is the final temperature of the mixture in the vessel?

N.B. This problem is important in connection with whether the mixture will explode.

Solution. The data needed are:

For air: $R = 53\cdot3$ ft lb$_f$/lb$_m$°F abs

                  $c_v = 0\cdot171$ Btu/lb$_m$°F

For hydrogen: $R = 772$ ft lb$_f$/lb$_m$°F abs

                  $c_v = 2\cdot43$ Btu/lb$_m$°F

The only difficulty in this problem is to organise the calculation in such a way as to retain clarity. This involves choosing a convenient notation, and working in symbols until the last possible moment. We use suffix a to represent air, and suffix b to represent hydrogen; the suffixes 1 and 2 represent the initial and final states respectively; the a and b are omitted from properties of the mixture; V represents the vessel volume. The system chosen is the mass of hydrogen, m_b, plus the mass of air, m_a, finally in the vessel (Fig. 15.10).

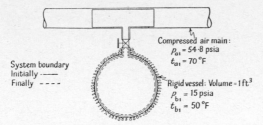

Fig. 15.10   Diagram used in the solution of the example.

From the Ideal Gas Rule,

$$m_b = \frac{p_{b_1} V}{R_b T_{b_1}} \qquad \dots \text{(15.50)}$$

$$= \frac{p_{b_2} V}{R_b T_2} \qquad \dots \text{(15.51)}$$

$$m_a = \frac{p_{a_2} V}{R_a T_2} \qquad \dots \text{(15.52)}$$

$$p_{a_1} v_{a_1} = R_a T_{a_1} \qquad \dots \text{(15.53)}$$

From the Gibbs-Dalton Law,

$$p_2 = p_{a_2} + p_{b_2} = p_{a_1} \qquad \dots \text{(15.54)}$$

From the First Law

$$Q - W = \Delta U \qquad \dots \text{(15.55)}$$

In this case

$$Q = 0$$

W, the work done by the moving boundary, $= -p_{a_1}(m_a \cdot v_{a_1})$

and $\Delta U = m_b c_{v_b}(T_2 - T_{b_1}) + m_a c_{v_a}(T_2 - T_{a_1})$ from the Gibbs-Dalton Law.

Hence eq. (15.55) becomes

$$m_a p_{a_1} v_{a_1} = m_b c_{v_b}(T_2 - T_{b_1}) + m_a c_{v_a}(T_2 - T_{a_1})$$

and so $\quad m_a[p_{a_1} v_{a_1} - c_{v_a}(T_2 - T_{a_1})] = m_b c_{v_b}(T_2 - T_{b_1}) \qquad \dots \text{(15.56)}$

Known are: $p_{a_1}, p_{b_1}, T_{a_1}, T_{b_1}, V, c_{v_a}, c_{v_b}, R_a, R_b$

Unknown are: $m_a, m_b, v_{a_1}, T_2, p_{a_2}, p_{b_2}$

The six equations suffice to yield the six unknowns. We are required to determine T_2 so we combine the six equations to eliminate the other five unknowns.

Substituting in eq. (15.54) from eq. (15.51) and eq. (15.52) we have

$$(m_a R_a + m_b R_b) \frac{T_2}{v} = p_{a_1}$$

and hence
$$m_a = \frac{1}{R_a} \left(\frac{p_{a_1} V}{T_2} - m_b R_b \right) \qquad \dots \quad (15.57)$$

Then in eq. (15.56) substitute for m_a from eq. (15.57), to give

$$\frac{1}{R_a} \left(\frac{p_{a_1} V}{T_2} - m_b R_b \right) [p_{a_1} v_{a_1} - c_{v_a}(T_2 - T_{a_1})] = m_b c_{v_b}(T_2 - T_{b_1})$$
$$\dots \quad (15.58)$$

Finally substitute in eq. (15.58) for m_b from equation (15.50) and for $p_{a_1} v_{a_1}$ from eq. (15.53) to give

$$\frac{1}{R_a} \left(\frac{p_{a_1} V}{T_2} - \frac{p_{b_1} V}{T_{b_1}} \right) [R_a T_{a_1} - c_{v_a}(T_2 - T_{a_1})] = \frac{p_{b_1} V}{R_b T_{b_1}} c_{v_b}(T_2 - T_{b_1})$$

which reduces to

$$\left(\frac{p_{a_1}}{T_2} - \frac{p_{b_1}}{T_{b_1}} \right) \left[T_{a_1} - \frac{c_{v_a}}{R_a}(T_2 - T_{a_1}) \right] = \frac{p_{b_1}}{T_{b_1}} \cdot \frac{c_{v_b}}{R_b} (T_2 - T_{b_1}) \quad \dots \quad (15.59)$$

T_2 is the only unknown in eq. (15.59). Inserting the given data in eq. (15.59) we have

$$\left(\frac{54 \cdot 8 \times 144}{T_2} - \frac{15 \times 144}{510} \right) \left[530 - \frac{0 \cdot 171 \times 778}{53 \cdot 3} (T_2 - 530) \right]$$
$$= \frac{15 \times 144}{510} \times \frac{2 \cdot 43 \times 778}{772} (T_2 - 510)$$

or $\left(\dfrac{7890}{T_2} - 4 \cdot 24 \right) [530 - 2 \cdot 495(T_2 - 530)] = 10 \cdot 37(T_2 - 510)$

Hence
$$T_2 = 661°F \text{ abs} = 201°F \qquad \dots \quad \textit{Answer.}$$

Remarks. 1. A quadratic in T_2 is obtained. The second value of T_2 which satisfies the equation is a negative absolute temperature and is therefore inadmissible as a solution.

2. The final mixture temperature T_2 is independent of the vessel volume V, since V does appear in eq. (15.59). This means that for given initial conditions the gases will mix in the same mass *ratio* to produce the same final conditions, irrespective of the magnitude of V; we would expect this in view of the Gibbs-Dalton relations. V will, of course, affect the magnitudes of both m_a and m_b, but not their ratio.

3. Note that when the data are inserted in eq. (15.59) the mechanical equivalent of heat, 778 ft lb$_f$/Btu, has to be included to make the units consistent.

Adiabatic saturation of air

As our first example of the application of the First Law to a mixture of an Ideal Gas and a condensable vapour, we consider the addition of water to air in a constant-pressure adiabatic process resulting in a saturated mixture. The process, which is called *adiabatic saturation*, is most easily followed on the h-y diagram for the prevailing pressure. First however we prove a general result relating to mixing processes represented on such diagrams.

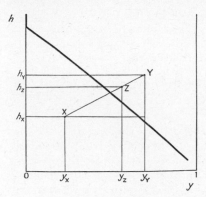

Fig. 15.11 Illustrating the mixing rule.

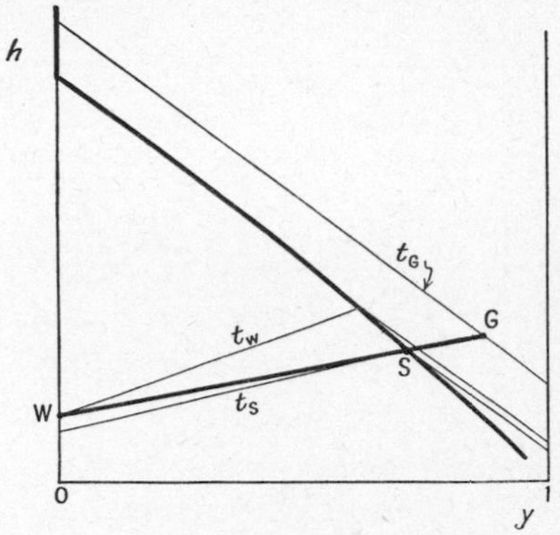

Fig. 15.12 Enthalpy–composition diagram for air-H_2O showing an adiabatic saturation process.

The mixing rule. If X and Y are the state-points of two air-H_2O systems on an h-y diagram (Fig. 15.11), and these two systems are mixed together adiabatically at constant pressure in the mass proportions m_X to m_Y, the state-point Z for the resultant system lies on the line XY and divides it so that

$$\frac{ZY}{XZ} = \frac{m_X}{m_Y} \qquad \cdots \ (15.60)$$

Proof. From the First Law applied to the constant-pressure adiabatic process, $\Delta h = 0$ and therefore

$$m_X h_X + m_Y h_Y = (m_X + m_Y)h_Z$$

i.e.
$$\frac{m_X}{m_Y} = \frac{h_Y - h_Z}{h_Z - h_X} \qquad \cdots \ (15.61)$$

The principle of conservation of mass applied to air in the process yields

$$m_X y_X + m_Y y_Y = (m_X + m_Y)y_Z$$

i.e.
$$\frac{m_X}{m_Y} = \frac{y_Y - y_Z}{y_Z - y_X} \qquad \cdots \ (15.62)$$

Equations (15.61) and (15.62) interpreted geometrically on the h–y diagram provide the required result.

Adiabatic saturation on the h-y diagram. Fig. 15.12 shows an *h-y* diagram. G represents the initial state of the air-steam mixture while W represents the state of the water which is to be mixed with it. How much water must be added, if the resultant mixture is to comprise saturated air?

The above mixing rule shows that the state-point for the resultant mixture must lie on the line WG. But it must also lie on the saturation line. The required state-point is therefore S, where WG cuts the saturation line.

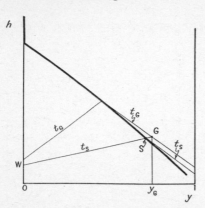

The required mass ratio m_W/m_G is given by the mixing rule as the ratio of two lengths

$$\frac{m_W}{m_G} = \frac{SG}{WS} \quad \dots \quad (15.63)$$

Fig. 15.13   Showing how the mixture content of an air-H$_2$O mixture may be evaluated from wet-and-dry bulb thermometer readings.

Wet-bulb temperature. It has already been stated on p. 298 above that the wet-bulb temperature is approximately that corresponding to adiabatic saturation. But clearly the latter temperature, for given gas condition, G, depends on the temperature of the water which is supplied. The experimental conditions in wet-and-dry-bulb hygrometers are usually such that the water supplied to the wick is already at the wet-bulb temperature. S is therefore fixed by the condition that W and S must lie on the same isotherm.

In hygrometry the usual problem is to evaluate the moisture content of the air from the measured values t_S and t_G. Fig. 15.13 shows that these values fix the line WS (which now is the isotherm, t_S in the mixed-phase region) and also the gas-phase isotherm, t_G, on which G lies. Hence G is determined uniquely as their intersection, and so y_G is obtained.

Evaluation of this result can of course be obtained by means of tables of properties of steam and air alone. This however usually involves a considerable amount of trial-and-error, which is avoided by use of the *h-y* diagram.

The Steady-Flow Energy Equation applied to air-water mixtures

As our final illustration of the First Law applied to mixtures, we consider a problem arising in the design of a cooling-tower. Fig. 15.14 illustrates a natural-draught cooling-tower used for cooling the water used in the condenser of a steam power plant. The warm water from the condenser enters the tower and is sprayed on to a packing constructed of wooden slats, over which it flows under gravity; it drips from the bottom of the packing, having been cooled by contact with air, and is collected and returned to the plant. The air enters at the bottom of the tower, and rises up through the packing, increasing meanwhile in temperature and moisture content, and leaves through the top of the tower. The circulation of air is caused by the buoyancy of the warmed air; the difference in hydrostatic pressure between the top and bottom of the packing exactly balances the flow resistance caused by the packing.

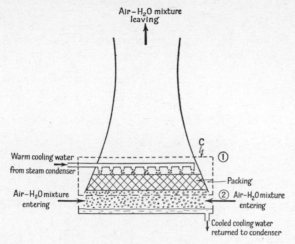

Fig. 15.14 Illustrating the example on the cooling tower.

EXAMPLE

Problem. Water enters a cooling tower at 70°F and leaves at 50°F. The air enters at 45°F and 50% relative humidity, and leaves, saturated, at 65°F. Determine the ratio of mass flow rates of entering water and air, and the percentage of entering water which leaves with the air as steam. The pressure may be taken as 14·7 psia throughout.

Solution. This problem is most easily solved analytically if we adopt as our basis 1 lb$_m$ of *dry air* entering the cooling tower; for the leaving dry air mass flow is the same. This means that it is simplest to express steam contents in terms of specific humidity. We first calculate these humidities.

At air entry, section 2, ω_2 is given by equation (15.48)

$$\omega_2 = 0\cdot5 \times \frac{18}{29} \times \frac{p}{14\cdot7 - p}$$

$$= 0\cdot5 \times \frac{18}{29} \times \frac{0\cdot1475}{14\cdot7 - 0\cdot1475} \quad \text{from Steam Tables}$$

$$= 0\cdot00315 \quad \text{lb}_m \text{ H}_2\text{O/lb}_m \text{ dry air}$$

At air exit, section 1, ω_1 is given by

$$\omega_1 = 1 \times \frac{18}{29} \times \frac{p}{14\cdot7 - p}$$

$$= \frac{18}{29} \times \frac{0\cdot306}{14\cdot7 - 0\cdot306} \quad \text{from Steam Tables}$$

$$= 0\cdot0132 \quad \text{lb}_m \text{ H}_2\text{O/lb}_m \text{ dry air}$$

The mass of water vaporising, m_v, is therefore

$$m_v = \omega_1 - \omega_2$$
$$= 0.0132 - 0.00315$$
$$= 0.00905 \ lb_m/lb_m \ \text{dry air}$$

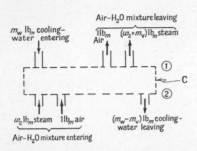

Fig. 15.15 Diagram showing the streams entering and leaving the control surface C of Fig. 15.14.

To obtain the mass of water m_w entering, we apply the Steady-Flow Energy Equation to a control volume enclosing the cooling tower. The Gibbs-Dalton Law is used implicitly by treating the enthalpies of the components separately. There is no heat flux or external work, and the gravitational and kinetic energies will be neglected. The enthalpy of the entering steam (mass ω_2) will be taken as the saturation enthalpy for the entering air temperature h_{g_2}. Fig. 15.15 shows the various streams. The S.F.E.E. eq. (8.27) gives

$$0 = 1 \times 0.24(t_{a_1} - 32) + (\omega_2 + m_v)h_{g_1} + (m_w - m_v)h_{w_2}$$
$$- 1 \times 0.24(t_{a_2} - 32) - \omega_2 h_{g_2} - m_w h_{w_1}$$

$$\therefore \quad m_w = \frac{0.24(t_{a_1} - t_{a_2}) + \omega_2(h_{g_1} - h_{g_2}) + m_v(h_{g_1} - h_{w_2})}{h_{w_1} - h_{w_2}}$$

$$= \frac{0.24(65 - 45) + 0.00315(1090.2 - 1081.5) + 0.00905(1090.2 - 18.1)}{38.0 - 18.1}$$

$$= \frac{4.8 + 0.0274 + 9.74}{19.9}$$

$$= \frac{14.57}{19.9}$$

$$= 0.731 \ lb_m \ \text{water}/lb_m \ \text{of dry air}. \qquad \dots \ \textit{Answer.}$$

N.B. The contribution of the vaporised steam to the energy equation $m_v(h_{g_1} - h_{w_2})$ is an important one (9.74 in 14.57). This is one reason why direct contact of water and air is preferred to a construction in which vaporisation is prevented. (The other is cheapness of construction.)

The required answers are now quickly obtained. The mass flow ratio is 0.731 as just shown. The percentage of water vaporised is

$$100 \times \frac{m_v}{m_w} = \frac{100 \times 0.00905}{0.731}$$

$$= 1.24\% \qquad \dots \ \textit{Answer.}$$

N.B. This vaporised water, together with any that is carried away by the air in droplet form, has to be made up from some external supply. However the quantity to be supplied is obviously very much less than if no cooling tower were used and all the water had to be replaced from a river.

THE SECOND LAW APPLIED TO GASEOUS MIXTURES

In Chapter 14, where reversible adiabatic processes undergone by air were discussed, we have already implicitly applied the Second Law of Thermodynamics to systems comprising gaseous mixtures. We conclude the present chapter by justifying the procedure of Chapter 14 by reference to the Gibbs-Dalton Law. The discussion is restricted to isentropic processes. Firstly Perfect Gas mixtures are discussed, and secondly mixtures including a condensable vapour.

Reversible adiabatic expansion of a Perfect* Gas mixture

Pure substances satisfying the Perfect Gas definition have simple algebraic relations between their properties when undergoing isentropic processes, as shown in Chapter 14. For example, for such a substance and process,

$$pv^{\gamma} = \text{constant} \qquad \ldots \quad (15.64)$$

It will now be shown that the same is true of *mixtures* of Perfect Gases.

p–v–T relations in an isentropic process. For a single component of a gas, designated by suffix a, we have

$$s_{a_2} - s_{a_1} = c_{v_a} \ln \left(\frac{T_2}{T_1}\right) + R_a \ln \left(\frac{V_2}{V_1}\right) \qquad \ldots \quad (15.65)$$

Therefore for a mixture of masses m_a, m_b, m_c ... of gases a, b, c ..., the entropy change in any process $(s_2 - s_1)$ is given by the Gibbs-Dalton Law as

$$(m_a + m_b + m_c + \ldots)(s_2 - s_1) = (m_a c_{v_a} + m_b c_{v_b} + \ldots) \ln \left(\frac{T_2}{T_1}\right)$$
$$+ (m_a R_a + m_b R_b + \ldots) \ln \left(\frac{V_2}{V_1}\right) \qquad \ldots \quad (15.66)$$

Here T and V do not have letter subscripts because they are the same for each component.

Now if we define c_v and R for the mixture by the weighted averaging equations

$$c_v \equiv \frac{m_a c_{v_a} + m_b c_{v_b} + \ldots}{m_a + m_b + \ldots} \qquad \ldots \quad (15.67)$$

and

$$R \equiv \frac{m_a R_a + m_b R_b + \ldots}{m_a + m_b + \ldots} \qquad \ldots \quad (15.68)$$

eq. (15.66) becomes

$$s_2 - s_1 = c_v \ln \left(\frac{T_2}{T_1}\right) + R \ln \left(\frac{V_2}{V_1}\right) \qquad \ldots \quad (15.69)$$

This is of course the same equation as holds for a chemically pure substance.

* N.B. *Not* for Ideal Gases in general.

Since for any component we have

$$c_{p_a} = c_{v_a} + R_a \qquad \ldots \text{ (15.70)}$$

it is easy to show that a mixture specific heat at constant pressure, defined by

$$c_p \equiv \frac{m_a c_{p_a} + m_b c_{p_b} + \cdots}{m_a + m_b + \cdots} \qquad \ldots \text{ (15.71)}$$

obeys the equation

$$c_p = c_v + R \qquad \ldots \text{ (15.72)}$$

This completes the parallelism and it only remains to define a mixture specific heat ratio γ, by

$$\gamma = \frac{c_p}{c_v} = \frac{m_a c_{p_a} + m_b c_{p_b} + \cdots}{m_a c_{v_a} + m_b c_{v_b}} \qquad \ldots \text{ (15.73)}$$

and to carry out the steps already shown in Chapter 14 (pp. 259, 260), in order to demonstrate that the mixture obeys the relations

$$pv^\gamma = \text{constant etc.,} \qquad \ldots \text{ (15.74)}$$

when carrying out a process of constant entropy.

Warning. It should be noted that, γ is not formed from the γ's of the components by a direct weighting procedure, i.e.

$$\gamma \neq \frac{m_a \gamma_a + m_b \gamma_b + \cdots}{m_a + m_b + \cdots}$$

Energy interchange between components. Suppose two Perfect Gases having different γ's are mixed together; the mixture γ will have an intermediate value. If not mixed, the gas with the higher γ would become cooler, on expanding isentropically through a fixed pressure ratio from a given initial temperature, than the gas with the lower γ. If they are mixed before the expansion takes place both components must have equal temperatures at all times. We infer that there is an energy interchange[*] between the components to bring this temperature equality about. A consequence is that although the entropy of the mixture is constant, the entropy of the gas with the lower γ decreases, while that of the gas with the higher γ increases during the expansion.

Reversible adiabatic expansion of steam and air

In conclusion the method of calculating the p–v–T relations for an isentropically expanding mixture of steam and air will be indicated. The fundamental principles are (i) the entropy *of the mixture* remains constant, not however the entropies of the components; (ii) the volume occupied by the air is the same as that occupied by the steam; (iii) the temperatures of the two components are equal at all times; (iv) the pressure of the mixture is equal to the sum of the partial pressures.

[*] Since this interchange takes place on the molecular scale it cannot be classified as heat or work.

Typical problem. Given a mixture of steam and air at an initial pressure and temperature, determine the $p-v-T$ relations during isentropic expansion.

Method of solution. It is most convenient to derive the volume-temperature relation first. A suitable procedure is as follows. For any given specific volume of the mixture, guess the corresponding temperature. This yields the air entropy from the algebraic formula eq. (14.43), assuming air to be a Perfect Gas, and the steam entropy from interpolation in Steam Tables. The latter is somewhat complicated because the steam pressure is not known; an *h-s* chart with constant volume and constant temperature lines drawn on it would enable *s* for steam to be found without interpolation.

The mixture entropy is thus calculated and compared with that of the initial mixture. If the two quantities are equal, the guessed temperature is correct. If not, a new guess is made. In this way the temperature corresponding to the chosen specific volume is found by trial-and-error.

The partial pressures of steam and air are then obtained respectively from Steam Tables (or charts) and the Ideal Gas Rule. The mixture pressure is the sum of the partial pressures.

In this way the complete $p-v-T$ relation for the expansion can be worked out. The procedure is tedious however and, if condensation does not occur, is usually replaced by the approximate assumption that steam is a Perfect Gas.

BIBLIOGRAPHY

Gibbs, J. W., *Collected Works*, Longmans, 1931.
Institution of Heating and Ventilation Engineers *Psychrometric Chart*.
Keenan, J. H., *Thermodynamics*, J. Wiley and Sons and Chapman & Hall, 1941.
Mollier, R., *Z.V.D.I.*, Vol 67 (1923) pp. 869-872, Vol 73 (1929) pp. 1009-1013.
Spalding, D. B., *Graphical Method of Calculating Heat Transfer, Condensation and Vaporisation Rates in Processes involving Water-Steam-Air Mixtures.* Institution of Mechanical Engineers. Vol 172 (1958) No 28.

CHAPTER 15—PROBLEMS

15.1 A rigid vessel contains a mixture of 1 lb_m of carbon monoxide (CO) and 1 lb_m of hydrogen (H_2) at a pressure of 30 psia and a temperature of 65°F.
Assuming CO and H_2 to be Ideal Gases evaluate:
  (i) the partial pressures of the components;
  (ii) the volume and specific volume of the mixture;
  (iii) the volumetric analysis;
  (iv) the molal analysis;
  (v) the Gas Constant, the specific heats and γ of the mixture.
Use the following data:
Atomic weights: C = 12·01, H = 1·008, O = 16. Specific heat at constant pressure: for CO, c_p = 0·252 Btu/lb_m °F; for H_2, c_p = 3·99 Btu/lb_m °F. The Universal Gas Constant $\mathcal{R}$ = 1·986 Btu/lb mole °F abs.

15.2 Heat transfer to the mixture of problem 15.1 at constant volume raises its pressure to 60 psia. Assuming the mixture to be a Perfect Gas evaluate:

(i) the final temperature of the mixture;

(ii) the increases in the specific enthalpy, the specific internal energy and the specific entropy;

(iii) the magnitude of the heat transfer.

15.3 Re-consider problem 15.2 given that the change of state was brought about by stirring work in the absence of heat transfer. In this case evaluate the magnitude of the stirring work.

15.4 (a) A cylinder, fitted with a piston, contains $0.02\ \text{lb}_m$ of a Perfect Gas ($M = 15$, $c_p = 0.2\ \text{Btu/lb}_m\ °\text{F}$) at a pressure of 15 psia and a temperature of 60°F. Calculate the volume of the gas.

(b) With the piston held stationary, $0.03\ \text{lb}_m$ of a second Perfect Gas ($M = 40$, $c_p = 0.26\ \text{Btu/lb}_m\ °\text{F}$) is introduced into the cylinder. It is found that the temperature of the contents of the cylinder has risen to 100°F. For the mixture, evaluate:

(i) the final pressure;

(ii) the specific heats and γ.

(c) The mixture now undergoes a fully resisted expansion to a final specific volume of $30\ \text{ft}^3/\text{lb}_m$ as the piston moves slowly outwards; the process may be represented by $pV^{1.4}$ = constant where p is the mixture pressure and V the corresponding mixture volume. Evaluate the final pressure, the work done by the mixture and the magnitude and sign of the heat transfer. Evaluate also the increase in specific entropy during the process.

(d) What would have been the final pressure and the work done if the expansion in (c) had been reversible and adiabatic. In this case evaluate the increase in the entropy of each component.

The Universal Gas Constant $\mathscr{R} = 1.986\ \text{Btu/lb mole }°\text{F abs.}$

15.5 Methane gas and air are mixed adiabatically in steady flow in the mass ratio of 1 : 20. The air stream flows steadily into the mixing chamber at a pressure of 16 psia; the methane is at a pressure of 40 psia and the mixed gas stream flows steadily out of the mixing chamber at a pressure of 15 psia. The temperature of the methane and of the air at entry to the mixing chamber are both 60°F. Flow velocities and changes in elevation are negligible. Evaluate:

(i) the temperature of the mixture stream;

(ii) the partial pressure of the gases in the mixture stream;

(iii) the increase in the entropy of the gases due to mixing, per lb_m of mixture.

Assume methane and air to be Perfect Gases and use the following data:

Molecular weight: CH_4, 16.04: Air, 28.97.

Specific heat at constant pressure: CH_4, $c_p = 0.53\ \text{Btu/lb}_m°\text{F}$; air, $c_p = 0.24\ \text{Btu/lb}_m°\text{F}$.

The Universal Gas Constant $\mathscr{R} = 1.986\ \text{Btu/lb}_m\ °\text{F abs.}$

15.6 (a) A rigid vessel containing 2 ft³ of carbon monoxide at a temperature of 60°F and a pressure of 25 psia is connected, via a valve and a short pipe, to a second rigid vessel containing 3 ft³ hydrogen at a temperature of 60°F and a pressure of 25 psia. The vessels, the valve and the pipeline are well insulated. The valve, which initially is shut, is opened so allowing the two gases to mix; after a time conditions become uniform throughout the vessels. Assuming carbon monoxide and hydrogen to be Perfect Gases and using the data given in problem 15.1, evaluate:

(i) the temperature of the mixture;

(ii) the partial pressures of the components;

(iii) the specific volume of the mixture;

(iv) the gravimetric analysis;

(v) the molal analysis;

(vi) the Gas Constant, the specific heats and γ of the mixture;

(vii) the increase in the entropy of the system comprising the two gases.

(b) the two vessels in (a) are connected, through a valve, to a third insulated vessel of volume 5 ft³. By opening the valve the third vessel, which initially is evacuated, is put into communication with the two inter-connected vessels containing the gas mixture. What are the temperature and pressure when conditions throughout the three vessels have become uniform?

(c) What would have been the final temperature and pressure if the three vessels had been put into communication simultaneously?

15.7 A rigid insulated vessel contains 0.1 lb$_m$ of hydrogen at a pressure of 15 psia and a temperature of 60°F. The vessel is connected to a pipeline containing carbon monoxide; the pressure and temperature in the pipeline are maintained at 60 psia and 70°F respectively. Carbon monoxide is allowed to flow into the vessel until the pressure of the mixture in the vessel has risen to 50 psia. Evaluate the temperature and the mass of the mixture in the vessel.

Assume carbon monoxide and hydrogen to be Perfect Gases and use the data given in Problem 15.1.

15.8 (a) 0.02 lb$_m$ of steam and 0.18 lb$_m$ of air form a gaseous mixture at a temperature of 300°F and a pressure of 30 psia. Determine (i) the partial pressures of the steam and air, (ii) the specific volume, and (iii) the specific internal energy of the mixture. In the latter case specify the datum state which you are using.

Assume air and steam to be Perfect Gases and use the following data: for air $R = 53.3$ ft lb$_f$/lb$_m$°F abs and $c_p = 0.24$ Btu/lb$_m$°F; for steam $R = 85.8$ ft lb$_f$/lb$_m$°F abs and $c_p = 0.48$ Btu/lb$_m$°F.

(b) Recalculate (a) using the Superheated Steam Table (Appendix B). In this case again specify the datum you are using.

15.9 (a) A vessel of 200 ft³ capacity initially contains a mixture of air and saturated water vapour at a temperature of 100°F and a pressure of 2 psia. Evaluate the mass of air and vapour in the vessel.

(b) Subsequently 2.3 lb$_m$ of air leak into the vessel and 0.31 lb$_m$ of water vapour condenses. Determine the temperature pressure and of the mixture in the vessel.

Assume air to be an Ideal Gas.

15.10 A closed rigid vessel of capacity 40 ft³ contains an air-H_2O mixture at a pressure of 100 psia and a temperature of 250°F. The H_2O, which is present in both the liquid and vapour phases, has a total mass of 10 lb$_m$.

Heat transfer from the contents of the vessel reduces the temperature to 50°F. Evaluate:

(i) the final pressure;

(ii) the mass of water which condenses;

(iii) the magnitude of the heat transfer;

(iv) the increase in the entropy of the contents of the vessel.

Assume air to be a Perfect Gas with $R = 53.3$ ft lb$_f$/lb$_m$°F abs and $c_p = 0.24$ Btu/lb$_m$°F.

15.11 Evaluate h and y for a saturated air-stream mixture at a temperature of 190°F and a pressure of 1 atm. Check your result against Fig. 25.7.

15.12 A vessel contains a mixture of air and steam at a pressure of 14·7 psia and a temperature of 80°F. The mass ratio of air to steam is 99 : 1.

Assuming air and steam to be Perfect Gases evaluate:
  (i) the partial pressures of the air and the steam;
  (ii) the specific volume of the mixture;
  (iii) the specific enthalpy of the mixture (datum 32°F);
  (iv) the specific internal energy of the mixture;
  (v) the specific entropy of the mixture (datum 32°F, 14·7 psia).
Use the following data: R for steam = 85·8 ft lb_f/lb_m°F abs; R for air = 53·3 ft lb_f/lb_m°F abs.

15.13 For the mixture of problem 15.12 evaluate:
  (i) the composition, y;
  (ii) the specific humidity, ω, in grains/lb_m (7000 grains ≡ 1 lb_m);
  (iii) the relative humidity, ϕ;
  (iv) the dew point;
  (v) the temperature to which the air must be cooled at constant volume to reach saturation. Check the answers to (ii), (iii) and (iv) against the Psychrometric Chart, Fig. 15.6.

15.14 For the mixture of problem 15.12 compare the values of relative humidity corresponding to the various definitions given on pp. 296, 298.

c_p for steam = 0·48, for air = 0·24 Btu/lb_m°F.

15.15 One cubic foot of the mixture of problem 15.12 is contained in a well-insulated cylinder fitted with a non-conducting piston. Liquid water is added to the mixture as the piston moves slowly to keep the pressure constant at 14·7 psia. Evaluate the adiabatic saturation temperature and the mass of water added when the water temperature is (a) 100°F, and (b) 66°F. Compare the values of saturation temperature with the wet-bulb temperature obtained from the Psychrometric Chart, Fig. 15.6.

15.16 An air-H_2O mixture at a pressure of 1 atm and a temperature of 80°F has a relative humidity of 20 per cent. The mixture flows steadily into a cooler at the rate of 800 ft³/min. and emerges at a temperature of 40°F. The pressure drop in the cooler is negligible. Evaluate:
  (a) the specific humidity of the mixture entering and leaving the cooler;
  (b) the relative humidity of the cooled mixture;
  (c) the heat transfer rate from the mixture.

15.17 Recalculate problem 15.16 given that the relative humidity of the mixture entering the cooler is 80 per cent. In this case determine the quantity of liquid water leaving the cooler.

15.18 An air-H_2O mixture at a pressure of 1 atm, a temperature of 32°F and a relative humidity of 40 per cent is to be "conditioned" to a temperature of 80°F and a relative humidity of 60 per cent by successively passing it, in steady flow, through a heater and an adiabatic spray chamber. Water at a temperature of 40°F is sprayed into the heated air at the rate of 0·015 lb_m per pound of dry air, any excess being drained from the spray chamber at a temperature of 40°F. The air duct is well insulated and the pressure may be assumed to be 1 atm throughout.

Evaluate:
  (i) the rate at which water is drained from the spray chamber;
  (ii) the temperature of the mixture leaving the heater;
  (iii) the heat transfer to the mixture in Btu per pound of mixture.

15.19 One pound of an air-H_2O mixture at a pressure of 1 atm, a temperature of 400°F and a composition y of 0·8 is mixed with 0·5 lb_m of an air-H_2O

mixture at a pressure of 1 atm, a temperature of 190°F and a composition of 0·2. Evaluate the composition and enthalpy of the resultant mixture and the quantity of liquid water contained in it. Check the calculation against the h-y chart, Fig. 15.7.

15.20 Plot to scale the saturation line and a few isotherms of an h-y chart for air-H_2O at a pressure of 1 atm. The chart should be about 10 in. square.

15.21 Steam escapes from a safety valve at a pressure of 1 atm with 50°F superheat into dry air at a temperature of 80°F. Will the jet be visible? (Solve with the aid of the chart of problem 15.20, assuming that the various states in the jet are found by adiabatic mixture of the steam and air and that their state points lie on the line joining the initial steam and air state points. If that line crosses the saturation line, condensation occurs and the droplets enable the jet to be seen.)

15.22 Air flowing in from an ocean is at a temperature of 50°F and has a relative humidity of 80 per cent. It passes over a mountain range. Assuming that the air-steam mixture changes isentropically (with $\gamma = 1·4$), determine the height of the mountain range which will just cause clouds to form at the peaks. The pressure-altitude relation may be taken as $p = 30 - 9 \times 10^{-4}z$ in. Hg where z is the height in feet above sea level.

CHAPTER 16

FUELS AND COMBUSTION

INTRODUCTION
The engineering importance of combustion

We have seen that one way of producing mechanical power is to construct a heat engine which exchanges heat with two systems: one at a high temperature and the other at a low temperature. Now, except in rare circumstances, systems of widely differing temperatures are not found in nature close together; they must therefore be constructed by man. The most common procedure is to use the atmosphere or a river as the low-temperature reservoir, and to provide a high-temperature heat source by burning fuel with air. It is in this way that a considerable proportion of the world's power is produced, usually in conjunction with steam power plants.

However this is not the only way of producing power from the combustion of fuel. Internal-combustion engines operate on the different principle of compressing the fuel and air, burning it at a pressure above that of the atmosphere, and then expanding the products of combustion into the atmosphere. Cars, lorries and aircraft are propelled in this way.

It is therefore important for the engineer to know the properties of available fuels and of their combustion products, to be able to calculate the temperature which can be reached in burning and the maximum work that can be obtained from a given quantity of fuel. We therefore have to make an excursion into chemical thermodynamics.

In doing so we touch on a subject which is vital to other branches of engineering also. For example, the operations of the metallurgical industry can only be understood through knowledge of the interactions between the fuel used in smelting and the metal-bearing ores, and the various metals which make up an alloy. Chemical thermodynamics is even more important to the chemical engineer, who can only plan his operations with the aid of quantitative knowledge of what reactions are possible, how they depend on pressure and temperature, and what changes in composition and energy accompany them.

The science of chemical change

Broadly speaking the scientific knowledge needed in designing plant for carrying out combustion or other chemical reactions consists of two parts. Firstly, it is necessary, as just implied, to calculate the direction which a reaction can be expected to take, together with the associated composition and energy changes. Secondly, we have to predict *how fast* the reaction will be and so *how big* a piece of equipment must be provided for a given output.

It is the first body of knowledge which comprises *chemical thermodynamics*, and it is only this aspect of chemical change which will be discussed in the present book. Our aim, moreover, is to introduce merely the fundamental ideas and their application to mechanical engineering.

The second body of knowledge is known as the science of *rate processes*, which may be regarded as thermodynamics with a time scale. The study of the rate of chemical reaction is known as *chemical kinetics*. It is beyond the scope of this book.

Similar restrictions to the scope of thermodynamics have already been noted. Although heat has been extensively discussed above, the calculations have been about its magnitude in any process, not the time taken for the process to occur; the latter theme belongs to the science of *heat transfer*. In Chapter 15, the thermodynamics of mixtures was discussed; how long a given mixing process will take, and how this depends on the area of contact between the mixing substances, can only be discovered by studying the subject known as *mass transfer*.

The nature of chemical thermodynamics

The subsequent discussion of combustion will reveal that chemical thermodynamics has three main aspects, corresponding to the three natural laws: the Law of Conservation of Matter, the First Law of Thermodynamics, and the Second Law of Thermodynamics.

The first aspect is known as *stoichiometry*. It is concerned with the relations between the composition of the reactants, e.g. the fuel and air, and the composition of the products. It necessitates an understanding of the chemical constitution of matter, and involves accounting for each of the chemical elements as they change partners in the reaction.

In Chapter 6 it was emphasised that the First Law is completely general. In later chapters however we imposed the restriction that the chemical state of the system should not change. Now this restriction must be removed, and we must study the heat, work and energy changes in processes undergone by systems which are not pure substances.

The Second Law gives two types of information about chemical reactions. Firstly, by distinguishing between reversible and irreversible processes, it tells us whether a given reaction will go forwards or backwards; whether, for example, we can ever expect combustion products to decompose spontaneously into fuel and oxygen. Secondly, the Second Law makes it possible to determine how much work can be obtained by burning a fixed mass of fuel; this gives us a standard against which the performance of actual power plants can be measured. In the present book, this aspect of chemical thermodynamics is only briefly touched on.

Summary of the remainder of the chapter

The treatment will follow the sub-division of the subject which has just been indicated. In the first section, the composition of fuels will be discussed together with the methods of calculating the composition of the combustion products from the fuel/air ratio, and vice versa.

The second section introduces enthalpies of reaction and formation, and the calorific values of fuels. It is shown how the temperatures attained in burning mixtures can be calculated, and how much heat can be transferred from the products of combustion.

The final section deals with the entropy changes which occur during reaction, and explains their relation to the maximum possible work output. This makes it possible to define and discuss the efficiency of internal combustion engines.

Symbols

c_p	Specific heat at constant pressure.	U_{fg}	Increase in internal energy of a pure substance during vaporisation, per lb mole.
H'	Enthalpy of a chemical substance.		
H'_f	Enthalpy of formation of a chemical substance.	u_{fg}	Increase in internal energy of a pure substance during vaporisation, per lb_m.
$[\Delta H']_{p,t}$	Increase in enthalpy of a chemical substance in a constant-pressure, isothermal reaction.	V	System volume.
		W	Net work done by a system.
		W_x	External work.
H_{fg}	Latent heat of vaporisation of a pure substance, per lb mole.	x	Air-fuel ratio by mass.
		x_{stoich}	Stoichiometric air-fuel ratio by mass.
h_{fg}	Latent heat of vaporisation of a pure substance, per lb_m.	y	Air-fuel ratio by volume.
		$\overline{CV}$	Calorific value of a fuel.
		$\overline{LCV}$	Lower (or net) calorific value of a fuel.
h	Specific enthalpy of a pure substance.	$\overline{HCV}$	Higher (or gross) calorific value of a fuel.
m	Mass.		
$\dot m$	Mass flow rate.	η_c	Combustion efficiency.
n	Number of moles.	η_h	Heating efficiency.
p	Pressure.	$\eta_{i.c.}$	Efficiency of an internal combustion engine.
Q	Heat transfer.		
$\mathscr{R}$	Universal Gas Constant.		
S'	Entropy of a chemical substance.	*Subscripts*	
		P	Products.
T	Absolute temperature.	R	Reactants.
t	Temperature.	0, 1, 2 ...	States of a fluid.
U'	Internal energy of a chemical substance.		
$[\Delta U']_{v,t}$	Increase in energy of a chemical substance in a constant-volume, isothermal reaction.		

STOICHIOMETRY

Chemical composition

We begin with a resumé of some facts about the constitution of matter which are normally treated in a school chemistry course.

The chemical elements. All matter is made up of a limited variety of elementary substances, the *chemical elements*. In combustion, the most important reacting elements are carbon, hydrogen and oxygen; they are denoted by the capital letters, C, H, and O, respectively.

Atoms. A quantity of a chemical element is not indefinitely divisible into smaller and smaller amounts, but must be regarded as consisting of a collection of tiny particles which cannot be split.* These particles are the *atoms*. They are so small that 1 lb_m of oxygen, for example, comprises $8 \cdot 5 \times 10^{24}$ of them. Atomic masses on the scale that makes the mass of the oxygen atom 16, i.e. *atomic weights*, are given in Table 16.1 for elements of importance in combustion.

TABLE 16.1. *Atomic weights of elements.*

Element	O	H	C	S	N
Atomic weight	16	1·008	12·01	32·06	14·01

Molecules. The individual atoms of a chemical element are rarely found in a "free" state. Even in a substance comprising only one chemical element, for example, hydrogen gas, the atoms are almost always found tied together in pairs; this fact is expressed by writing the formula for hydrogen gas as H_2. Oxygen and nitrogen gases also consist as a rule of multitudes of particles each of which comprises two atoms; their formulae are accordingly O_2 and N_2 respectively.

Atoms need not "mate" with others of their own kind, however, but can form close bonds with atoms of different elements. Thus steam comprises particles each of which contains two hydrogen atoms and one oxygen atom: its formula is accordingly H_2O. The groups of atoms are known as *molecules*, and it is their constitution that determines the chemical and other properties of the substance in which they occur.

The inter-atomic forces which bind together the atoms in the molecule only operate over very small distances. It is therefore usual for each molecule to consist of only a small number of atoms; for larger groups of atoms would be only weakly bound and so would easily be de-composed. Carbon and hydrogen form the most notable exceptions to this general rule: their elements can jointly form molecules comprising some scores of atoms.

A consequence of the atomic and molecular construction of matter is that the ratio of the numbers of atoms of the elements in a substance must be a fairly simple fraction; 2 : 1 in the case of hydrogen and oxygen in steam. If the masses are expressed in molal units (e.g. lb. mole) the mass ratios therefore also form simple fractions. This is a major reason for using different mass units for the different substances: the arithmetic is made simpler thereby.

* Modern knowledge of nuclear physics does not invalidate this statement. For when an atom is split it ceases to have the properties of the original chemical element. Such nuclear changes are not considered in this chapter.

Oxides. In combustion the atoms of an oxygen molecule become parted; they then form new molecules jointly with atoms of carbon and hydrogen which are originally in the fuel molecules. The new molecules are known as *oxides.* Thus steam is an oxide of hydrogen.

Carbon forms two common oxides. The first, known as carbon monoxide, consists of molecules each containing one atom of carbon and one of oxygen; it has the chemical formula CO. The second, carbon dioxide, has two oxygen atoms and one carbon atom in its molecule; it has the formula CO_2. Both these substances are gaseous at normal temperatures and pressures; for most engineering purposes they may be regarded as Ideal Gases.

Fuels

It is convenient to classify fuels according to the phase in which they are normally handled. The gaseous fuels are chemically the simplest; liquid fuels contain more complex molecules; while solid fuels often have so complicated a molecular structure that full knowledge of their constitution is not yet available.

Gaseous fuels. Gaseous fuels are stored naturally beneath the earth in many parts of the world, often in the vicinity of oilfields. Where natural gas is not available, gaseous fuels have to be manufactured, usually by the treatment of coal. They are convenient to transport in pipes over short distances, particularly around the furnaces and engines in which they are employed. We will list some of the more important chemical substances which occur in these fuels.

The simplest is *hydrogen,* H_2, which is a major constituent of manufactured gas derived from coal.

Carbon monoxide, CO, is a fuel, as well as being an oxide, because it can combine with more oxygen to form carbon dioxide, CO_2. Carbon monoxide is also found in manufactured gases, both in that which is supplied in a town's gas system, and in so-called *producer gas.* The latter is manufactured for use in furnaces and engines by the simple process of burning coke with a limited supply of air.

The other gaseous fuels of chief importance are combinations of carbon and hydrogen, the so-called *hydrocarbons.* The simplest is *methane,* which has the chemical formula CH_4, signifying that its molecule contains one atom of carbon and four atoms of hydrogen. It is a major constituent of natural gas. A whole family of further fuels can be formed by adding to a methane molecule further carbon and hydrogen atoms in the ratio 1 : 2. Thus *ethane* has the formula C_2H_6, *propane* has the formula C_3H_8, *butane* is C_4H_{10}, and so on. This family is known as the *paraffins.* They also are found in natural gas.

It is not possible to take a paraffin molecule and form new substances by adding further hydrogen atoms to the molecule. Paraffin hydrocarbons are therefore called *saturated.* However hydrocarbon molecules can exist which have fewer hydrogen atoms combined with a given number of carbon atoms than has the corresponding paraffin; such hydrocarbons are called *unsaturated*. The best-known example is the gas *acetylene* which has two carbon atoms and two hydrogen atoms in its molecule; its formula is accordingly C_2H_2. Others are *ethylene*, C_2H_4, *propylene*, C_3H_6, and so on. Many of them are found naturally, but some (acetylene is one) have to be manufactured.

Most gaseous fuels are mixtures of several gases, including some, such as nitrogen, which are not easily oxidised. Table 16.2 contains volumetric analyses of typical fuels used industrially. The components may be regarded as Ideal Gases under atmospheric conditions; the volumetric analysis is therefore the same as the molal analysis (see Chapter 15, p. 285).

TABLE 16.2. *Volumetric analyses of some fuel gas mixtures* (%)

	CO	H_2	CH_4	C_2H_4	C_2H_6	C_4H_8	O_2	CO_2	N_2
Coal gas (Town gas)	9	53·6	25	—	—	3	0·4	3	6
Producer gas	29	12	2·6	0·4	—	—	—	4	52
Blast furnace gas	27	2	—	—	—	—	—	11	60
Natural gas (English)	1	—	93	—	3	—	—	—	3
Natural gas (American)	—	—	80	—	18	—	—	—	2
Natural gas (Russian)	—	1	93	—	3·5	—	—	2	0·5

Liquid fuels. There is no clear-cut boundary between gaseous and liquid fuels, since one can be transformed into the other as a result of a change in temperature and pressure. Most liquid fuels are hydrocarbons, either saturated or unsaturated. As the molecular weight increases as a result of an increased number of carbon and hydrogen atoms in the molecule, the boiling point of the substance at atmospheric pressure rises. Roughly speaking, hydrocarbon molecules containing six or more carbon atoms in the molecule have boiling points in excess of atmospheric temperature; such hydrocarbons are therefore classified as liquid fuels.

Table 16.3 contains the names, chemical formulae, molecular weights and atmospheric boiling points of hydrocarbon fuels. Both gaseous and liquid fuels are included so that the trend can be perceived.

The fuels used in practice are invariably mixtures; often some hundreds of different varieties of molecule can be found in a single fuel sample. This does not, however, usually create difficulty for the combustion engineer, since all he needs to know about the fuel composition are the relative numbers or masses of carbon and hydrogen atoms in the sample. Table 16.4 gives some typical data. It will be seen that elements other than carbon and hydrogen are normally present, notably sulphur. There are also traces of incombustible impurities which are lumped together under the designation *ash*.

The composition of a fuel, expressed in terms of the percentage masses of the chemical elements, is known as the *ultimate analysis* of the fuel. It is most useful in the case of solid fuels, for which the molecular structure is too complex to be unravelled. For liquid hydrocarbon fuels it is often sufficiently accurate to take the ultimate analysis as 85·8% C and 14·2% H; this corresponds to a 1 : 2 ratio of number of carbon atoms to number of hydrogen atoms.

TABLE 16.3. *Boiling points of hydrocarbon fuels*

Name	Chemical formula	Molecular weight (rounded-off)	Boiling point (°F) at $p = 1$ atm
Methane	CH_4	16	−258·5
Ethylene	C_2H_4	28	−155
Ethane	C_2H_6	30	−128·3
Propylene	C_3H_6	42	−53·6
n-Butane	C_4H_{10}	58	31
n-Pentane	C_5H_{12}	72	97
Benzene	C_6H_6	78	171
Toluene	C_7H_8	92	231
n-Octane	C_8H_{18}	114	258

TABLE 16.4. *Liquid fuels: mass analysis* (%)

Fuel	Carbon	Hydrogen	Sulphur	Ash etc.
Aviation petrol (100 Octane)	85·1	14·9	0·01	—
Motor petrol	85·5	14·4	0·1	—
Vaporising oil	86·2	12·9	0·3	—
Motor benzole	91·7	8·0	0·3	—
Kerosene	86·3	13·6	0·1	—
Diesel oil, distilled (Gas oil)	86·3	12·8	0·9	—
Light fuel oil	86·2	12·4	1·4	—
Heavy fuel oil	86·1	11·8	2·1	—
Residual fuel oil (Bunker C)	88·3	9·5	1·2	1·0

Solid fuels. The simplest solid fuel chemically is pure carbon. Alone among the fuels mentioned so far, it burns in the solid phase; oxygen has to diffuse to the carbon surface and the gaseous oxides are formed there. The gaseous and liquid fuels discussed above burn in the gaseous phase, the liquids vaporising before burning. The boiling point of carbon at normal pressures is well above the temperatures attained in flames.

The solid fuels which are obtained by mining consist mainly of carbon, together with hydrogen, sulphur and some incombustible ash. According to their chemical and physical properties, they are called anthracite, bituminous coal, brown coal, or peat. Some of their typical properties are indicated in Table 16.5. Anthracite is the most valuable, and peat the least. For comparison wood is included also.

TABLE 16.5. *Some properties of solid fuels*

Fuel	Moisture content of good commercial fuel % by weight	Ultimate analysis of good commercial fuel % by weight in dry fuel					Volatile matter % by weight in dry fuel
		C	H	O	N+S	Ash	
Anthracite	1	90·27	3·00	2·32	1·44	2·97	4
Bituminous Coal	2	81·93	4·87	5·98	2·32	4·90	25
Lignite	15	56·52	5·72	31·89	1·62	4·25	50
Peat	20	43·70	6·42	44·36	1·52	4·00	65
Wood	15	42·5	6·78	49·87	0·85	Trace	80

The chemical elements comprising industrial solid fuels are bound together, often fairly loosely, into complex molecules of high molecular weight. The incombustible ash is interspersed in the fuel both in minute particles and also in larger lumps. In addition there is always a certain amount of water in the fuel, some of it chemically combined, some merely admixed; for a fuel from a given mine, the moisture content varies according to the conditions of treatment and storage.

Engineers keep a check on the quality of solid fuel with which they are supplied by carrying out what is called a *proximate analysis*. By heating at atmospheric pressure to successively higher temperatures, with intermediate weighings, the percentages of moisture, volatile matter, combustible solids and ash are determined. The volatile matter mentioned is that driven off at temperatures above 212°F, and so excludes the water; it consists chiefly of hydrocarbons of high molecular weight.

Standard testing methods have been laid down by the British Standards Institute and the American Society for Testing Materials (See Bibliography).

Exhaust gases. Fuel and air form the input streams to most combustion appliances. The output stream is invariably gaseous, apart from the ash and possibly some condensed water. The exhaust gas stream therefore contains the products of combustion: the oxides of hydrogen, carbon and, if present, sulphur; excess oxygen and unburned fuel; and nitrogen and other chemically inert gases flowing through the plant. Whether any of the steam condenses depends on the temperature of the exhaust gas and the partial pressure of steam in it. The most usual oxide of sulphur is the dioxide, SO_2.

Chemical change

Chemical reaction is the process in which the interatomic bonds in the reactant molecules are broken, followed by the re-arrangement of the atoms thus set free in new molecular combinations: the product molecules. Combustion is the particular class of chemical reaction in which the products are oxides. Thus new chemical substances appear while old ones disappear, the actual atoms remaining the same. From this it is clear that chemical reaction is not an interaction between systems like heat and work; it is a change *within* a system. It is recognised by the change in the chemical properties of the system.

Chemical equations. In order to keep track of chemical reactions we make use of an accounting system which is expressed symbolically in the form of an equation. Thus the reaction in which methane burns with oxygen to carbon dioxide and steam is described by the equation:

$$CH_4 + 2\ O_2 = CO_2 + 2\ H_2O \qquad \dots \quad (16.1)$$

The convention adopted differs from that of ordinary algebra. The symbols for the reactant molecules appear on the left and those for the product molecules on the right. Each molecular symbol is multiplied by a numeral (which may be unity, and therefore omitted) signifying the relative number of molecules taking part. In setting up such an equation usually the molecular symbols are written down first and the multiplying numerals are then prefixed in a way that conforms with the *Principle of Conservation of Matter*. This states that the number of atoms of any chemical element in the reactants is the same as the number in the products.

In eq. (16.1) if the CH_4 symbol has the coefficient unity, so must the CO_2 symbol to balance the number of carbon atoms. Since hydrogen only appears in the products in the form H_2O, there must be two H_2O molecules to give the same number of H atoms (four) in both products and reactants. This fixes the number of oxygen atoms in the products as four (two in CO_2, two in $2H_2O$); thus two oxygen molecules must appear on the left-hand side.

By combining eq. (16.1) with the atomic weight data* given in Table 16.1 we obtain the relative masses of the reactants and products taking part in the reaction:

$$16\ lb_m\ CH_4 + 64\ lb_m\ O_2 = 44\ lb_m\ CO_2 + 36\ lb_m\ H_2O$$

or on a molal basis

$$1\ mole\ CH_4 + 2\ moles\ O_2 = 1\ mole\ CO_2 + 2\ moles\ H_2O.$$

* It is usually adequate to use the "rounded-off" values of atomic weights.

Merely writing a chemical equation tells little about the chemical reaction, not even whether it is possible that it should proceed in the direction indicated, i.e. from left to right. Questions of possibility have to be discussed in terms of the Second Law of Thermodynamics. For the present, however, we will take it that combustion reactions in which carbon- and hydrogen-bearing fuels are completely oxidised can always proceed spontaneously, *if sufficient oxygen is available* and the appropriate combustion equipment is provided. CO_2 and H_2O are therefore regarded as the products of *complete combustion*. Only when the products are at extremely high temperatures is this assumption invalid.

Often substances are present which take no part in the chemical reaction, for example nitrogen when air is the source of oxygen. Such inert substances are usually omitted from the chemical equation; if it is found convenient to take note of them the appropriate symbols are the same on both sides of the equation. Thus taking 100 moles of air to consist of a mixture of 21 moles of oxygen and 79 moles of nitrogen, the equation for the reaction of methane with just sufficient air to cause complete combustion could be written

$$CH_4 + 2\,O_2 + 2 \times \tfrac{79}{21}\,N_2 = CO_2 + 2\,H_2O + 2 \times \tfrac{79}{21}\,N_2 \quad \ldots \quad (16.2)$$

The calculation of composition change

Identity of system analysis and control volume analysis in the case of composition. In this section a number of commonly useful equations and methods relating to the composition changes occurring in combustion will be set down. The discussion will be in terms of a system, i.e. a fixed body of matter, contained, for example, in a reaction vessel. The procedure is identical however if steady flow has to be analysed by means of a control volume; then the masses within the system are merely replaced by the masses crossing the control volume boundary.

Combustion with air: mass units. Consider a fuel of ultimate analysis: $100\,m_C$ % C, $100\,m_H$ % H, $100\,m_O$ % oxygen, $100\,m_A$ % ash. Let the system contain $1\,lb_m$ of fuel and $x\,lb_m$ of air, consisting of $0.232\,lb_m\ O_2/lb_m$ air and $0.768\,lb_m\ N_2/lb_m$ air. We will calculate the composition of the exhaust gases, assuming that *complete combustion* takes place.

The carbon burns according to the equation

$$C + O_2 = CO_2 \qquad \ldots \quad (16.3)$$

The corresponding masses are

$$m_C\ lb_m\ C, \qquad \tfrac{32}{12}\,m_C\ lb_m\ O_2, \qquad \tfrac{44}{12}\,m_C\ lb_m\ CO_2$$

since the molecular weights of C, O_2 and CO_2 are 12, 32 and 44 respectively.

For hydrogen (molecular weight $= 2$), the reaction and corresponding masses are

$$H_2 + \tfrac{1}{2}\,O_2 = H_2O \qquad \ldots \quad (16.4)$$

$$m_H\ lb_m\ H_2, \qquad \tfrac{16}{2}\,m_H\ lb_m\ O_2, \qquad \tfrac{18}{2}\,m_H\ lb_m\ H_2O$$

The substances present at the end of reaction are CO_2, H_2O, O_2, N_2 and ash. We consider each in turn.

CO_2:   the final mass is $\frac{44}{12} m_C$, as already stated.

H_2O: the final mass is $\frac{18}{2} m_H$, as already stated.

O_2:   The initial mass is m_O lb_m supplied in the fuel and $0 \cdot 232x$ lb_m supplied in the air. The quantity consumed in the reaction, as has been seen, is $\frac{32}{12} m_C + \frac{16}{2} m_H$ lb_m.

The final mass is therefore:

$$m_O + 0 \cdot 232x - \frac{32}{12} m_C - \frac{16}{2} m_H.$$

N_2:   The mass supplied is $0 \cdot 768x$ lb_m. Since nitrogen takes no part in the reaction, this is the final mass also.

Ash: The initial and final masses are both m_A lb_m.

The *exhaust gases*, if at sufficiently high temperature, comprise CO_2, H_2O (as steam), O_2 and N_2. If the temperature is reduced sufficiently, the steam condenses. We will calculate the composition of the resulting *dry* gases; it will be remembered that it is the dry gas analysis which is given by the Orsat apparatus (p. 299).

The total mass of dry exhaust gas (CO_2, O_2 and N_2) is

$$\underbrace{\frac{44}{12} m_C}_{CO_2} + \underbrace{m_O + 0 \cdot 232x - \frac{32}{12} m_C - \frac{16}{2} m_H}_{O_2} + \underbrace{0 \cdot 768x}_{N_2}$$

which simplifies to

$$m_C - \frac{16}{2} m_H + m_O + x$$

This represents the original mass of $1 + x$ less the masses of the ash and condensed steam.

The *mass analysis* of the dry exhaust gas is therefore

$$(\tfrac{44}{12} m_C \times 100)/(m_C - \tfrac{16}{2} m_H + m_O + x) \qquad \% \; CO_2$$

$$\{(m_C + 0 \cdot 232x - \tfrac{32}{12} m_C - \tfrac{16}{2} m_H) \times 100\}/\{m_C - \tfrac{16}{2} m_H + m_O + x\} \; \% \; O_2$$

and $\qquad (0 \cdot 768x \times 100)/(m_C - \tfrac{16}{2} m_H + m_O + x) \qquad \% \; N_2$

For comparison with measurements made with an Orsat apparatus, the *volumetric*, i.e. *the molal analysis* of the dry gases is required. The procedure is as follows:—

The molecular weights of CO_2, O_2 and N_2 will be taken as 44, 32 and 28 respectively. Then the numbers of moles present are:

$$\tfrac{1}{44} \times \tfrac{44}{12} m_C, \qquad \text{i.e.} \quad \tfrac{1}{12} m_C \text{ lb mole } CO_2$$

$$\tfrac{1}{32}(m_O + 0 \cdot 232x - \tfrac{32}{12} m_C - \tfrac{16}{2} m_H) \text{ lb mole } O_2$$

and $\qquad\qquad \tfrac{1}{28} \times 0 \cdot 768x \text{ lb mole } N_2$.

The total number of moles is therefore obtained by addition as:—

$$\tfrac{1}{32}(m_O + 0 \cdot 232x - \tfrac{16}{2} m_H) + \tfrac{1}{28} \times 0 \cdot 768x$$

The *molal analysis* is therefore:—

$$\{\tfrac{1}{12} m_C \times 100\}/\{\tfrac{1}{32}(m_O + 0.232x - \tfrac{16}{2} m_H) + (0.768x/28)\} \qquad \% \text{ CO}_2$$

$$\{\tfrac{1}{32}(m_O + 0.232x - \tfrac{32}{12} m_C - \tfrac{16}{2} m_H) \times 100\}/$$
$$\{\tfrac{1}{32}(m_O + 0.232x - \tfrac{16}{2} m_H) + (0.768x/28)\} \qquad \% \text{ O}_2$$

and $(\tfrac{1}{28} \times 0.768x \times 100)/$

$$\{\tfrac{1}{32}(m_O + 0.232x - \tfrac{16}{2} m_H) + \tfrac{1}{28} \times 0.768x\} \qquad \% \text{ N}_2$$

Deduction of air-fuel ratio from exhaust gas analysis. The above results are often used to calculate the mass of air x supplied per unit mass of fuel from the exhaust gas analysis, which is easily measured. For if the percentage of CO_2 in the gas is known, together with the ultimate analysis of the fuel (i.e. m_C, m_H and m_O), x can be calculated.

The same can be done if the percentage of O_2 is measured. In general the value of x calculated from the CO_2 percentage will differ slightly from that calculated from the O_2 percentage. This is a result of experimental inaccuracy. Normally the CO_2 value is the more reliable.

Stoichiometric air-fuel ratio. It is of interest to calculate the minimum value of x which would supply sufficient oxygen for complete combustion. This is known as the *stoichiometric* or "theoretical" air-fuel ratio, x_{stoich}; it is calculated by equating the final mass of oxygen to zero. Thus

$$m_O + 0.232x_{stoich} - \tfrac{32}{12} m_C - \tfrac{16}{2} m_H = 0$$

that is, $$x_{stoich} = \frac{\tfrac{32}{12} m_C + \tfrac{16}{2} m_H - m_O}{0.232} \qquad \dots \quad (16.5)$$

For a hydrocarbon fuel x_{stoich} is usually about 15; for a coal it is nearer 11.

Excess air. It is undesirable to supply more than the stoichiometric quantity of air when fuel is being burned for heating purposes, because the excess air merely lowers the gas temperature and so lowers the heat transfer rate. However, since it is seldom possible to mix the fuel and air completely uniformly, some *excess air* must be provided, in order to avoid the still less desirable phenomenon of incompletely burned fuel passing out of the furnace in the exhaust gases. The quantity of excess air is usually expressed as a percentage, viz.

$$\text{per cent excess air} = \frac{x - x_{stoich}}{x_{stoich}} \times 100\%$$

Usually a value of 20% excess air is regarded as acceptably low. Gas turbines however must operate with about 300% excess air in order to avoid melting the turbine blades.

Mixture strength. For petrol engines a different procedure is adopted for comparing x and x_{stoich}. The reason for this is that petrol engines are used for applications (e.g. motor cars) which demand a wide range of operating conditions. As a consequence, the air-fuel ratio, x, varies considerably and can have values both above and below x_{stoich}. In these circumstances, therefore, it is usual to express the variation in air-fuel ratio in terms of the *mixture strength* defined by the relation

$$\text{Mixture strength} = \frac{x_{stoich}}{x} \times 100 \text{ per cent} \qquad \text{...} \quad (16.6)$$

A typical range of mixture strength is from a *weak* mixture of 90% to a *rich* mixture of 120%. The terms "weak" and "rich" exemplify respectively the deficiency and the excess of the fuel in a given quantity of air entering the engine as compared with the stoichiometric quantity of fuel. The "theoretical" or stoichiometric air-fuel ratio corresponds to a mixture strength of 100%.

Consequences of deficient air supply. If the air-fuel ratio is less than x_{stoich}, the above assumption of complete combustion of fuel would lead to the absurd conclusion that the concentration of oxygen in the exhaust gases was negative; the assumption is therefore wrong. What the exhaust gases actually consist of is then hard to determine, and involves Second Law considerations. An approximate rule however is to assume that first all the carbon is burned to the monoxide, CO, and that thereafter any remaining oxygen is equally shared between this gas, oxidising to CO_2, and the hydrogen, oxidising to H_2O. The exhaust gases then comprise CO_2, CO, H_2O, H_2 and N_2 if the fuel is a hydrocarbon.

Combustion with air: molal units. If the fuel has a known molecular constitution and weight, the calculation of the volumetric exhaust gas analysis is more easily performed in molal units throughout. This is particularly the case when the fuel consists of a mixture of Ideal Gases. An example now follows:—

EXAMPLE 1

Problem. The volumetric analysis of a producer gas is 26% CO, 12% H_2, 7% CO_2, and 55% N_2. y ft³ of air are supplied for each ft³ of fuel (both measured at standard* conditions). What is the volumetric analysis of the dry exhaust gases?

Solution. We suppose 1 lb mole of gas and y lb mole of air constitute the system, making use of the fact throughout that numbers of moles are proportional to standard volumes. The reactions are:—

$$\begin{array}{cccc} CO & + & \tfrac{1}{2}O_2 & = & CO_2 \\ \text{1 mole} & & \tfrac{1}{2}\text{ mole} & & \text{1 mole} \end{array} \qquad \text{...} \quad (16.7)$$

$$\begin{array}{cccc} H_2 & + & \tfrac{1}{2}O_2 & = & H_2O \\ \text{1 mole} & & \tfrac{1}{2}\text{ mole} & & \text{1 mole} \end{array} \qquad \text{...} \quad (16.8)$$

* Usually $p = 30$ in. Hg; $t = 60°F$.

Air consists, we assume, of 21% O_2 and 79% N_2 by volume. Treating each component of the exhaust gases in turn, we have:—

CO_2: 0·07 moles are supplied. 0·26 moles result from the combustion of CO. Finally, therefore we have 0·33 moles CO_2.

H_2O: None is supplied. 0·12 moles result from combustion of H_2.

O_2: 0·21 y moles are supplied. $\frac{1}{2} \times 0\cdot26 + \frac{1}{2} \times 0\cdot12$ moles are consumed in the oxidation of CO and H_2 respectively. Finally we have $0\cdot21y - 0\cdot13 - 0\cdot06 = 0\cdot21y - 0\cdot19$ moles O_2.

N_2: 0·55 moles are supplied in the fuel, and 0·79y moles in the air. Finally therefore we have $0\cdot55 + 0\cdot79y$ moles N_2.

The total number of moles of non-condensable gas (i.e. excluding H_2O) is therefore

$$0\cdot33 + 0\cdot21y - 0\cdot19 + 0\cdot55 + 0\cdot79y, \text{ i.e. } 0\cdot69 + y \text{ moles.}$$

The volumetric analysis of the dry exhaust gas is therefore

$$\frac{0\cdot33}{y + 0\cdot69} \times 100 \qquad \% \ CO_2$$

and

$$\frac{0\cdot21y - 0\cdot19}{y + 0\cdot69} \times 100 \qquad \% \ O_2$$

$$\frac{0\cdot79y + 0\cdot55}{y + 0\cdot69} \times 100 \qquad \% \ N_2 \qquad \dots \textit{Answer}$$

Remarks. (i) The stoichiometric air-fuel ratio in terms of volumes is given by putting the oxygen concentration in the exhaust gases equal to zero; thus $y_{\text{stoich}} = 0\cdot19 \div 0\cdot21 = 0\cdot905$ ft³ air/ft³ producer gas.

(ii) With the stoichiometric air-fuel ratio, the CO_2 percentage has its highest possible value of $33 \div (0\cdot69 + 0\cdot905) = 20\cdot7\%$. Measurement of the CO_2 percentage in the exhaust gases is often used as a control on the excess air quantity; the operator of the furnace tries to keep it as high a value as possible consistent with the non-appearance of CO and H_2 in the exhaust. Values of 18% are common for solid fuels and gases such as producer gas directly derived from them. Liquid fuels and gaseous hydrocarbons give CO_2 percentages of around 15% in stoichiometric combustion.

(iii) The total number of gaseous moles changes from $1 + y$ to $0\cdot69 + y$ in the combustion, a decrease of 0·31 moles. If the H_2O does not condense, the final number of gaseous moles is $0\cdot81 + y$, representing a decrease of 0·19 moles. At constant temperature and pressure therefore, the volume of gas suffers a decrease in combustion.

Air-fuel ratio deduced from the carbon-nitrogen ratio. If the exhaust gas analysis is being used solely to calculate the air-fuel ratio, the quickest procedure is usually to deduce the latter from the ratio of carbon to nitrogen in exhaust. This will be illustrated by an example.

EXAMPLE 2

Problem. A fuel contains 84% carbon by mass and no nitrogen. The composition of the exhaust gas produced by combustion with air is 14% CO_2, 0·5% CO, 5% O_2 and 80·5% N_2 by volume. Determine the air-fuel ratio x.

Solution. 1 mole of exhaust gas contains 0·14 moles of (monatomic) carbon in the CO_2, 0·005 moles of (monatomic) carbon in the CO, and 0·805 moles of (diatomic) nitrogen. The mass ratio of carbon to nitrogen in the exhaust gas is therefore

$$\frac{12(0·14 + 0·005)}{28 \times 0·805} = 0·0772$$

Since 1 lb_m of air contains 0·768 lb_m of nitrogen, the carbon-nitrogen ratio in the reactants is

$$\frac{0·84}{0·768x}$$

Since the ratios before and after combustion must be equal we have

$$x = \frac{0·84}{0·768 \times 0·772} = 14·2 \qquad \dots \; Answer$$

Condensation of moisture. We conclude this section by illustrating the determination of the phase of the H_2O present in the exhaust gases. Usually it is undesirable for condensation to occur within the heating equipment, for oxides of sulphur, even if present only in small concentration in the gas, can dissolve in the droplets of water and seriously corrode metal surfaces.

EXAMPLE 3

Problem. A furnace burns the producer gas of example 1; 1·2 cubic feet of air are supplied per cubic foot of gas. What is the minimum temperature allowable for any surface in contact with the flue gas if condensation is not to occur when the gas pressure is 14·2 psia?

Solution. We have to determine the dew-point of the gases. From the previous calculation, 1 mole of fuel produces

$$0·33 \text{ moles } CO_2$$
$$0·12 \text{ moles } H_2O$$
$$0·21 \times 1·2 - 0·19 = 0·062 \text{ moles } O_2$$
$$0·55 + 0·79 \times 1·2 = 1·499 \text{ moles } N_2$$

$$\text{Total} \qquad 2·011 \text{ moles}$$

Treating the steam as an Ideal Gas, its partial pressure is therefore $14·2 \times \dfrac{0·12}{2·011} = 0·849$ psia. From Steam Tables, Appendix B, the temperature at which this partial pressure is also the saturation pressure is 96·3°F. Therefore no part of the metal surface should fall below 96·3°F. ... *Answer.*

THE FIRST LAW OF THERMODYNAMICS APPLIED TO COMBUSTION

Energy and enthalpy

All systems and processes obey the First Law of Thermodynamics; energy and enthalpy are concepts therefore of universal application. When dealing with a pure substance it was found convenient to give special symbols to these quantities; we follow the same practice now that chemical reaction has to be allowed for. First a special sort of system will be defined; *the chemical substance*. The analogy with the pure substance should be clear.

Definition. A system which is homogeneous in composition will be called a chemical substance.

As with the pure substance, chemical substances will be considered in the absence of effects due to gravity, motion, capillarity, electricity and magnetism. Energy terms due to the first two of these influences can be added when required, as before.

Internal energy. The internal energy of a chemical substance, i.e. its energy in the absence of the above effects, will be denoted by the symbol U'. For a system of unit mass the lower case symbol u' is used. The units are Btu or ft lb$_f$ as before.

Enthalpy. The enthalpy of a chemical substance is given the symbol H' and defined by

$$H' = U' + pV \qquad \ldots \quad (16.9)$$

where p and V are respectively the pressure and volume of the system. The lower case symbol h' is used for systems of unit mass.

Relations between the zeros. Energy is only defined by the First Law as a difference (eq. 6.5); the state of zero internal energy can therefore be chosen arbitrarily. This choice fixes the zero of enthalpy also. Another relation between zeros peculiar to chemical substances will now be discussed.

Dependence of U' and H' on chemical aggregation. Whereas all the properties of a pure substance, including its internal energy and enthalpy, are fixed by the specification of two independent properties, e.g. pressure and specific volume, this is not true of a chemical substance; the state of chemical aggregation must be specified as well. Consider, for example, a system comprising hydrogen and oxygen. Let the two elements be present at first as hydrogen and oxygen gases (the reactant state), and finally in the form of steam molecules (the product state). If the pressures and specific volumes are the same in both states, it follows that the final temperature must exceed the initial temperature because of the reduction in the number of molecules in the system.* U' and H' also alter.

Consequently we are not free, when chemical reactions are in question, to choose independently the zeros of internal energies of chemical substances which may be transformed into each other by reaction. This will become clearer from the analysis which follows.

Energy and enthalpy changes in isothermal reactions

The changes of internal energy and enthalpy which result from chemical reaction depend on the initial and final states of the system. Attention will first be concentrated on changes in which the initial and final

---

* This is seen most clearly if the reactants and the products are assumed to be Ideal Gases; the conclusion is, however, a general one.

22

temperatures are the same. In considering such changes, it is to be noted that we do not require that the temperature should remain constant during the reaction. It seldom will. The temperature may change temporarily provided that it returns to the initial value. For brevity, however, we speak of constant-temperature or isothermal reactions.

Temperature alone does not determine the state, so in addition we specify that either the final volume or the final pressure must be equal to its initial value.

Constant-volume isothermal reaction: $[\Delta U']_{v,t}$. If a chemical substance changes its composition from a reactant to a product state by chemical reaction at constant temperature and *volume*, the internal energy of the system in the final (product) state, U'_P, is related to the internal energy in the initial (reactant) state, U'_R, through the First Law, eq. (6.5).

From eq. (6.5), in the absence of shear work we have

$$Q = \Delta E$$
$$= U'_P - U'_R$$
$$= [\Delta U']_{v,t} \qquad \ldots \quad (16.10)$$

where $[\Delta U']_{v,t} \equiv$ increase in internal energy of the chemical system, the subscripts v and t denoting that the reaction has taken place at constant volume and constant temperature. $[\Delta U']_{v,t}$ is obtained experimentally by measuring the heat transfer Q.

Constant-pressure-isothermal reaction: $[\Delta H']_{p,t}$. For a chemical reaction carried out at constant temperature and *pressure* we have, from the First Law, eq. (6.5), that

$$Q - W = U'_P - U'_R$$

Here the work W in the absence of shear work is given by

$$W = \int p \, dV$$

and so, for a constant-pressure reaction;

$$W = p \int dV$$
$$= p(V_P - V_R)$$

where $V_P =$ volume of the chemical system in the final (product) state,

and $V_R =$ volume of the chemical system in the initial (reactant) state. It follows that

$$Q - p(V_P - V_R) = U'_P - U'_R$$
or
$$Q = (U'_P + pV_P) - (U'_R + pV_R)$$
$$= H'_P - H'_R \quad \text{from eq. (16.9)}$$
$$= [\Delta H']_{p,t} \qquad \ldots \quad (16.11)$$

where $[\Delta H']_{p,t} =$ increase in enthalpy of the chemical system in a constant-pressure, constant temperature reaction.

In this case it is $[\Delta H']_{p,t}$ which is obtained experimentally by measuring the heat transfer Q.

Relation between $[\Delta U']_{v,t}$ *and* $[\Delta H']_{p,t}$. From the derivation of eq. (16.11), it is evident that normally the internal energy increase and the enthalpy increase have different values. They are identical in magnitude only when the volume change $\Delta V = (V_P - V_R)$ is zero. In general, as has been seen above, the change in the number of moles, or a change of phase, will cause ΔV to be finite.

Reactions in Ideal Gases. When the reactants and products are Ideal Gases, the lack of dependence of their internal energies and enthalpies on volume and pressure makes it permissible to drop one of the subscripts; we therefore write $[\Delta U']_t$ and $[\Delta H']_t$ simply. However, the first quantity is still only equal to the heat transfer to the surroundings in a constant-volume reaction, while the second only equals the heat transfer in a constant-pressure reaction or in a steady-flow process with zero external work. The last result follows from the Steady-Flow Energy Equation (eq.) (8.22).

These conclusions also hold fairly closely when solid or liquid phases are present in reactant or product; for U' and H' for solids and liquids depend only mildly on pressure. The Gibbs-Dalton Law implies that $[\Delta U']_t$ and $[\Delta H']_t$ are not influenced by the extent to which individual components of the system are mixed. The *phase* of the components is important however, as will be shown below.

For reactions between Ideal Gases an algebraic relation between $[\Delta U']_t$ and $[\Delta H']_t$ may be developed as follows. From the definition of enthalpy, eq. (16.9), we have

$$[\Delta H']_t = [\Delta U']_t + \Delta[pV]_t.$$

Now from the Ideal Gas Rule, on a molal basis, we may write

$$p_R V_R = n_R \mathscr{R} T$$

and

$$p_P V_P = n_P \mathscr{R} T$$

where n_R and n_P are the numbers of moles of gaseous reactants and products respectively, and T is the absolute temperature at which the isothermal reaction is carried out.

Hence

$$\Delta[pV]_t = [p_P V_P - p_R V_R]$$

$$= (n_P - n_R)\mathscr{R} T$$

It follows that

$$[\Delta H']_t = [\Delta U']_t + (n_P - n_R)\mathscr{R} T \qquad \ldots \quad (16.12)$$

When the change in the number of moles is zero, $[\Delta H']_t$ and $[\Delta U']_t$ are numerically equal.

EXAMPLE 4

Problem. For the reaction $CO + \frac{1}{2}O_2 = CO_2$, when carried out at 77°F $[\Delta H']_t = -4348$ Btu/lb$_m$ of CO. Evaluate $[\Delta U']_t$ at 77°F.

Solution. We make use of eq. (16.12) as follows:

$$n_R = 1 \text{ mole CO} + \tfrac{1}{2} \text{ mole } O_2 = 1\tfrac{1}{2} \text{ moles}$$

$$n_P = 1 \text{ mole } CO_2$$

$$\therefore \qquad (n_P - n_R)\mathscr{R}T = (1 - 1\tfrac{1}{2}) \times 1{\cdot}986 \times (77 + 460)$$

$$= -533 \text{ Btu/lb mole CO}$$

$$[\Delta H']_t = -4348 \text{ Btu/lb}_m \text{ CO}$$

$$= -4348 \times 28 \text{ Btu/lb mole CO}$$

$$= -121{,}745 \text{ Btu/lb mole CO}$$

since the molecular weight of CO is 28.
Therefore in eq. (16.12) we have

$$-121{,}745 = [\Delta U']_t - 533$$

or $$[\Delta U']_t = -121{,}212 \text{ Btu/lb mole of CO} \qquad \dots \textit{Answer}$$

$$= -4329 \text{ Btu/lb}_m \text{ CO} \qquad \dots \textit{Answer}$$

Remarks: 1 The increase in U', $[\Delta U']_t$, and the increase in H', $[\Delta H']_t$, are negative, i.e. U' and H' *decrease*. This is invariably the case in isothermal combustion reactions, which are thus given the name *exothermic*, because the direction of the heat transfer is *outwards* (See eq. (16·10)).

2. There is a reduction in the number of moles in this case; $(n_P - n_R)$ is negative.

3. Note that n_P and n_R are the numbers of *gaseous* moles present. If any of the reactants or products are present as solids or liquids, they are ignored in computing $(n_P - n_R)$. For example, in the reaction

$$C + O_2 = CO_2$$

in which the carbon is present as a solid reactant, $n_R = 1$, and $n_P = 1$. It follows from eq. (16.12) that for this case $[\Delta H']_t = [\Delta U']_t$.

Final remark on the relation between the zeros. If the internal energy of a reactant system is arbitrarily defined to be zero, and then a constant-temperature, constant-volume reaction ensues, it is now clear that the internal energy of the resultant product system cannot be arbitrarily defined. For a definite heat transfer occurs in the process, so the final internal energy is fixed; it is $[\Delta U']_{v,t}$, according to eq. (16.10). The enthalpies are determined, by reason of the definition (16.9).

Dependence of $[\Delta U']_{v,t}$ and $[\Delta H']_{p,t}$ on temperature and phase

The effect of temperature. The increases in internal energy and enthalpy in a given change of state depend on the condition of the experiment, chiefly on the temperature. This may be illustrated by plotting the internal energy of a substance versus temperature for a fixed volume. For Ideal Gases it does not matter what volume is chosen, of course.

Fig. 16.1 shows such a plot for a system comprising initially hydrogen and oxygen gases mixed in stoichiometric proportions. The units of internal energy are Btu per lb mole of H_2, per $\tfrac{1}{2}$lb mole of O_2, or per lb mole of H_2O. The volume is supposed sufficiently large (and therefore the pressure sufficiently small) for all three substances, H_2, O_2 and H_2O, to act as Ideal Gases.

The upper curve gives the internal energy for the reactant gas ($H_2 + \frac{1}{2}O_2$); the lower gives that of the product (steam). It will be seen that the vertical spacing between them varies, being in fact less at the higher temperature than at the lower. Now this vertical distance measures the

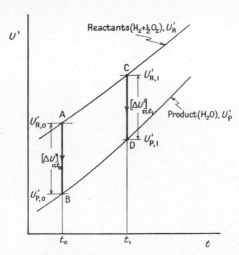

Fig. 16.1   The internal energy-temperature diagram
for the reaction $H_2 + \frac{1}{2}O_2 = H_2O$

negative of $[\Delta U']_{v,t}$; for an isothermal reaction corresponds to a shift from the upper to the lower curve along a line of constant temperature. The distance changes with temperature because the c_V of the products differs from the c_V of reactants, c_V being the local slope of the internal energy curve; there is, after all, no reason why the two c_V's should be the same. Only if, by chance, the c_V of the products were the same function of temperature as that of the reactants would the increase in internal energy be a constant at all temperatures.

Standard values of $[\Delta U']_{v,t}$ *and* $[\Delta H']_{p,t}$. It might be thought that the variation of $[\Delta U']_{v,t}$ with temperature would make it necessary for values for various temperatures to be tabulated in data books. Reflexion shows however that, provided internal energy data for the pure reactants and products are available, a single value of $[\Delta U']_{v,t}$ will suffice.

Suppose that a measurement of the increase in the internal energy in a constant-volume, isothermal reaction is given at a fixed temperature, t_0; for example, at 77°F (25°C) and large volume, $[\Delta U']_{v,t}$ for the hydrogen-oxygen reaction is —104,036 Btu/lb mole of H_2. Then the two points A and B on Fig. 16.1 can be plotted, above same arbitrary base-line. Internal energy data for the gases H_2, O_2 and H_2O will then enable the two curves passing through A and B to be drawn. The increase in internal energy at any other temperature, say t_1, is then given as the intercept CD which these curves make on the vertical corresponding to t_1.

Normally it is not necessary to plot the curves. Instead an algebraic equivalent is used, using number subscripts to denote temperatures, namely

$$(U'_{P,1} - U'_{R,1}) = (U'_{P,0} - U'_{R,0}) + (U'_{P,1} - U'_{P,0}) - (U'_{R,1} - U'_{R,0})$$

i.e. $\quad [\Delta U']_{v,t_1} = [\Delta U']_{v,t_0} + (U'_{P,1} - U_{P,0}) - (U'_{R,1} - U'_{R,0})$

$$\dots \quad (16.13)$$

the truth of which will be recognised by studying its geometrical equivalent, namely

$$\left.\frac{C}{D}\right| = \left.\frac{A}{B}\right| + \left.\frac{C}{A}\right| - \left.\frac{D}{B}\right|$$

where $\left.\dfrac{X}{Y}\right|$ is a symbol used to denote "vertical height of X above Y". A sketch of Fig. 16.1 should always be used as an aid in getting the signs right in eq. (16.13).

The enthalpy changes in constant-pressure isothermal reactions are similarly related as follows:

$$(H'_{P,1} - H'_{R,1}) = (H'_{P,0} - H'_{R,0}) + (H'_{P,1} - H'_{P,0}) - (H'_{R,1} - H'_{R,0})$$

i.e. $\quad [\Delta H']_{p,t_1} = [\Delta H']_{p,t_0} + (H'_{P,1} - H'_{P,0}) - (H'_{R,1} - H'_{R,0})$

The value of $[\Delta U']_{v,t}$ at a standard temperature, t_0, often 25°C (77°F), is known as the *standard increase in internal energy at constant-volume*. Correspondingly, $[\Delta H']_{p,t}$ at the standard temperature is known as the *standard increase in enthalpy at constant-pressure*. Values tabulated in data books are usually quoted for low pressure, i.e. large volume, under which conditions the substances may be taken as Ideal Gases. Correction for a change in pressure may be made in the same way as for temperature if U'–p and H'–p data are available for the substances in question; the correction is often negligible.

The First Law applied to non-isothermal reactions. Diagrams such as Fig. 16.1 are useful for illustrating the application of the First Law to non-isothermal processes also. We consider as an example the application of the Steady-Flow Energy Equation to a flow process in which a combustible stream (reactants) of state 1 enters a machine while combustion products at state 2 flow out (Fig. 16.2). How are the heat and shaft work related to the change of state?

Fig. 16.3 shows an H'–t diagram for the substances in question, which will be taken as Ideal Gases so that no statement about pressure need be made. The S.F.E.E., eq. (8.22) gives

$$Q - W_x - \Delta\left(\frac{V^2}{2g_0} + \frac{gz}{g_0}\right) = H'_{P,2} - H'_{R,1} \qquad \dots \quad (16.14)$$

The left-hand side of eq. (16.14) is given and the final state has to be evaluated. Knowing the initial state, the enthalpy-temperature relations of the substances and the constant-pressure increase in enthalpy at temperature t_0, $[\Delta H']_{t_0}$, the evaluation may be done with the aid of an equation derived similarly to (16.13); it is

$$H'_{P,2} - H'_{R,1} = (H'_{P,2} - H'_{P,0}) - (H'_{R,1} - H'_{R,0}) + (H'_{P,0} - H'_{R,0})$$
$$= (H'_{P,2} - H'_{P,0}) - (H'_{R,1} - H'_{R,0}) + [\Delta H']_{t_0}$$
$$\dots \quad (16.15)$$

The first two brackets on the right-hand side are obtained directly from the enthalpy-temperature tables for the products and reactants.

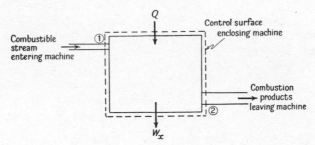

Fig. 16.2   Illustrating a steady-flow combustion process

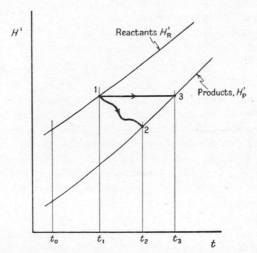

Fig. 16.3   Enthalpy-temperature diagram used in the discussion of steady-flow combustion processes.

Temperature rise in constant-enthalpy combustion. A case of particular interest is that in which the enthalpy change is zero. This arises in adiabatic steady-flow (or constant-pressure) reaction in the absence of shaft work or significant changes in kinetic and gravitational energy, for example in a well-lagged combustion chamber. Since H' does not change, the product state resulting from the initial state 1 must correspond to the point 3 in Fig. 16.3. The diagram therefore affords a simple means for the determination of the temperature rise.

In the absence of an accurately plotted H-$'t$ diagram, t_3 is calculated from eq. (16.15). With $H'_{P,2}$ replaced by $H'_{P,3}$ and with $H'_{P,3}$ put equal to $H'_{R,1}$, the useful form of this equation is

$$(H'_{P,3} - H'_{P,0}) = (H'_{R,1} - H'_{R,0}) - [\Delta H']_{t_0} \quad \dots \quad (16.16)$$

The first term on the right-hand side is evaluated from enthalpy-temperature data for the reactants; the second term is looked up in tables of standard increases in enthalpy; the bracket on the left-hand side is then used for the determination of t_3 from enthalpy-temperature data for the products.

Three alternative forms of eq. (16.16) in terms of specific heats will now be given without comment. Their equivalence may be perceived by study of Fig. 16.3. They are:—

$$\bar{C}_{\mathrm{PP},03}(t_3 - t_0) = \bar{C}_{\mathrm{PR},01}(t_1 - t_0) - [\Delta H']_{t_0} \quad \dots \quad (16.17)$$

$$\bar{C}_{\mathrm{PP},13}(t_3 - t_1) = - [\Delta H']_{t_1} \quad \dots \quad (16.18)$$

$$0 = \bar{C}_{\mathrm{PR},13}(t_1 - t_3) - [\Delta H']_{t_3} \quad \dots \quad (16.19)$$

- These equations are useful when mean specific heat tables are available instead of enthalpy tables. Since $\bar{C}_p$ depends on the temperature range (see p. 255), which is not known in each case before the calculation starts, a trial-and-error procedure has to be used.

It will be evident from comparison of eq. (16.18) and eq. (16.19) that in the particular case in which the specific heats of products and reactants are equal $[\Delta H']_t$ is independent of temperature.

The effects of the phase of the substances. So far we have assumed that the reactants and products are in the gaseous phase. However liquid and solid fuels have to be considered, and at least one product of common combustion reactions, H_2O, is easily condensable. The effects of the pressure of non-gaseous phases will be illustrated by two examples.

Firstly, we consider once more the U'-t diagram for the H_2—O_2—H_2O system. Fig. 16.4 shows the same curves as Fig. 16.1, but an additional curve has been added, namely, that for the products in the liquid (water) phase. This curve lies below that for steam by a distance corresponding to the quantity denoted earlier (p. 155) by u_{fg}, multiplied by the molecular weight of steam. This is U_{fg}, the internal energy increase in vaporisation per lb mole of steam. It varies, of course, with temperature.

Fig. 16.4 shows that the negative of $[\Delta U']_t$, i.e. the vertical distance between the reactant and product curves, is greater when the product is condensed than when it is not. The relations are:

$$- [\Delta U']_{t_{\mathrm{water}}} = - [\Delta U']_{t_{\mathrm{steam}}} + n U_{fg}$$

i.e.

$$[\Delta U']_{t_{\mathrm{water}}} = [\Delta U']_{t_{\mathrm{steam}}} - n U_{fg}$$

and

$$[\Delta U']_{t_{\mathrm{water}}} = [\Delta U']_{t_{\mathrm{steam}}} - m u_{fg}$$

where n is the number of moles of H_2O in the system and m is its mass. Calculations are carried out with the aid of Fig. 16.4, or the corresponding tabulated data, in the same way as above.

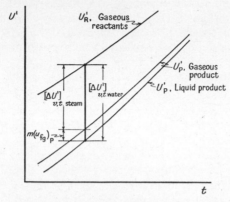

Fig. 16.4   Showing the effect of the phase of the products on $[\Delta U']_{v,t}$.

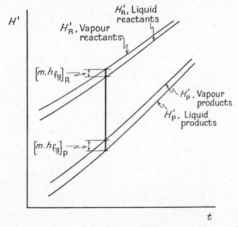

Fig. 16.5   Showing the effect of phase on the enthalpies of the reactants and products.

Corresponding relations, in terms of enthalpy, may also be deduced. These are:

$$[\Delta H']_{t_{water}} = [\Delta H']_{t_{steam}} - nH_{fg}$$

$$[\Delta H']_{t_{water}} = [\Delta H']_{t_{steam}} - mh_{fg} \qquad \ldots \quad (16.20)$$

where H_{fg} is the latent heat of vaporisation of steam per lb mole.

Secondly, we consider the $H'-t$ diagram of a system in which the reactants as well as the products may be present in liquid form. Fig. 16.5 might represent the enthalpy-temperature relations for a mixture of a condensable hydrocarbon with air. The upper reactant curve is valid if the hydrocarbon is in the vapour phase; the lower line holds if it is liquid. The two product curves correspond to the two possible phases of the H_2O produced. The vertical distance between the alternative curves is equal to the latent heat of vaporisation of the condensable substance, multiplied by the proportion which that substance comprises of the mass of the system. It is evident that, in stating the values of a $[\Delta U']_t$ and $[\Delta H']_t$, the phase of both products and reactants must be completely specified.

Enthalpy of formation

In the last section it was shown how the necessity to tabulate the increases in internal energy and enthalpy for various temperatures may be avoided by reference to the values of these quantities at a standard temperature. We now discuss a similar device for avoiding tabulation of the standard increases in internal energy and enthalpy of all the multitudinous reactions which may actually occur. This involves the consideration of one reaction only for each substance together with the specification of arbitrary states of the elements to which are assigned zero values of enthalpy.

For each substance, the reaction considered is one under specified standard conditions (usually 77°F and 1 atm) in which the substance is formed from its constituent chemical elements; it is a particular sort of standard reaction of the type mentioned earlier on p. 333.

Examples of datum states of the elements to which are assigned zero values of enthalpy are:

Oxygen: diatomic* gas (O_2) at 77°F, 1 atm.

Hydrogen: diatomic* gas (H_2) at 77°F, 1 atm.

Carbon: graphite, solid (C) at 77°F, 1 atm.

The data pertaining to such reactions is presented as *enthalpy of formation*†, H'_f, which we define as follows:—

The enthalpy of formation of a chemical substance is the enthalpy of the product in a constant-pressure, isothermal reaction, in which the substance is the only product and the reactants are the chemical elements in their datum states.

Some values of enthalpy of formation, H'_f, are given in Table 16.6. The meaning of the definition and of the data given in Table 16.6 will be exemplified by the reaction

$$C_{solid} + \tfrac{1}{2}O_2 = CO$$

Table 16.6 gives H'_f for CO as $-47,549$ Btu/lb mole CO.
For any reaction, we have the definition

$$[\Delta H']_{p,t} = H'_P - H'_R$$

---

* The monatomic gases at the same temperatures and pressures will have corresponding positive values of enthalpy of formation.

† Commonly the symbol ΔH_f is used instead of H'_f.

Now since the reactants are chemical elements in their datum states, $H'_R = 0$; on the other hand $H'_P = H'_f$ for CO.

Hence $$[\Delta H']_{p,t} = H'_f \text{ for CO.}$$

By writing the enthalpy of the product, H'_P, as H'_f we emphasise the special nature and conditions of the reaction. If the zero values of enthalpy are not introduced, the data for the reaction would be presented as:—

Standard $[\Delta H']_{p,t} = -47,549$ Btu/lb mole CO.

The enthalpy of formation concept, with its associated zero values of enthalpy simplifies, the calculations of $[\Delta H']_{p,t}$ for more complicated reactions. Example 5 below illustrates this.

TABLE 16.6. *Enthalpy of formation*

Substance	Reaction	State	H'_f Btu/lb mole of substance
O_2	—	gas at 77°F, 1 atm	0, by definition
H_2	—	gas at 77°F, 1 atm	0, by definition
C	—	solid at 77°F, 1 atm	0, by definition
CO_2	$C + O_2 = CO_2$	gas at 77°F, 1 atm	$-169,294$
CO	$C + \frac{1}{2}O_2 = CO$	gas at 77°F, 1 atm	$-47,549$
H_2O	$H_2 + \frac{1}{2}O_2 = H_2O$	gas at 77°F, 1 atm	$-104,036$
H_2O	$H_2 + \frac{1}{2}O_2 = H_2O$	liquid at 77°F, 1 atm	$-122,971$
CH_4	$C + 2H_2 = CH_4$	gas at 77°F, 1 atm	$-32,200$
C_2H_6	$2C + 3H_2 = C_2H_6$	gas at 77°F, 1 atm	$-36,425$

Internal energy of formation. A procedure similar to that given above for enthalpy of formation could be adopted for internal energy of formation. However, since for Ideal Gases $[\Delta U']_t$ can be obtained from $[\Delta H']_t$ via eq. (16.12), it suffices to consider enthalpy of formation only.

Deduction of increase in enthalpy of reaction from enthalpy of formation.
The use of data for enthalpy of formation to obtain the standard increase in enthalpy in any reaction will now be illustrated by an example. The technique is to ascribe the appropriate values of enthalpy of formation to each of the reactants and products to obtain H'_R and H'_P; their difference then gives $[\Delta H']_{p,t}$.

EXAMPLE 5

Problem. Steam reacts with solid carbon to form carbon monoxide and hydrogen (water-gas). Determine the increase in enthalpy per lb mole at 77°F and 1 atm.

Solution. The chemical equation is

$$C + H_2O = CO + H_2$$

The reactants (on the left-hand side of the equation) have enthalpy H'_R given by

$$H'_R = H'_{f,c} + H'_{f,steam}$$

Inserting the values of H'_f from Table 16.6 we obtain

$$H'_R = 0 + (-104,036 \text{ Btu/lb mole } H_2O) \times 1 \text{ lb mole } H_2O$$

$$= -104,036 \text{ Btu.}$$

Similarly $H'_P = H'_{f,CO} + H'_{f,H_2}$

$$= (-47,549 \text{ Btu/lb mole CO}) \times 1 \text{ lb mole CO} + 0$$

$$= -47,549 \text{ Btu}$$

$\therefore$ $[\Delta H']_{p,t} = H'_P - H'_R$

$$= -47,549 - (-104,036)$$

$$= +56,487 \text{ Btu.} \qquad \qquad \dots Answer$$

Comment. The reaction is endothermic; heat must be transferred to the system from the surroundings. This may be seen from eq. (16.11) which states

$$Q = [\Delta H']_{p,t}$$

$$= +54,487 \text{ Btu in this case.}$$

Heat of reaction; heat of formation

So far we have considered the internal energy and enthalpy changes which result from reaction in a system comprising a chemical substance. The application of the First Law to such systems led to eq. (16.10) and eq. (16.11) which state how $[\Delta U']_{v,t}$ and $[\Delta H']_{p,t}$ are related to Q, the heat transfer *to the system*. We now consider the effects which the reaction in the system has *on the surroundings*.

Heat of reaction. In a constant-volume, isothermal reaction, the heat transfer *to the surroundings*, $-Q$, is, from eq. (16.10) equal to the *negative* of the increase in the internal energy of the system, $-[\Delta U']_{v,t}$; $-[\Delta U']_{v,t}$ is called the *constant-volume heat of reaction*. Similarly for an isothermal reaction at constant pressure, the *negative* of the increase in enthalpy, $-[\Delta H']_{p,t}$, is called the *constant-pressure heat of reaction*. Clearly, heats of reaction are of great interest in heating applications.

Standard heats of reaction. It will be recalled (p. 333) that in order to limit the amount of tabulated data on chemical reaction, standard values of $[\Delta U']_{v,t}$ and $[\Delta H']_{p,t}$ were used. Correspondingly the negatives of these quantities become standard heats of reactions: the value of $-[\Delta U']_{v,t}$ at a standard temperature, often 77°F (25°C) is known as the *standard heat of reaction at constant volume;* $-[\Delta H']_{p,t}$ at the standard temperature is known as the *standard heat of reaction at constant pressure*. These standard heats of reaction may be regarded respectively as alternatives to the standard values of $[\Delta U']_{v,t}$ and $[\Delta H']_{p,t}$ for the presentation of tabulated data on chemical reaction; the corresponding quantities are equal in magnitude but of opposite sign.

Heat of formation. In parallel with the above pattern, the heat of formation of a substance is the negative of its enthalpy of formation, $-H'_f$. Again it is to be regarded as an alternative way of presenting reaction data.

EXAMPLE 6.

Problem. In the reaction $C + O_2 = CO_2$ the enthalpy of formation at 77°F (25°C) and 1 atm. is $-169,294$ Btu/lb mole of CO_2 (from Table 16.6).

Evaluate (a) the standard heat of reaction at constant pressure, i.e. at 77°F and 1 atm;

(b) the heat of reaction when the reactants are at 100°F and the products at 1000°F.

Take the following values of mean specific heat, $\bar{c}_p$: $C = 0.2$; $O_2 = 0.236$; $CO_2 = 0.246$ Btu/lb$_m$ °F. The gaseous reactants and products may be assumed to be Ideal Gases.

Solution (a).

$$H'_f = -169,294 \text{ Btu/lb mole } CO_2$$

$$= [\Delta H']_t$$

since H'_f assumes zero values for C and O_2 at 77°F.

Hence the standard heat of reaction at constant pressure

$$= -[\Delta H']_t$$

$$= 169,294 \text{ Btu/lb mole } CO_2$$

or $\qquad = 169,294 \text{ Btu/lb mole C}$

or $\qquad = \dfrac{169,294}{12} = 14,108 \text{ Btu/lb}_m \text{ C} \qquad \dots \quad Answer (a)$

Solution (b)

Using subscripts 1 and 2 to denote the temperatures 100°F and 1000°F respectively, and subscript 0 to denote the standard temperature, we have, from eq. (16.15)

$$H'_{P,2} - H'_{R,1} = (H'_{P,0} - H'_{R,0}) + (H'_{P,2} - H'_{P,0}) - (H'_{R,1} - H'_{R,0})$$

Now

$$(H'_{P,0} - H'_{R,0}) = [\Delta H']_t = -169,294 \text{ Btu/lb mole } CO_2$$

$$(H'_{P,2} - H'_{P,0}) = m\bar{c}_p(t_2 - t_0) \text{ for the only product,}$$
$$\text{namely, } CO_2.$$

$$= 44 \times 0.246 \times (1000 - 77) = 10,000 \text{ Btu/lb mole } CO_2$$

$$(H'_{R,1} - H'_{R,0}) = m\bar{c}_p(t_1 - t_0) \text{ for C} + m\bar{c}_p(t_1 - t_0) \text{ for } O_2$$

$$= 12 \times 0.02 \times (100 - 77) + 32 \times 0.236 \times (100 - 77)$$

$$= 229 \text{ Btu/lb mole } CO_2$$

Hence

$$H'_{P,2} - H'_{R,1} = -169,294 + 10,000 - 229$$

$$= -159,513 \text{ Btu/lb mole } CO_2$$

∴   Heat of reaction

$$= 159,513 \text{ Btu/lb mole } CO_2 \qquad \dots \quad Answer (b)$$

Calorific value

"Heat of reaction" and "heat of formation" are terms originating in chemical thermodynamics. The mechanical engineer is more exclusively concerned with combustion reaction and uses a different terminology. We begin this section with a definition:

The calorific value of a fuel is the heat of reaction at constant pressure of the reaction in which the fuel burns completely with oxygen.

Complete combustion usually implies that the oxides are carbon dioxide and steam (or water). If sulphur is present in the fuel, the appropriate oxide is the dioxide, SO_2. Other oxidisable elements, such as vanadium, are normally present in such small quantities as to make it immaterial what oxides are formed.

The calorific value, also called *heating value*, is expressed as Btu/lb_m of fuel, Btu/lb mole of fuel, or Btu/standard ft^3 of fuel according to convenience. Reference to a unit of fuel makes it unnecessary to know how much air happens to be mixed with the fuel, though of course this must exceed the stoichiometric quantity if combustion is to be complete. It is likewise immaterial whether air or pure oxygen is the oxidant.

In accordance with the the foregoing analysis, the calorific value of a fuel, $\overline{CV}$, is related to the increase in enthalpy in the reaction, $[\Delta H']_{p,t}$, by

$$\overline{CV} = -[\Delta H']_{p,t}$$

Higher and lower calorific values. It has been seen above that the phase of the reactants and products influences the magnitudes of the internal energy and enthalpy increases. It follows, therefore, that the calorific value of a fuel will be also so influenced. The terms *higher calorific value*, $\overline{HCV}$, and *lower calorific value*, $\overline{LCV}$, are used respectively to distinguish the cases in which any H_2O formed is in the liquid or the gaseous phase. The same distinction is sometimes rendered by the terms "gross" and "net". The two calorific values are related, through eq. (16.20), as follows:

$$\overline{HCV} = \overline{LCV} + mh_{fg}$$

where m is the mass of H_2O produced per pound of fuel and h_{fg} is the latent heat of vaporisation of water at the standard temperature. In practice h_{fg} is taken as 1050 Btu/lb_m although it actually depends somewhat on the pressure and the temperature.

The phase of the fuel, if in question, must be stated separately.

Some typical calorific values of fuels are given in Table 16.7.

Mixtures of fuels. It is a consequence of the Gibbs-Dalton Law that the calorific value of a mixed fuel can be determined by simple addition. We give as an example the calculation of the calorific value of the producer gas of example 1 on p. 326.

TABLE 16.7. *Typical calorific values of fuels*

Solid fuels

Fuel	Calorific value, Btu/lb$_m$ (Bomb calorimeter, 60°F)	
	Higher	Lower
Anthracite	14,868	14,580
Bituminous coal	14,400	13,932
Lignite	9,306	8,766
Peat	6,840	6,228
Wood	6,804	6,156
Coke	13,212	13,104

Liquid fuels

Fuel	Calorific value, Btu/lb$_m$ (Bomb calorimeter, 60°F)	
	Higher	Lower
Aviation petrol (100 octane)	20,340	18,918
Motor petrol	20,160	18,792
Vaporising oil	19,800	18,576
Motor benzole	18,045	17,280
Kerosene	19,854	18,558
Diesel oil, distilled (Gas oil)	19,764	18,558
Light fuel oil	19,260	18,090
Heavy fuel oil	18,900	17,784
Residual fuel oil (Bunker C)	18,080	17,180

Gaseous fuels

Fuel	Calorific value Btu/ft^3 at 60°F, 30 in. Hg	
	Higher	Lower
Coal gas (Town gas)	540	482·2
Producer gas	162·7	161·7
Blast furnace gas	92·3	91·3
Natural gas (English)	977·2	879·7
Carbon monoxide, CO	318	318
Hydrogen, H$_2$	320	270

EXAMPLE 7

Problem. Determine the higher calorific value of a producer gas of volumetric analysis 26% CO, 12% H_2, 7% CO_2 and 55% N_2.

Solution. Using the data in Table 16.7, we draw up the following table:—

Gas	$\overline{HCV}$ of pure gas Btu/ft³ at 60°F, 30 in. Hg.	Volume fraction	Contribution to $\overline{HCV}$ of mixture. Btu/ft³ at 60°F, 30 in. Hg.
CO	318	0·26	$0·26 \times 318 = 82·7$
H_2	320	0·12	$0·12 \times 320 = 38·4$
			Total $= 121·1$

The answer is therefore 121·1 Btu/ft³ at 60°F, 30 in. Hg. The CO_2 and N_2 of course make no contribution to the calorific value of the mixture.

Measurement of calorific values. The engineer needs to have simple means of measuring the calorific values of the fuels with which he is supplied. *Calorimeters* are used for this purpose. They are of two types: *steady-flow* calorimeters and *bomb* (or constant-volume) calorimeters. The first type is used for measurements on gaseous fuels, the second for liquid and solid fuels.

Fig. 16.6 shows a gas calorimeter. The fuel gas is mixed with sufficient air to ensure complete combustion and absence of condensation of the steam in the exhaust gases. Since the process is one of steady-flow at low velocity in the absence of external work, the enthalpy decrease of the gas stream is equal to the heat transferred to the surroundings, which is measured by the temperature rise of the cooling water. The gas calorimeter therefore measures the higher calorific value of the fuel gas; the lower calorific value can then be calculated, knowing the quantity of steam in the exhaust and the latent heat of vaporisation of steam.

Steady-flow techniques are more difficult to devise for liquid and gaseous fuels; it is easier to carry out an experiment at *constant volume*. Fig. 16.7 shows a bomb calorimeter used for solid fuel. A sample of fuel is placed in the bomb, into which pure oxygen is then forced under pressure. Ignition is effected by an electric current passed through a wire in contact with the fuel. When combustion is complete the temperature rise of the bomb and its surrounding water bath is measured; since this temperature rise amounts only to a few degrees, the reaction can be regarded as isothermal although a correction can be applied if great accuracy is required.

Two other corrections are needed if the bomb calorimeter is to yield the calorific value of the fuel. Firstly, we note that, since the experiment is at constant volume rather than constant pressure, it measures $-[\Delta U']_{v,t}$ rather than $-[\Delta H']_{p,t}$; these quantities differ because of the change in the number of gaseous moles during the reaction; eq. (16.12) enables $-[\Delta H']_{p,t}$ to be deduced from the measured $-[\Delta U']_{v,t}$. Secondly, the conditions of the experiment are usually such that most of the steam condenses; the measurement therefore gives more nearly the higher calorific value than the lower. However a small but calculable proportion of the steam remains in the vapour phase, so a small correction has to be

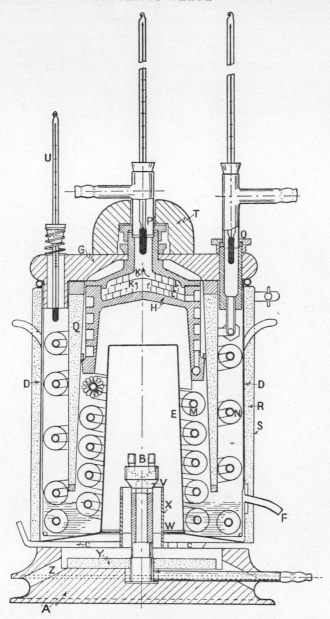

Fig. 16.6 Gas Calorimeter (Boys).

A. Wood base	G. Wood lid	R. Felt jacket
B. Gas burners	H. Mixing chamber	S. Bright sheet metal
C. Metal plate	K. Dished plates	T. Wood shield
D. Metal vessel	M. Inner coil	W. Ferrule
E. Copper chimney	N. Outer coil	X. Fibre tube
F. Condensed water	O. Inlet water box	Y. Felt disc
outlet	Q. Baffle	Z. Holes in base

applied. Often the experimental accuracy, or the use to which the data are to be put, renders it unnecessary to apply these corrections; in this case the heat transfer from the fuel and oxygen to their surroundings is simply taken as the higher calorific value of the fuel.

Standard methods of measuring calorific values have been laid down by the British Standards Institute and the American Society for Testing Materials (see bibliography).

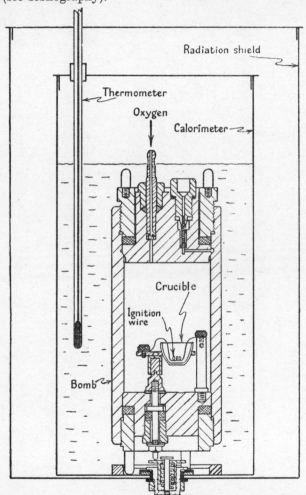

Fig. 16.7 Bomb calorimeter (Griffin-Sutton) (stirrer omitted).

The efficiency of combustion appliances

The discussion of the application of the First Law of Thermodynamics to combustion processes will be concluded by mention of two ways in which the performance of combustion equipment may be compared with an absolute standard. These involve the concepts of combustion efficiency, η_c, and heating efficiency, η_h.

Combustion efficiency. In the foregoing sections we have considered reactions which go to completion, i.e. in which all the carbon and hydrogen in the fuel leave the equipment in the form of CO_2 and H_2O. This desirable result is sometimes difficult to achieve, the main causes of failure being incomplete mixing of fuel and air in the combustion chamber and inadequate time of residence in the chamber for the reaction to be completed. The extent to which combustion is completed is measured by the *combustion efficiency*, η_c, defined in such a way that η_c is 100% if combustion is complete and 0% if no combustion has taken place.

Various definitions of η_c are in use; each has its own advantages and fields of convenient application. One which is susceptible of easy measurement is the so-called "CO_2 efficiency", defined as

$$\eta_c \equiv \frac{\text{actual volumetric\% } CO_2 \text{ exhaust gases}}{\substack{\text{volumetric\% } CO_2 \text{ exhaust gases from the same} \\ \text{fuel and air streams if combustion is complete.}}} \quad \ldots \quad (16.21)$$

It has the disadvantage that if all the carbon were completely burned while the hydrogen escaped combustion, η_c would appear as 100%*. This situation rarely arises in practice.

Another definition of η_c may be used if the combustion chamber is adiabatic. It is the "temperature rise efficiency", defined as

$$\eta_c \equiv \frac{\text{actual temperature rise of gases in chamber}}{\substack{\text{temperature rise which would occur} \\ \text{if combustion were complete.}}} \quad \ldots \quad (16.22)$$

This avoids the disadvantage of the former definition, but is more difficult to measure and is restricted to adiabatic combustion chambers.

Heating efficiency. The most important measure of performance from the point of view of the designer of heating equipment is the "heating efficiency", η_h. This is defined as

$$\eta_h = \frac{\text{heat transferred from gases to material to be heated}}{\substack{\text{maximum possible heat transfer} \\ \text{in isothermal reaction}}} \quad \ldots \quad (16.23)$$

The denominator is of course the calorific value of the fuel. The numerator is less than this in practice because (*a*) the exhaust gases rarely leave the equipment at as low a temperature as the entering fuel and air streams; (*b*) heat is transferred wastefully to the surroundings of the equipment because of inadequate insulation; (*c*) the combustion efficiency may not be 100%. The heating efficiency of a well-designed steam boiler is of the order of 85%; the heating efficiency of an open coal fire on the other hand, regarding the room as the system to be heated, is nearer 15%.

* Or very nearly. The number of moles in the exhaust gas would differ somewhat from those of the products of complete combustion so that CO_2 efficiency would not be quite 100%.

Opinion varies as to whether the higher or the lower calorific value should be used as the denominator of η_h. On the one hand it may be argued that the steam in the exhaust gases could be condensed; then the higher calorific value is appropriate. On the other hand, such condensation has to be avoided as a rule lest oxides of sulphur should dissolve in the water to form acid and cause corrosion; in this case it may be thought more "fair" to the heat transfer equipment to use the lower calorific value. However the important thing is to make known on what basis any quoted heating efficiency has been calculated.

EXAMPLE 8

Problem. A boiler generates 11 pounds of steam per pound of fuel burned, when fired with fuel oil having an $\overline{HCV}$ of 18,000 Btu/lb$_m$. The feed water is supplied at a temperature of 140°F and the steam is produced at a pressure of 600 psia and a temperature of 900°F. Calculate the heating efficiency of the boiler.

Solution. Applying the S.F.E.E. to the H_2O flowing steadily through the boiler, and neglecting the kinetic and potential energy terms, we have

Heat transfer to H_2O in the boiler, $Q = h_{steam} - h_{feed}$

From the Steam Tables, Appendix B

$$h_{steam} = 1462 \cdot 5 \text{ Btu/lb}_m$$

$$h_{feed} = 107 \cdot 9 \text{ Btu/lb}_m$$

$$\therefore \qquad Q = 1354 \cdot 6 \text{ Btu/lb}_m \text{ steam.}$$

The heating efficiency, often called the *boiler efficiency*, is then obtained from eq. (16.23) as

$$\eta_h = \frac{11 \times 1354 \cdot 6}{18000} \times 100\%$$

$$= 82 \cdot 8\% \qquad \text{based on the } \overline{HCV}. \quad \dots \quad Answer$$

THE SECOND LAW OF THERMODYNAMICS APPLIED TO COMBUSTION

The entropy of a chemical substance

Just as values can be ascribed to the internal energy and enthalpy of a chemical substance, each substance in a definite state has a definite value of entropy. The symbol S' will be used for this quantity. The remarks made earlier about the restrictions on the choice of arbitrary zeros of U' and H' apply to S' also; if the entropy of a given chemical substance in a reactant state is arbitrarily put equal to zero, the entropy of the system in any product state is fixed.

Entropy change in adiabatic reaction. It is a consequence of the Second Law that the entropy of an adiabatic system can only increase (eq. (13.33), p. 226). Consequently any chemical substance which can react spontaneously under adiabatic conditions is found to have a higher entropy after reaction than before it.

The *possibility* of any reaction can therefore be determined by comparing the entropy of the reactants with the entropy of the (supposed) products, bearing in mind of course that the temperatures of the products and reactants will in general differ because the reaction is adiabatic. To do this it is necessary to have data available on the entropies of the materials in question. We shall not discuss here how these are determined.

Entropy change in isothermal reaction. Since the changes of U' and H' in chemical reactions have been discussed above largely for isothermal reactions, it is desirable to re-formulate the above statement about the possibility of reaction accordingly.

In Chapter 13 it was shown (eq. (13.35) p. 227) that for any process

$$dQ \leqslant T\, dS' \qquad \ldots \quad (16.24)$$

where dQ is an infinitesimal heat transfer, T is the absolute temperature of the system and dS' is the change in entropy of the (chemical) system.

Application of the First Law to processes in which shear work, electrical work, gravity, motion, capillarity, etc. are absent yields

$$dQ = dU' \text{ if the process is at constant volume} \quad \ldots \quad (16.25)$$

and $\qquad dQ = dH'$ if the process is at constant pressure $\ldots$ (16.26)

Combining eq. (16.25) and eq. (16.26) in turn with the Second Law statement (16.24), we obtain

$$dU' - T\, dS' \leqslant 0 \text{ for a constant-volume process} \quad \ldots \quad (16.27)$$

and $\qquad dH' - T\, dS' \leqslant 0$ for a constant-pressure process $\ldots$ (16.28

Since we are considering only changes in which T is constant* there is no need to restrict ourselves to infinitesimal changes. Eq. (16.27) and eq. (16.28) can therefore be integrated, giving

$$\Delta U' - T\Delta S' \leqslant 0\dagger$$

or $(U' - TS')_P - (U' - TS')_R \leqslant 0$ for a constant volume process

$$\ldots \quad (16.29)$$

and $\qquad\qquad \Delta H' - T\Delta S' \leqslant 0\dagger$

or $(H' - TS')_P - (H' - TS')_R \leqslant 0$ for a constant pressure process

$$\ldots \quad (16.30)$$

Our criterion for the possibility of isothermal chemical reaction can now be formulated. It is:—

An isothermal chemical reaction is only possible at constant volume, if $U' - TS'$ for the products is less than $U' - TS'$ for the reactants. Isothermal reaction is only possible at constant pressure, in the absence of shear and electrical work, if $H' - TS'$ for the products is less than $H' - TS'$ for the reactants.

---

* i.e. isothermal reaction. See p. 329.

† To conform with the nomenclature used earlier in this chapter we should write $[\Delta U']_{v,t}$ and $[\Delta H']_{p,t}$. We omit the brackets here for clarity.

The possibility of combustion reactions. Table 16.8 contains data for the changes of $H' - TS'$ for reactions important in combustion, at 77°F and 1 atm pressure.

Examination of Table 16.8 reveals two features. The first is that $\Delta(H' - TS')$ is indeed negative; the reactions are therefore possible, as common experience asserts.* The second is that $\Delta(H' - TS')$ has very nearly the same value as $\Delta H'$, indicating that the contribution of the entropy change at constant temperature is small. Closer study shows that S' increases in the reactions leading to H_2O and CO_2, but decreases in that leading to CO.

TABLE 16.8

Reaction	$\Delta H'$ Btu/lb mole	$\Delta(H' - TS')$ Btu/lb mole
$H_2 + \frac{1}{2}O_2 = H_2O_{gas}$	−104,036	−102,787
$C + O_2 = CO_2$	−169,294	−169,144
$C + \frac{1}{2}O_2 = CO$	−47,549	−48,963

Work done by a chemically-reacting system

In the introduction to this chapter it was stated that the Second Law furnishes (*a*) a criterion for the possibility of chemical reaction, and (*b*) a means of determining the maximum attainable work. Having discussed the first of these we now turn to the second. As a preliminary, we first consider how it is that any of the reactions of Table 16.8 can ever be reversed; we know that H_2O can be split into H_2 and O_2, yet $\Delta(H' - TS')$ for this reaction is *positive* (i.e. >0). How can this be?

Reflexion about how H_2O is decomposed in practice, namely by means of an electrolytic cell, reveals the answer to the query; for a flow of electricity counts as external work, which was specifically excluded in deriving eq. (16.30). External work, W_x, here means work other than pdV work at the (constant pressure) system boundary. (cf. p. 111 for the corresponding definition for a control volume). We now remedy this restriction, considering only constant-pressure isothermal processes.

The First Law yields $dQ - dW_x = dH'$ ... (16.31)

Combining this equation with (16.24) and integrating, yields

$$W_x \leqslant - (\Delta H' - T\Delta S')   \quad ... (16.32)$$

* This conclusion requires qualification. What if there is an intermediate state, occurring before complete reaction, in which $H' - TS'$ is even lower than in the completely reacted state? Then the reaction will proceed to this intermediate state and no farther. This is not merely an academic point; there are indeed always such intermediate states, although at low temperatures they are so close to the state of complete reaction as to be indistinguishable for practical purposes. At the higher temperatures occurring in petrol engines and rocket motors on the other hand, the intermediate equilibrium states are far indeed from those of complete combustion. The theory of this phenomenon is found in more advanced texts than the present, usually under the heading of "dissociation". This word implies that reaction goes to completion and then partly retraces its steps; i.e. the products "dissociate". This is not the way things really happen, but it is quite a useful way of imagining them.

In electrolysis W_x is negative. This enables the condition eq. (16.32) to be satisfied even though $(\Delta H' - T\Delta S')$ is positive.

The maximum work in chemical reaction. Eq. (16.32) enables an important practical question to be answered: given a fuel-air mixture, how much work can be obtained from isothermal constant-pressure reaction? The answer is obtained by replacing the inequality by an equality, namely:

$$W_{x,max} = -(\Delta H' - T\Delta S') \qquad \ldots \quad (16.33)$$

Examination of Table 16.8 shows that, since the $T\Delta S'$ terms are small, the maximum work quantity is very nearly equal to $\Delta H'$ and therefore to the calorific value, $\overline{CV}$, for both hydrogen and carbon combustion. This result holds for all fuels used in practice. Symbolically we write

$$W_{x,max} \approx \overline{CV} \qquad \ldots \quad (16.34)$$

Efficiency of internal-combustion engines. Although much of the world's power is produced by petrol and diesel engines, and by "open-cycle" gas turbines, these were specifically excluded from the consideration of efficiency advanced in Chapter 10. Eq. (16.33) makes if possible to remedy this omission by defining an efficiency $\eta_{i.c.}$ for internal combustion engines, as

$$\eta_{i.c.} \equiv \frac{W_x}{W_{x,max}} \qquad \ldots \quad (16.35)$$

wherein W_x is the shaft work produced by the engine and $W_{x,max}$ is equal to $-(\Delta H' - T\Delta S')$ for the fuel used, evaluated at the constant pressure and temperature of the surrounding atmosphere.

However, since the term $T\Delta S'$ is so small, and since actual engines anyway deliver much less than the maximum possible power, it is sufficient in practice to use an approximate expression, obtained by combining eq. (16.34) and eq. (16.35), namely

$$\eta_{i.c.} \approx \frac{W_x}{\overline{CV}} \qquad \ldots \quad (16.36)$$

Once again opinions differ as to whether the higher or the lower calorific value should be used in the denominator.

Values of $\eta_{i.c.}$ which are obtained in practice vary from about 20% for the simplest gas-turbine engines, to about 40% for advanced Diesel engines. Petrol engines have efficiencies between 30% and 35%.

EXAMPLE 9

Problem. An industrial gas-turbine engine develops 6300 horse-power and has a specific fuel consumption of 0.76 lb$_m$ of fuel/h.p. h. The higher calorific value of the fuel used is 18,300 Btu/lb$_m$ of fuel. Calculate the efficiency, $\eta_{i.c.}$ of the engine.

Solution. The shaft work, W_x, is given by

$$W_x = \frac{6300 \times 550}{778} = 4460 \text{ Btu/s.}$$

in which the factor 550 is the equivalent of 1 horse-power in ft lb$_f$/s and the factor 778 is the mechanical equivalent of heat in ft lb$_f$/Btu.

From eq. (16.34) we have

$$W_{x,max} = \overline{CV} \text{ Btu/lb}_m \text{ of fuel}$$
$$= \overline{CV} \times \dot{m}_{fuel} \text{ Btu/s.}$$

where $\dot{m}_{fuel}$ = mass flow rate of fuel in lb_m/s.

In this case $\dot{m}_{fuel} = \dfrac{0 \cdot 76 \times 6300}{3600} = 1 \cdot 33 \text{ lb}_m \text{ fuel/s.}$

$\therefore \qquad\qquad W_{x,max} \approx 18{,}300 \times 1 \cdot 33 = 24{,}350 \text{ Btu/s.}$

Hence from eq. (16.35) we have

$$\eta_{i.c.} = \frac{4460}{24{,}350} \times 100\% = 18 \cdot 3\% \qquad \ldots \text{ } Answer$$

EXAMPLE 10

Problem. An automobile petrol engine develops 65 brake horse-power. The mixture strength is 110% and the engine air consumption is $7 \cdot 5 \text{ lb}_m/\text{min.}$ The stoichiometric air-fuel ratio of the fuel used is $14 \cdot 5$ and the higher calorific value of the fuel is $19{,}000 \text{ Btu/lb}_m$. Determine (*a*) the specific fuel consumption in $\text{lb}_m/\text{bhp h}$, and (*b*) the efficiency, $\eta_{i.c.}$.

Solution. First we determine the air-fuel ratio, x, of the mixture entering the engine.

From eq. (16.6) we have

$$\text{Mixture strength} = \frac{x_{stoich}}{x} \times 100\%$$

$\therefore \qquad\qquad x = 14 \cdot 5 \times \dfrac{100}{110} = 13 \cdot 18$

Then from the air consumption and x we deduce the fuel consumption, $\dot{m}_{fuel}$ as follows:

$$\dot{m}_{fuel} = \frac{7 \cdot 5}{13 \cdot 18} = 0 \cdot 569 \text{ lb}_m \text{ fuel/min.}$$

Hence the specific fuel consumption =

$$\frac{0 \cdot 569 \times 60}{65} = 0 \cdot 525 \text{ lb}_m \text{ fuel/b.h.p h} \qquad \ldots \text{ } Answer \text{ } (a)$$

The shaft work $W_x = \dfrac{65 \times 550 \times 60}{778} = 3170 \text{ Btu/min}$

and $\qquad W_{x,max} = \overline{CV} \times \dot{m}_{fuel}$ from eq. (16.34)

$$= 19{,}000 \times 0 \cdot 569 = 10{,}820 \text{ Btu/min.}$$

$\therefore \qquad\qquad \eta_{i.c.} = \dfrac{3170}{10{,}820} \times 100 = 29 \cdot 3\% \qquad \ldots \text{ } Answer \text{ } (b)$

The upper limit of efficiency of internal-combustion engines. A major difference between $\eta_{i.c.}$ and the heat engine efficiency of Chapter 10 must be emphasised. Whereas the latter is limited by the temperature of the available reservoirs, no such limitation is imposed on the efficiency of an internal-combustion engine. According to the Second Law, $\eta_{i.c.}$, can reach 100%.

Internal-combustion engines should therefore be judged more strictly than, for example, steam power plants. A Diesel engine giving 40% efficiency is wasting 60% of the available power. Engineers cannot be satisfied until a much greater approach to the permissible limit has been achieved.

One way of doing this has been mentioned already in Chapter 11 (pp. 189, 196). This is the fuel cell. It is currently the most hopeful development in the effort materially to increase the efficiency of man's usage of fuel.

BIBLIOGRAPHY

Code for the Sampling and Analysis of Flue Gases. B.S. 1756. British Standards Institution, 1952.

Fuel Oils for Burners. B.S. 742. British Standards Institution, 1947.

Fuel, Petroleum, Aromatic Hydrocarbons and Engine Anti-freezes. American Society for Testing Materials Standards, Part 5, 1955.

Fuels for Oil Engines. B.S. 209. British Standards Institution, 1947.

Sampling and Analysis of Coal and Coke. B.S. 735. British Standards Institution, 1944.

Selected Values of Properties of Hydrocarbons. Circular C 461, National Bureau of Standards, 1947.

Specification for Testing the Calorific Value of Coal Gas: General Notification of the Gas Referees. H.M. Stationery Office, 1930.

Standard Methods for Testing Petroleum and its Products. Institute of Petroleum, 1952.

SPIERS, H. M., *Technical Data on Fuel.* The British National Committee, World Power Conference, 1955.

CHAPTER 16—PROBLEMS

Notes.

1. Air contains 23·2% by mass of oxygen
   21·0% by volume of oxygen.

2. Assume all gaseous reactants to be Ideal Gases.

16.1 (*a*) A solid fuel, having a composition by mass of 84% carbon, 14% hydrogen and 2% sulphur, is burned completely with oxygen. Determine the minimum quantity of oxygen required, and the mass composition and the molal composition of the products of combustion.

(*b*) The fuel of (*a*) is burned completely with air. Determine the minimum quantity of air required and the mass composition and molal composition of the products of combustion.

16.2 (*a*) A stoichiometric mixture of *n*-octane (C_8H_{18}) and air burns completely. Determine the stoichiometric air-to-fuel ratio by mass and the molal composition of the products of combustion.

(*b*) A six-cylinder, four-stroke reciprocating engine uses *n*-octane as fuel. The engine develops 160 hp when running at a speed of 3600 rev/min at a mixture strength of 100 per cent. The specific fuel consumption is 0·48 lb_m/hp h. Evaluate the volumes (in in.^{3}) of liquid octane and of atmospheric air consumed per working cycle per cylinder assuming combustion to be complete. The density of liquid octane is 44·3 lb_m/ft^3 and the atmospheric pressure and temperature are 14·6 psia and 70°F respectively; R for air is 53·3 ft lb_f/lb_m°F abs.

16.3 A liquid fuel has a composition by mass of 84% carbon and 16% hydrogen. The fuel is used in an engine at a mixture strength of 115 per cent.

On the assumption that all the hydrogen is burned completely and that there is no 'free' oxygen in the exhaust gas estimate:

    (i) the molal composition of the exhaust gas;

    (ii) the Orsat analysis of the exhaust gas.

16.4 A boiler consumes fuel of composition by mass of 82% carbon, 5% hydrogen, 6% oxygen and 7% ash. The volumetric composition of the dry flue gas is 13·2% carbon dioxide, 1·5% carbon monoxide, 6·8% oxygen, 78·5% nitrogen.

Evaluate (i) the air-fuel ratio;

              (ii) the percentage excess air supplied;

              (iii) the volume of air handled by the boiler fans in ft^3/min given that the hourly fuel consumption of the boiler is 1000 lb$_m$. Assume that the air enters the fans at a pressure of 14·55 psia and a temperature of 110°F; R for air is 53·3 ft lb/lb$_m$ °F abs.

16.5 The fuel of problem 16.1 is burned in a boiler with 40 per cent excess air. The fuel as fired contains 3 per cent by mass of moisture and the air supplied has a relative humidity of 50 per cent. The temperature and pressure of the air supplied are 90°F and 1 atm; the pressure of the flue gas is 14·3 psia. Assuming the fuel to be burned completely evaluate:

    (i) the molal composition of the flue gas;

    (ii) the mass of H_2O in the flue gas per pound of *dry* fuel burned;

    (iii) the dew point of the flue gas.

16.6 A fuel gas has a volumetric composition of 30% carbon monoxide, 10% hydrogen, 3% methane, 5% carbon dioxide and 52% nitrogen. The gas is burned in a furnace the air-fuel ratio by volume being 2. Assuming combustion to be complete, determine the volumetric analysis of the dry exhaust gas.

16.7 A stoichiometric mixture of carbon monoxide and oxygen is contained in a rigid vessel of volume 100 in^3 at a pressure of 1 atm and a temperature of 77°F.

When the mixture is ignited and burns completely, it is found that a heat transfer of 11·9 Btu from the contents of the vessel is required to restore their temperature to 77°F. Assuming carbon monoxide and oxygen to be Ideal Gases evaluate:

    (i) the number of moles of carbon monoxide and oxygen in the vessel.

    (ii) the internal energy increase of reaction at 77°F in Btu/lb mole of CO;

    (iii) the final pressure of the contents of the vessel;

    (iv) the enthalpy increase of reaction at 1 atm, 77°F.

16.8 For the combustion of carbon to carbon monoxide at 77°F, 1 atm, the enthalpy increase is −47,549 Btu/lb mole CO.

(*a*) For the reaction $2C + O_2 = 2CO$, plot, to scale, the $H' - t$ diagram using the following data for mean specific heat at constant pressure (Btu/lb$_m$ °F; datum 32°F).

t°F	200	400	600	800	1000	1200
C	0·193	0·221	0·251	0·278	0·300	0·317
O_2	0·220	0·223	0·228	0·231	0·235	0·239
CO	0·249	0·249	0·252	0·254	0·257	0·261

(*b*) Evaluate the heat of reaction at 1200°F.

(*c*) Determine the product temperature in a constant-pressure reaction in which the heat transfer to the surroundings is 3418 Btu/lb$_m$ of carbon. The temperature of the reactants is 32°F.

16.9 The enthalpy increase of reaction of liquid octane (C_8H_{18}) with oxygen at a pressure of 1 atm and a temperature of 77°F is −19,100 Btu/lb$_m$ of octane when the H_2O product is in the vapour state.

(i) Sketch the $H' - t$ diagram, showing the reactant curves corresponding to the liquid and gaseous octane states and the product curves corresponding to the liquid and vapour H_2O states.

(ii) Evaluate the internal energy increase of reaction for these conditions.

(iii) Calculate the enthalpy increase of reaction and the internal energy increase of reaction of liquid octane at a temperature of 260°F when the H_2O product is in the vapour state. Use the following values of mean specific heat at constant pressure: liquid octane, 0·41 Btu/lb$_m$ °F; CO_2, 0·215 Btu/lb$_m$ °F; steam, 0·48 Btu/lb$_m$ °F; O_2, 0·22 Btu/lb$_m$ °F.

(iv) The latent heat of vaporisation of octane at a temperature of 260°F is 128 Btu/lb$_m$; the latent heat of vaporisation of H_2O at this temperature may be taken as 1055 Btu/lb$_m$. Calculate the enthalpy increase of reaction and the internal energy increase of reaction of gaseous octane at a temperature of 260°F when the H_2O product is in the liquid state.

16.10 For the complete combustion of carbon at a temperature of 77°F and a pressure of 1 atm the enthalpy increase is −14,108 Btu/lb$_m$ of carbon; at a temperature of 1,470°F and a pressure of 1 atm the enthalpy increase is −14,311 Btu/lb$_m$ of C. The mean specific heat of carbon between 77°F and 1,470°F is 0·25 Btu/lb$_m$ °F, and of oxygen is 0·243 Btu/lb$_m$ °F. Evaluate the mean specific heat of CO_2 for this temperature range.

16.11 Carbon monoxide is burned adiabatically in steady flow at atmospheric pressure with 100 per cent excess air. The CO is supplied to the gas burner at a temperature of 300°F and the air at a temperature of 100°F. The standard enthalpy increase of reaction at 1 atm, 77°F is −121,745 Btu/lb mole of carbon monoxide. Sketch the $H' - t$ diagram and hence calculate the temperature of the combustion products assuming combustion to be complete. Use the following values of mean specific heat at constant pressure: CO, 0·262 Btu/lb$_m$ °F; O_2, 0·240 Btu/lb$_m$ °F; N_2, 0·260 Btu/lb$_m$ °F; CO_2, 0·261 Btu/lb$_m$ °F.

16.12 Calculate the calorific value of carbon monoxide, in Btu/lb$_m$ using the enthalpy of formation data given in Table 16.6.

16.13 (a) Ethane gas, C_2H_6, is burned completely with oxygen at a constant pressure of 1 atm. The reactants and products are both at a temperature of 77°F and the H_2O product is in the liquid state. Using the data given in Table 16.6 evaluate

(i) the enthalpy increase of reaction;

(ii) the heat of reaction;

(iii) the higher and lower calorific values.

(b) Ethane gas is burned completely in adiabatic steady flow with 50 per cent excess of pure oxygen. The reactants are at a temperature of 77°F. Determine the temperature of the combustion products using the following values of mean specific heat at constant pressure: CO_2, 0·25 Btu/lb$_m$ °F; O_2, 0·245 Btu/lb$_m$ °F; steam, 0·48 Btu/lb$_m$ °F.

16.14 (a) Recalculate problem 16.13 (a) assuming the reaction to take place in air. The specific heat of nitrogen at constant pressure may be taken as 0·26 Btu/lb$_m$ °F.

(b) Recalculate problem 16.13 (b) assuming 50% excess air to be supplied.

16.15 Determine the higher and lower calorific values of the fuel gas of problem 16.6 in Btu/ft^3 at 60°F, 30 in. Hg when (a) dry, (b) saturated with water vapour. Use the data given in Table 16.7.

16.16 Kerosene having a composition by mass of 86·5% carbon, 13·5% hydrogen, is burned adiabatically in the combustion chamber of an open-cycle gas-turbine engine; the air-fuel ratio is 63 : 1 by mass. The fuel is supplied to the chamber at a temperature of 60°F and the air at a temperature of 462°F. The measured CO_2 content of the dry products of combustion is 3·18 per cent by volume and the measured products temperature is 1,530°F. The higher calorific value of kerosene is 19,854 Btu/lb$_m$.

Evaluate (i) the "CO_2 efficiency";
          (ii) the "temperature rise efficiency";

Use the following values of mean specific heat at constant pressure (Btu/lb$_m$ °F): O_2, 0·243; N_2, 0·261; CO_2, 0·261; steam, 0·48.

16.17 (a) By applying the Steady-Flow Energy Equation to the fuel-air stream as it flows through a steam boiler show that the so-called 'energy account' may be written

$$\overline{LCV} = q_1 + q_u + m\bar{c}_p(t - t_0)$$

where q_1 is the heat transfer to the H_2O in the boiler per lb$_m$ of fuel burned,
     q_u is the unmeasured ('unaccounted-for') heat transfer (to the surroundings) per lb$_m$ of fuel burned,
     m is the mass of flue gas per lb$_m$ of fuel burned,
     $\bar{c}_p$ is the mean specific heat at constant pressure of the flue gas,
     t is the flue-gas temperature,
     t_0 is the $\overline{LCV}$ datum temperature.
Assume that the fuel and air are supplied to the boiler at t_0.

(b) A boiler generates steam at a pressure of 300 psia and a temperature of 600°F from feed water at a temperature of 150°F; the quantity of steam produced is 11·3 lb$_m$ per lb$_m$ of oil fuel burned. The oil fuel used has a composition by mass of 88% carbon, and 12% hydrogen, and a $\overline{LCV}$ of 17,200 Btu/lb$_m$ (datum 60°F). The Orsat analysis of the flue gas is 10·6% CO_2, 7·4% O_2, 82% N_2; the CO content is negligible. The flue gas temperature is 644°F.

(i) Draw up the "energy account" given that $\bar{c}_p = 0·245$ Btu/lb$_m$ °F.

(ii) Evaluate the heating efficiency of the boiler based on the $\overline{LCV}$.

16.18 (a) The $\overline{LCV}$ of light fuel oil is 19,260 Btu/lb$_m$. What is the maximum power which could be produced by the reaction of this fuel with air at constant pressure at the rate of 1 lb$_m$/min. (Neglect the entropy change occurring during the reaction.)

(b) An open-cycle gas-turbine engine burns the fuel oil of (a). The specific fuel consumption of the engine is 0·7 lb$_m$ fuel/h.p. hour. Evaluate $\eta_{l.c.}$, the efficiency of the engine.

16.19 In the formation of steam by the reaction of hydrogen with oxygen at a temperature of 77°F and a pressure of 1 atm, the enthalpy increase is −104,036 Btu/lb mole of steam. Correspondingly the entropy of the product steam is 0·0655 Btu/°F less than the entropy of the reactants, per lb$_m$ of hydrogen present.

Evaluate the maximum work which could be produced by the isothermal reaction of hydrogen to steam at 77°F, 1 atm.

Appendix A

END NOTES

1. *Chapter* 2. p. 19. We could, for example, set up a standard spring and specify the unit of force as that force required to compress (or stretch) the spring a given amount.

This unit force, the "pound spring", lb_s, would, in general, cause a different acceleration, x ft/s², say, when acting upon 1 lb_m.

Applying Newton's Second Law to this case we have

$$1\ \mathrm{lb}_s = \frac{1\ \mathrm{lb}_m \times x\ \mathrm{ft/s^2}}{g_0}$$

whence $\qquad g_0 = x\ \dfrac{\mathrm{lb}_m\ \mathrm{ft}}{\mathrm{lb}_s\ \mathrm{s^2}}$

2. *Chapter* 2. p. 22. Consider, for example, the poundal, lb_m, ft, s, set of units for which $g_0 = 1\ \mathrm{lb}_m$ ft/pdl s². The weight of a body of mass $m\ \mathrm{lb}_m$ at a place where the local gravitational acceleration $g = 32\ \mathrm{ft/s^2}$ is given from eq. (2.5):

$$w = \frac{m(\mathrm{lb}_m) \times 32\ (\mathrm{ft/s^2})}{1\ \mathrm{lb}_m \times \mathrm{ft/pdl\ s^2}}$$

$$= 32\ m\ \mathrm{pdl}$$

That is, weight and mass are *not* equal numerically in this system of units.

3. *Chapter* 5. p. 71. This may be established by considering three systems:—
S_1, the standard system comprising 1 lb_m of water at atmospheric pressure.
S_2, any system at high temperature $T_1(>61°\mathrm{F}.)$ and
S_3, any system at low temperature $t_1(<60°\mathrm{F}.)$.

We compare the heat transfers when S_1 and S_2, S_2 and S_3 and S_1 and S_3 communicate in turn as follows:

(i) With S_1 at 60°F, raise its temperature to 61°F by heat transfer from S_2, which as a result falls in temperature from T_1 to T_2. By definition 1 Btu of heat is transferred from S_2 to S_1.

(ii) With S_2 restored to T_1, reduce its temperature to T_2 by heat transfer to S_3, which, as a result, rises in temperature from t_1 to t_2. Since S_2 performs the same process as in (i) the heat transfer to S_3 must also be 1 Btu.

(iii) With S_1 at 61°F reduce its temperature to 60°F by heat transfer to S_3. If S_3 is initially at t_1 its temperature will be found to have risen to t_2. But from (ii) 1 Btu of heat produced this same change of state in S_3. Therefore in reducing the temperature of S_1 from 61°F to 60°F 1 Btu of heat is transferred.

4. *Chapter* 6. p. 87. $W = 0$ because the block, in executing the same process, (i.e. its fall in level and its rise of temperature) could not have the rise of a weight as its *sole* external effect. This may be seen by supposing the real process to be replaced by the following processes. First the block slides frictionlessly down the plane to its final position so raising a weight; the temperature of the block is unchanged. Second, the temperature of the block is raised to the value attained in the real process by heat transfer from a hot body. Thus in completely establishing the final state of the real process two

357

effects have occurred in the imaginary surroundings, namely, the rise of a weight and heat transfer from a hot body. The rise of a weight has not been the *sole* effect and therefore we cannot conclude that work has been done.

5. *Chapter* 8. p. 122. Many books "explain" the fact that the enthalpy remains constant in some throttling process by statements such as "the pressure energy of the fluid is converted into kinetic energy in the small passages of the restriction; the kinetic energy is subsequently reconverted into heat (*sic*) by eddying motion downstream." We see no merit in this "explanation". It involves a bandying-about of statements to which no quantitative significance can be given, and usually loosens the student's grip on an extremely simple equation. It fails to "explain" the fact that the enthalpy also remains constant for flow in a rough pipe (for low velocities or an incompressible fluid), where the velocity distribution remains unchanged along the pipe.

6. *Chapter* 10. p. 172. This definition has been used to keep in line with Keenan. There are two objections to it: (i) Many people have become used to calling internal-combustion engines "heat engines"; they become upset when told they must stop. (ii) The bright student will ask "Well, what else could cross the boundaries of a thermodynamic system anyway?" What, indeed?

7. *Chapter* 13. p. 227. The use of q instead of Q in this analysis simplifies the diagram illustrating the situation. If Q is used, Fig. A. 1 is the appropriate diagram; it should be compared with Fig. 13.9.

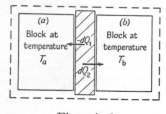

In Fig. A. 1 $-dQ_1$ and dQ_2, each with an arrow in the positive direction, represent the heat transfer for each component system (block) at temperatures T_a and T_b respectively. In addition, we must state that $-dQ_1 = dQ_2$ to complete the specification of the problem. In Fig. 13.9. the single symbol dq, with a single arrow denoting direction, represents simultaneously the heat transfer for each component system.

Fig. A. 1

8. *Chapter* 14. p. 247. We commonly say that for an incompressible fluid $u \approx f(t)$. The present proof shows that such a fluid in a constant-volume thermometer would register the absolute temperature T. However,

(*a*) the experimental difficulty is much greater, and

(*b*) the normally negligible dependence of u on p is not negligible in this application.

9. *Chapter* 15. p. 287. What about mixing two isotopes of the same gas? These have the same chemical properties but differing nuclear ones. These nuclear differences could be used, in principle, to effect a reversible interpenetration, so mixing causes an entropy increase. However if the practical possibility of reversible interpenetration is excluded, no difficulties arise from neglecting the entropy increase, provided that this is done consistently. Entropy is a man-made concept and we can trim its definition to suit our convenience and capabilities.

STEAM TABLES

The arbitrary datum state for zero enthalpy and entropy is that of saturated water at 32°F. (*This is a fictitious state-point obtained by extrapolating the data from the triple point at 32·02°F to 32°F*).

TABLE I
TRIPLE POINT DATA
TEMPERATURE: 32·02°F; PRESSURE: 0·088 psia.

	Enthalpy Btu/lb$_m$	Specific volume ft^3/lb$_m$
Ice ...	−143·3	0·01747
Water ...	0·02	0·01602
Steam ...	1075·8	3303

TABLE II

PROPERTIES OF SATURATED WATER AND SATURATED STEAM: TEMPERATURE TABLE*

Temp °F t	Abs Press psia p	Sat Liq ft³/lb_m v_f	Evap ft³/lb_m v_{fg}	Sat Vap ft³/lb_m v_g	Sat Liq Btu/lb_m h_f	Evap Btu/lb_m h_{fg}	Sat Vap Btu/lb_m h_g	Sat Liq Btu/lb_m°F s_f	Evap Btu/lb_m°F s_{fg}	Sat Vap Btu/lb_m°F s_g	Temp °F t
32	0·08854	0·01602	3306	3306	0·00	1075·8	1075·8	0·0000	2·1877	2·1877	32
35	0·09995	0·01602	2947	2947	3·02	1074·1	1077·1	0·0061	2·1709	2·1770	35
40	0·12170	0·01602	2444	2444	8·05	1071·3	1079·3	0·0162	2·1435	2·1597	40
45	0·14752	0·01602	2036·4	2036·4	13·06	1068·4	1081·5	0·0262	2·1167	2·1429	45
50	0·17811	0·01603	1703·2	1703·2	18·07	1065·6	1083·7	0·0361	2·0903	2·1264	50
60	0·2563	0·01604	1206·6	1206·7	28·06	1059·9	1088·0	0·0555	2·0393	2·0948	60
70	0·3631†	0·01606	867·8	867·9	38·04	1054·3	1092·3	0·0745	1·9902	2·0647	70
80	0·5069	0·01608	633·1	633·1	48·02	1048·6	1096·6	0·0932	1·9428	2·0360	80
90	0·6982	0·01610	468·0	468·0	57·99	1042·9	1100·9	0·1115	1·8972	2·0087	90
100	0·9492	0·01613	350·3	350·4	67·97	1037·2	1105·2	0·1295	1·8531	1·9826	100
110	1·2748	0·01617	265·3	265·4	77·94	1031·6	1109·5	0·1471	1·8106	1·9577	110
120	1·6924	0·01620	203·25	203·27	87·92	1025·8	1113·7	0·1645	1·7694	1·9339	120
130	2·2225	0·01625	157·32	157·34	97·90	1020·0	1117·9	0·1816	1·7296	1·9112	130
140	2·8886	0·01629	122·99	123·01	107·89	1014·1	1122·0	0·1984	1·6910	1·8894	140
150	3·718	0·01634	97·06	97·07	117·89	1008·2	1126·1	0·2149	1·6537	1·8685	150
160	4·741	0·01639	77·27	77·29	127·89	1002·3	1130·2	0·2311	1·6174	1·8485	160
170	5·992	0·01645	62·04	62·06	137·90	996·3	1134·2	0·2472	1·5822	1·8293	170
180	7·510	0·01651	50·21	50·23	147·92	990·2	1138·1	0·2630	1·5480	1·8109	180
190	9·339	0·01657	40·94	40·96	157·95	984·1	1142·0	0·2785	1·5147	1·7932	190
200	11·526	0·01663	33·62	33·64	167·99	977·9	1145·9	0·2938	1·4824	1·7762	200
210	14·123	0·01670	27·80	27·82	178·05	971·6	1149·7	0·3090	1·4508	1·7598	210
212	14·696	0·01672	26·78	26·80	180·07	970·3	1150·4	0·3120	1·4446	1·7566	212
220	17·186	0·01677	23·13	23·15	188·13	965·2	1153·4	0·3239	1·4201	1·7440	220
230	20·780	0·01684	19·365	19·382	198·23	958·8	1157·0	0·3387	1·3901	1·7288	230
240	24·969	0·01692	16·306	16·323	208·34	952·2	1160·5	0·3531	1·3609	1·7140	240
250	29·825	0·01700	13·804	13·821	216·48	945·5	1164·0	0·3675	1·3323	1·6998	250
260	35·429	0·01709	11·746	11·763	228·64	938·7	1167·3	0·3817	1·3043	1·6860	260
270	41·858	0·01717	10·044	10·061	238·84	931·8	1170·6	0·3958	1·2769	1·6727	270
280	49·203	0·01726	8·628	8·645	249·06	924·7	1173·8	0·4096	1·2501	1·6597	280
290	57·556	0·01735	7·444	7·461	259·31	917·5	1176·8	0·4234	1·2238	1·6472	290

300	1·6350	1·1980	0·4369	1179·7	910·1	269·59	6·466	6·449	0·01745	67·013	300
310	1·6231	1·1727	0·4504	1182·5	902·6	279·92	5·626	5·609	0·01755	77·68	310
320	1·6115	1·1478	0·4637	1185·2	894·9	290·28	4·914	4·896	0·01765	89·66	320
330	1·6002	1·1233	0·4769	1187·7	887·0	300·68	4·307	4·289	0·01776	103·06	330
340	1·5891	1·0992	0·4900	1190·1	879·0	311·13	3·788	3·770	0·01787	118·01	340
350	1·5783	1·0754	0·5029	1192·3	870·7	321·63	3·342	3·324	0·01799	134·63	350
360	1·5677	1·0519	0·5158	1194·4	862·2	332·18	2·957	2·939	0·01811	153·04	360
370	1·5573	1·0287	0·5286	1196·3	853·5	342·79	2·625	2·606	0·01823	173·37	370
380	1·5471	1·0059	0·5413	1198·1	844·6	353·45	2·335	2·317	0·01836	195·77	380
390	1·5371	0·9832	0·5539	1199·6	835·4	364·17	2·0836	2·0651	0·01850	220·37	390
400	1·5272	0·9608	0·5664	1201·0	826·0	374·97	1·8633	1·8447	0·01864	247·31	400
410	1·5174	0·9386	0·5788	1202·1	816·3	385·83	1·6700	1·6512	0·01878	276·75	410
420	1·5078	0·9166	0·5912	1203·1	806·3	396·77	1·5000	1·4811	0·01894	308·83	420
430	1·4982	0·8947	0·6035	1203·8	796·0	407·79	1·3499	1·3308	0·01910	343·72	430
440	1·4887	0·8730	0·6158	1204·3	785·4	418·90	1·2171	1·1979	0·01926	381·59	440
450	1·4793	0·8513	0·6280	1204·6	774·5	430·1	1·0993	1·0799	0·0194	422·6	450
460	1·4700	0·8298	0·6402	1204·6	763·2	441·4	0·9944	0·9748	0·0196	466·9	460
470	1·4606	0·8083	0·6523	1204·3	751·5	452·8	0·9009	0·8811	0·0198	514·7	470
480	1·4513	0·7868	0·6645	1203·7	739·4	464·4	0·8172	0·7972	0·0200	566·1	480
490	1·4419	0·7653	0·6766	1202·8	726·8	476·0	0·7423	0·7221	0·0202	621·4	490
500	1·4325	0·7438	0·6887	1201·7	713·9	487·8	0·6749	0·6545	0·0204	680·8	500
520	1·4136	0·7006	0·7130	1198·2	686·4	511·9	0·5594	0·5385	0·0209	812·4	520
540	1·3942	0·6568	0·7374	1193·2	656·6	536·6	0·4649	0·4434	0·0215	962·5	540
560	1·3742	0·6121	0·7621	1186·4	624·2	562·2	0·3868	0·3647	0·0221	1133·1	560
580	1·3532	0·5659	0·7872	1177·3	588·4	588·9	0·3217	0·2989	0·0228	1325·8	580
600	1·3307	0·5176	0·8131	1165·5	548·5	617·0	0·2668	0·2432	0·0236	1542·9	600
620	1·3062	0·4664	0·8398	1150·3	503·6	646·7	0·2201	0·1955	0·0247	1786·6	620
640	1·2789	0·4110	0·8679	1130·5	452·0	678·6	0·1798	0·1538	0·0260	2059·7	640
660	1·2472	0·3485	0·8987	1104·4	390·2	714·2	0·1442	0·1165	0·0278	2365·4	660
680	1·2071	0·2719	0·9351	1067·2	309·9	757·3	0·1115	0·0810	0·0305	2708·1	680
700	1·1389	0·1484	0·9905	995·4	172·1	823·3	0·0761	0·0392	0·0369	3083·7	700
705·4	1·0580	0	1·0580	902·7	0	902·7	0·0503	0	0·0503	3206·2	705·4

* Abridged from "Thermodynamic Properties of Steam," by Joseph H. Keenan and Frederick G. Keyes. Copyright, 1937, by Joseph H. Keenan and Frederick G. Keyes. Published by John Wiley & Sons, Inc., New York.

TABLE III

Properties of Saturated Water and Saturated Steam: Pressure Table*

Abs. Press psia	Temp °F	Specific Volume		Enthalpy			Entropy			Internal Energy		Abs Press psia
		Sat Liq ft³/lbm	Sat Vap ft³/lbm	Sat Liq Btu/lbm	Evap Btu/lbm	Sat Vap Btu/lbm	Sat Liq Btu/lbm °F	Evap Btu/lbm °F	Sat Vap Btu/lbm °F	Sat Liq Btu/lbm	Sat Vap Btu/lbm	
p	t	v_f	v_g	h_f	h_{fg}	h_g	s_f	s_{fg}	s_g	u_f	u_g	p
1·0	101·74	0·01614	333·0	69·70	1036·3	1106·0	0·1326	1·8456	1·9782	69·70	1044·3	1·0
2·0	126·08	0·01623	173·73	93·99	1022·2	1116·2	0·1749	1·7451	1·9200	93·98	1051·9	2·0
3·0	141·48	0·01630	118·71	109·37	1013·2	1122·6	0·2008	1·6855	1·8863	109·36	1056·7	3·0
4·0	152·97	0·01636	90·63	120·86	1006·4	1127·3	0·2198	1·6427	1·8625	120·85	1060·2	4·0
5·0	162·24	0·01640	73·52	130·13	1001·0	1131·1	0·2347	1·6094	1·8441	130·12	1063·1	5·0
6·0	170·06	0·01645	61·98	137·96	996·2	1134·2	0·2472	1·5820	1·8292	137·94	1065·4	6·0
7·0	176·85	0·01649	53·64	144·76	992·1	1136·9	0·2581	1·5586	1·8167	144·74	1067·4	7·0
8·0	182·86	0·01653	47·34	150·79	988·5	1139·3	0·2674	1·5383	1·8057	150·77	1069·2	8·0
9·0	188·28	0·01656	42·40	156·22	985·2	1141·4	0·2759	1·5203	1·7962	156·19	1070·8	9·0
10	193·21	0·01659	38·42	161·17	982·1	1143·3	0·2835	1·5041	1·7876	161·14	1072·2	10
14·696	212·00	0·01672	26·80	180·07	970·3	1150·4	0·3120	1·4446	1·7566	180·02	1077·5	14·696
15	213·03	0·01672	26·29	181·11	969·7	1150·8	0·3135	1·4415	1·7549	181·06	1077·8	15
20	227·96	0·01683	20·089	196·16	960·1	1156·3	0·3356	1·3962	1·7319	196·10	1081·9	20
25	240·07	0·01692	16·303	208·42	952·1	1160·6	0·3533	1·3606	1·7139	208·34	1085·1	25
30	250·33	0·01701	13·746	218·82	945·3	1164·1	0·3680	1·3313	1·6993	218·73	1087·8	30
35	259·28	0·01708	11·898	227·91	939·2	1167·1	0·3807	1·3063	1·6870	227·80	1090·1	35
40	267·25	0·01715	10·498	236·03	933·7	1169·7	0·3919	1·2844	1·6763	235·90	1092·0	40
45	274·44	0·01721	9·401	243·36	928·6	1172·0	0·4019	1·2650	1·6669	243·22	1093·7	45
50	281·01	0·01727	8·515	250·09	924·0	1174·1	0·4110	1·2474	1·6585	249·93	1095·3	50
55	287·07	0·01732	7·787	256·30	919·6	1175·9	0·4193	1·2316	1·6509	256·12	1096·7	55
60	292·71	0·01738	7·175	262·09	915·5	1177·6	0·4270	1·2168	1·6438	261·90	1097·9	60
65	297·97	0·01743	6·655	267·50	911·6	1179·1	0·4342	1·2032	1·6374	267·29	1099·1	65
70	302·92	0·01748	6·206	272·61	907·9	1180·6	0·4409	1·1906	1·6315	272·38	1100·2	70
75	307·60	0·01753	5·816	277·43	904·5	1181·9	0·4472	1·1787	1·6259	277·19	1101·2	75
80	312·03	0·01757	5·472	282·02	901·1	1183·1	0·4531	1·1676	1·6207	281·76	1102·1	80
85	316·25	0·01761	5·168	286·39	897·8	1184·2	0·4587	1·1571	1·6158	286·11	1102·9	85
90	320·27	0·01766	4·896	290·56	894·7	1185·3	0·4641	1·1471	1·6112	290·27	1103·7	90
95	324·12	0·01770	4·652	294·56	891·7	1186·2	0·4692	1·1376	1·6068	294·25	1104·5	95
100	327·81	0·01774	4·432	298·40	888·8	1187·2	0·4740	1·1286	1·6026	298·08	1105·2	100
110	334·77	0·01782	4·049	305·66	883·2	1188·9	0·4832	1·1117	1·5948	305·30	1106·5	110

120	1107·6	312·05	1·5878	1·0962	0·4916	1190·4	877·9	312·44	3·728	0·01789	341·25	120
130	1108·6	318·38	1·5812	1·0817	0·4995	1191·7	872·9	318·81	3·455	0·01796	347·32	130
140	1109·6	324·35	1·5751	1·0682	0·5069	1193·0	868·2	324·82	3·220	0·01802	353·02	140
150	1110·5	330·01	1·5694	1·0556	0·5138	1194·1	863·6	330·51	3·015	0·01809	358·42	150
160	1111·2	335·39	1·5640	1·0436	0·5204	1195·1	859·2	335·93	2·834	0·01815	363·53	160
170	1111·9	340·52	1·5590	1·0324	0·5266	1196·0	854·9	341·09	2·675	0·01822	368·41	170
180	1112·5	345·42	1·5542	1·0217	0·5325	1196·9	850·8	346·03	2·532	0·01827	373·06	180
190	1113·1	350·15	1·5497	1·0116	0·5381	1197·6	846·8	350·79	2·404	0·01833	377·51	190
200	1113·7	354·68	1·5453	1·0018	0·5435	1198·4	843·0	355·36	2·288	0·01839	381·79	200
250	1115·8	375·14	1·5263	0·9588	0·5675	1201·1	825·1	376·00	1·8438	0·01865	400·95	250
300	1117·1	392·79	1·5104	0·9225	0·5879	1202·8	809·0	393·84	1·5433	0·01890	417·33	300
350	1118·0	408·45	1·4966	0·8910	0·6056	1203·9	794·2	409·60	1·3260	0·01913	431·72	350
400	1118·5	422·6	1·4844	0·8630	0·6214	1204·5	780·5	424·0	1·1613	0·0193	444·59	400
450	1118·7	435·5	1·4734	0·8378	0·6356	1204·6	767·4	437·2	1·0320	0·0195	456·28	450
500	1118·6	447·6	1·4634	0·8147	0·6487	1204·4	755·0	449·4	0·9278	0·0197	467·01	500
550	1118·2	458·8	1·4542	0·7934	0·6608	1203·9	743·1	460·8	0·8424	0·0199	476·94	550
600	1117·7	469·4	1·4454	0·7784	0·6720	1203·2	731·6	471·6	0·7698	0·0201	486·21	600
650	1117·1	479·4	1·4374	0·7548	0·6826	1202·3	720·5	481·8	0·7083	0·0203	494·90	650
700	1116·3	488·8	1·4296	0·7371	0·6925	1201·2	709·7	491·5	0·6554	0·0205	503·10	700
750	1115·4	498·0	1·4223	0·7204	0·7019	1200·0	699·2	500·8	0·6092	0·0207	510·86	750
800	1114·4	506·6	1·4153	0·7045	0·7108	1198·6	688·9	509·7	0·5687	0·0209	518·23	800
850	1113·3	515·0	1·4085	0·6891	0·7194	1197·1	678·8	518·3	0·5327	0·0210	525·26	850
900	1112·1	523·1	1·4020	0·6744	0·7275	1195·4	668·8	526·6	0·5006	0·0212	531·98	900
950	1110·8	530·9	1·3957	0·6602	0·7355	1193·7	659·1	534·6	0·4717	0·0214	538·43	950
1000	1109·4	538·4	1·3897	0·6467	0·7430	1191·8	649·4	542·4	0·4456	0·0216	544·61	1000
1100	1106·4	552·9	1·3780	0·6205	0·7575	1187·8	630·4	557·4	0·4001	0·0220	556·31	1100
1200	1103·0	566·7	1·3667	0·5956	0·7711	1183·4	611·7	571·7	0·3619	0·0223	567·22	1200
1300	1099·4	580·0	1·3559	0·5719	0·7840	1178·6	593·2	585·4	0·3293	0·0227	577·46	1300
1400	1095·4	592·7	1·3454	0·5491	0·7963	1173·4	574·7	598·7	0·3012	0·0231	587·10	1400
1500	1091·2	605·1	1·3351	0·5269	0·8082	1167·9	556·3	611·6	0·2765	0·0235	596·23	1500
2000	1065·6	662·2	1·2849	0·4230	0·8619	1135·1	463·4	671·7	0·1878	0·0257	635·82	2000
2500	1030·6	717·3	1·2322	0·3197	0·9126	1091·1	360·5	730·6	0·1307	0·0287	668·13	2500
3000	972·7	783·4	1·1615	0·1885	0·9731	1020·3	217·8	802·5	0·0858	0·0346	695·36	3000
3206·2	872·9	872·9	1·0580	0	1·0580	902·7	0	902·7	0·0503	0·0503	705·40	3206·2

* Abridged from "Thermodynamic Properties of Steam" by Joseph H. Keenan and Frederick G. Keyes. Copyright, 1937, by Joseph H. Keenan and Frederick G. Keyes. Published by John Wiley & Sons, Inc., New York.

TABLE IV

PROPERTIES OF SUPERHEATED STEAM*

[Specific volume, v, ft³/lb$_m$; Enthalpy, h, Btu/lb$_m$; Entropy, s, Btu/lb$_m$°F]

Temperature—Degrees Fahrenheit

Abs Press psia (Sat Temp °F)		200	300	400	500	600	700	800	900	1000	1100	1200	1400	1600
1 (101·74)	v	392·6	452·3	512·0	571·6	631·2	690·8	750·4	809·9	869·5	929·1	988·7	1107·8	1227·0
	h	1150·4	1195·8	1241·7	1288·3	1335·7	1383·8	1432·8	1482·7	1533·5	1585·2	1637·7	1745·7	1857·5
	s	2·0512	2·1153	2·1720	2·2233	2·2702	2·3137	2·3542	2·3923	2·4283	2·4625	2·4952	2·5566	2·6137
5 (162·24)	v	78·16	90·25	102·26	114·22	126·16	138·10	150·03	161·95	173·87	185·79	197·71	221·6	245·4
	h	1148·8	1195·0	1241·2	1288·0	1335·4	1383·6	1432·7	1482·6	1533·4	1585·1	1637·7	1745·7	1857·4
	s	1·8718	1·9370	1·9942	2·0456	2·0927	2·1361	2·1767	2·2148	2·2509	2·2851	2·3178	2·3792	2·4363
10 (193·21)	v	38·85	45·00	51·04	57·05	63·03	69·01	74·98	80·95	86·92	92·88	98·84	110·77	122·69
	h	1146·6	1193·9	1240·6	1287·5	1335·1	1383·4	1432·5	1482·4	1533·2	1585·0	1637·6	1745·6	1857·3
	s	1·7927	1·8595	1·9172	1·9689	2·0160	2·0596	2·1002	2·1383	2·1744	2·2086	2·2413	2·3028	2·3598
14·696 (212·00)	v		30·53	34·68	38·78	42·86	46·94	51·00	55·07	59·13	63·19	67·25	75·37	83·48
	h		1192·8	1239·9	1287·1	1334·8	1383·2	1432·3	1482·3	1533·1	1584·8	1637·5	1745·5	1857·3
	s		1·8160	1·8743	1·9261	1·9734	2·0170	2·0576	2·0958	2·1319	2·1662	2·1989	2·2603	2·3174
20 (227·96)	v		22·36	25·43	28·46	31·47	34·47	37·46	40·45	43·44	46·42	49·41	55·37	61·84
	h		1191·6	1239·2	1286·6	1334·4	1382·9	1432·1	1482·1	1533·0	1584·7	1637·4	1745·4	1857·2
	s		1·7808	1·8396	1·8918	1·9392	1·9829	2·0235	2·0618	2·0978	2·1321	2·1648	2·2263	2·2834
40 (267·25)	v		11·040	12·628	14·168	15·688	17·198	18·702	20·20	21·70	23·20	24·69	27·68	30·66
	h		1186·8	1236·5	1284·8	1333·1	1381·9	1431·3	1481·4	1532·4	1584·3	1637·0	1745·1	1857·0
	s		1·6994	1·7608	1·8140	1·8619	1·9058	1·9467	1·9850	2·0212	2·0555	2·0883	2·1498	2·2069
60 (292·71)	v		7·259	8·357	9·403	10·427	11·441	12·449	13·452	14·454	15·453	16·451	18·446	20·44
	h		1181·6	1233·6	1283·0	1331·8	1380·9	1430·5	1480·8	1531·9	1583·8	1636·6	1744·8	1856·7
	s		1·6492	1·7135	1·7678	1·8162	1·8605	1·9015	1·9400	1·9762	2·0106	2·0434	2·1049	2·1621
80 (312·03)	v			6·220	7·020	7·797	8·562	9·322	10·077	10·830	11·582	12·332	13·830	15·352
	h			1230·7	1281·1	1330·5	1379·9	1429·7	1480·1	1531·3	1583·4	1636·2	1744·5	1856·5
	s			1·6791	1·7346	1·7836	1·8281	1·8694	1·9079	1·9442	1·9787	2·0115	2·0731	2·1303
100 (327·81)	v			4·937	5·589	6·218	6·835	7·446	8·052	8·656	9·259	9·860	11·060	12·258
	h			1227·6	1279·1	1329·1	1378·9	1428·9	1479·5	1530·8	1582·9	1635·7	1744·2	1856·2
	s			1·6518	1·7085	1·7581	1·8029	1·8443	1·8829	1·9193	1·9538	1·9867	2·0484	2·1056
120 (341·25)	v			4·081	4·636	5·165	5·683	6·195	6·702	7·207	7·710	8·212	9·214	10·213
	h			1224·4	1277·2	1327·7	1377·8	1428·1	1478·8	1530·2	1582·4	1635·3	1743·9	1856·0
	s			1·6287	1·6869	1·7370	1·7822	1·8237	1·8625	1·8990	1·9335	1·9664	2·0281	2·0854

P (sat. temp)		1	2	3	4	5	6	7	8	9	10	11
140 (353·02)	v	8·752	7·895	7·035	6·604	6·172	5·738	5·301	4·861	4·413	3·954	3·468
	h	1855·7	1743·5	1634·9	1581·9	1529·7	1478·2	1427·3	1376·8	1326·4	1275·5	1221·1
	s	2·0683	2·0110	1·9493	1·9163	1·8817	1·8451	1·8063	1·7645	1·7190	1·6683	1·6087
160 (363·53)	v	7·656	6·906	6·152	5·775	5·396	5·015	4·631	4·244	3·849	3·443	3·008
	h	1855·5	1743·2	1634·5	1581·4	1529·1	1477·5	1426·4	1375·7	1325·0	1273·1	1217·6
	s	2·0535	1·9962	1·9344	1·9014	1·8667	1·8301	1·7911	1·7491	1·7033	1·6519	1·5908
180 (373·06)	v	6·804	6·136	5·466	5·129	4·792	4·452	4·110	3·764	3·411	3·044	2·649
	h	1855·2	1742·9	1634·1	1581·0	1528·6	1476·8	1425·6	1374·7	1323·5	1271·0	1214·0
	s	2·0404	1·9831	1·9212	1·8882	1·8534	1·8167	1·7776	1·7355	1·6894	1·6373	1·5745
200 (381·79)	v	6·123	5·521	4·917	4·613	4·309	4·002	3·693	3·380	3·060	2·726	2·361
	h	1855·0	1742·6	1633·7	1580·5	1528·0	1476·2	1424·8	1373·6	1322·1	1268·9	1210·3
	s	2·0287	1·9713	1·9094	1·8763	1·8415	1·8048	1·7655	1·7232	1·6767	1·6240	1·5594
220 (389·86)	v	5·565	5·017	4·467	4·191	3·913	3·634	3·352	3·066	2·772	2·465	2·125
	h	1854·7	1742·3	1633·3	1580·0	1527·5	1475·5	1424·0	1372·6	1320·7	1266·7	1206·5
	s	2·0181	1·9607	1·8987	1·8656	1·8308	1·7939	1·7545	1·7120	1·6652	1·6117	1·5453
240 (397·37)	v	5·100	4·597	4·093	3·839	3·584	3·327	3·068	2·804	2·533	2·247	1·9276
	h	1854·5	1742·0	1632·9	1579·6	1526·9	1474·8	1423·2	1371·5	1319·2	1264·5	1202·5
	s	2·0084	1·9510	1·8889	1·8558	1·8209	1·7839	1·7444	1·7017	1·6546	1·6003	1·5319
260 (404·42)	v	4·707	4·242	3·776	3·541	3·305	3·067	2·827	2·582	2·330	2·063	......
	h	1854·2	1741·7	1632·5	1579·1	1526·3	1474·2	1422·3	1370·4	1317·7	1262·3	......
	s	1·9995	1·9420	1·8799	1·8467	1·8118	1·7748	1·7352	1·6922	1·6447	1·5897	......
280 (411·05)	v	4·370	3·938	3·504	3·286	3·066	2·845	2·621	2·392	2·156	1·9047	......
	h	1854·0	1741·4	1632·1	1578·6	1525·8	1473·5	1421·5	1369·4	1316·2	1260·0	......
	s	1·9912	1·9337	1·8716	1·8383	1·8033	1·7662	1·7265	1·6834	1·6354	1·5796	......
300 (417·33)	v	4·078	3·674	3·269	3·065	2·859	2·652	2·442	2·227	2·005	1·7675	......
	h	1853·7	1741·0	1631·7	1578·1	1525·2	1472·8	1420·6	1368·3	1314·7	1257·6	......
	s	1·9835	1·9260	1·8638	1·8305	1·7954	1·7582	1·7184	1·6751	1·6268	1·5701	......
350 (431·72)	v	3·493	3·147	2·798	2·622	2·445	2·266	2·084	1·8980	1·7036	1·4923	......
	h	1853·1	1740·3	1630·7	1577·0	1523·8	1471·1	1418·5	1365·5	1310·9	1251·5	......
	s	1·9663	1·9086	1·8463	1·8130	1·7777	1·7403	1·7002	1·6563	1·6070	1·5481	......
400 (444·59)	v	3·055	2·751	2·445	2·290	2·134	1·9767	1·8161	1·6508	1·4770	1·2851	......
	h	1852·5	1739·5	1629·6	1575·8	1522·4	1469·4	1416·4	1362·7	1306·9	1245·1	......
	s	1·9513	1·8936	1·8311	1·7977	1·7623	1·7247	1·6842	1·6398	1·5894	1·5281	......

* Abridged from "Thermodynamic Properties of Steam," by Joseph H. Keenan and Frederick G. Keyes. Copyright, 1937, by Joseph H. Keenan and Frederick G. Keyes. Published by John Wiley & Sons, Inc., New York.

TABLE IV (contd)

PROPERTIES OF SUPERHEATED STEAM*

[Specific volume, v, ft³/lb$_m$; Enthalpy, h, Btu/lb$_m$; Entropy, s, Btu/lb$_m$°F]

Temperature—Degrees Fahrenheit

Abs Press psia (Sat Temp °F)		500	550	600	620	640	660	680	700	800	900	1000	1200	1400	1600
450 (456·28)	v	1·1231	1·2155	1·3005	1·3332	1·3652	1·3967	1·4278	1·4584	1·6074	1·7516	1·8928	2·170	2·443	2·714
	h	1238·4	1272·0	1302·8	1314·6	1326·2	1337·5	1348·8	1359·9	1414·3	1467·7	1521·0	1628·6	1738·7	1851·9
	s	1·5095	1·5437	1·5735	1·5845	1·5951	1·6054	1·6153	1·6250	1·6699	1·7108	1·7486	1·8177	1·8803	1·9381
500 (467·01)	v	0·9927	1·0800	1·1591	1·1893	1·2188	1·2478	1·2763	1·3044	1·4405	1·5715	1·6996	1·9504	2·197	2·442
	h	1231·3	1266·8	1298·6	1310·7	1322·6	1334·2	1345·7	1357·0	1412·1	1466·0	1519·6	1627·6	1737·9	1851·3
	s	1·4919	1·5280	1·5588	1·5701	1·5810	1·5915	1·6016	1·6115	1·6571	1·6982	1·7363	1·8056	1·8683	1·9262
550 (476·94)	v	0·8852	0·9686	1·0431	1·0714	1·0989	1·1259	1·1523	1·1783	1·3038	1·4241	1·5414	1·7706	1·9957	2·219
	h	1223·7	1261·2	1294·3	1306·8	1318·9	1330·8	1342·5	1354·0	1409·9	1464·3	1518·2	1626·6	1737·1	1850·6
	s	1·4751	1·5131	1·5451	1·5568	1·5680	1·5787	1·5890	1·5991	1·6452	1·6868	1·7250	1·7946	1·8575	1·9155
600 (486·21)	v	0·7947	0·8753	0·9463	0·9729	0·9988	1·0241	1·0489	1·0732	1·1899	1·3013	1·4096	1·6208	1·8279	2·033
	h	1215·7	1255·5	1289·9	1302·7	1315·2	1327·4	1339·3	1351·1	1407·7	1462·5	1516·7	1625·5	1736·3	1850·0
	s	1·4586	1·4990	1·5323	1·5443	1·5558	1·5667	1·5773	1·5875	1·6343	1·6762	1·7147	1·7846	1·8476	1·9056
700 (503·10)	v	……	0·7277	0·7934	0·8177	0·8411	0·8639	0·8860	0·9077	1·0108	1·1082	1·2024	1·3853	1·5641	1·7405
	h	……	1243·2	1280·6	1294·3	1307·5	1320·3	1332·8	1345·0	1403·2	1459·0	1513·9	1623·5	1734·8	1848·8
	s	……	1·4722	1·5084	1·5212	1·5333	1·5449	1·5559	1·5665	1·6147	1·6573	1·6963	1·7666	1·8299	1·8881
800 (518·23)	v	……	0·6154	0·6779	0·7006	0·7223	0·7433	0·7635	0·7833	0·8763	0·9633	1·0470	1·2088	1·3662	1·5214
	h	……	1229·8	1270·7	1285·4	1299·4	1312·9	1325·9	1338·6	1398·6	1455·4	1511·0	1621·4	1733·2	1847·5
	s	……	1·4467	1·4863	1·5000	1·5129	1·5250	1·5366	1·5476	1·5972	1·6407	1·6801	1·7510	1·8146	1·8729
900 (531·98)	v	……	0·5264	0·5873	0·6089	0·6294	0·6491	0·6680	0·6863	0·7716	0·8506	0·9262	1·0714	1·2124	1·3509
	h	……	1215·0	1260·1	1275·9	1290·9	1305·1	1318·8	1332·1	1393·9	1451·8	1508·1	1619·3	1731·6	1846·3
	s	……	1·4216	1·4653	1·4800	1·4938	1·5066	1·5187	1·5303	1·5814	1·6257	1·6656	1·7371	1·8009	1·8595
1000 (544·61)	v	……	0·4533	0·5140	0·5350	0·5546	0·5733	0·5912	0·6084	0·6878	0·7604	0·8294	0·9615	1·0893	1·2146
	h	……	1198·3	1248·8	1265·9	1281·9	1297·0	1311·4	1325·3	1389·2	1448·2	1505·1	1617·3	1730·0	1845·0
	s	……	1·3961	1·4450	1·4610	1·4757	1·4893	1·5021	1·5141	1·5670	1·6121	1·6525	1·7245	1·7886	1·8474
1100 (556·31)	v	……	……	……	0·4738	0·4929	0·5110	0·5281	0·5445	0·6191	0·6866	0·7503	0·8716	0·9885	1·1031
	h	……	……	……	1255·3	1272·4	1288·5	1303·7	1318·3	1384·3	1444·5	1502·2	1615·2	1728·4	1843·8
	s	……	……	……	1·4425	1·4583	1·4728	1·4862	1·4989	1·5535	1·5995	1·6405	1·7130	1·7775	1·8363
1200 (567·22)	v	……	……	……	0·4222	0·4410	0·4586	0·4752	0·4909	0·5617	0·6250	0·6843	0·7967	0·9046	1·0101
	h	……	……	……	1243·9	1262·4	1279·6	1295·7	1311·0	1379·3	1440·7	1499·2	1613·1	1726·9	1842·5
	s	……	……	……	1·4243	1·4413	1·4568	1·4710	1·4843	1·5409	1·5879	1·6293	1·7025	1·7672	1·8263

Pressure (sat. temp)													
1400 (587·10)	v	0·8640	0·7727	0·6789	0·5805	0·5281	0·4714	0·4062	0·3912	0·3753	0·3580	0·3390	0·3174
	h	1840·0	1723·7	1608·9	1493·2	1433·1	1369·1	1295·5	1278·5	1260·3	1240·4	1218·4	1193·0
	s	1·8083	1·7439	1·6836	1·6093	1·5666	1·5177	1·4567	1·4419	1·4258	1·4079	1·3877	1·3639
1600 (604·90)	v	0·7545	0·6738	0·5906	0·5027	0·4553	0·4034	0·3417	0·3271	0·3112	0·2936	0·2733	
	h	1837·5	1720·5	1604·6	1487·0	1425·3	1358·4	1278·7	1259·6	1238·7	1215·2	1187·8	
	s	1·7926	1·7328	1·6669	1·5914	1·5476	1·4964	1·4303	1·4187	1·3952	1·3741	1·3489	
1800 (621·03)	v	0·6693	0·5968	0·5218	0·4421	0·3986	0·3502	0·2907	0·2760	0·2597	0·2407		
	h	1835·0	1717·3	1600·4	1480·8	1417·4	1347·2	1260·3	1238·5	1214·0	1185·1		
	s	1·7786	1·7185	1·6520	1·5752	1·5301	1·4765	1·4044	1·3855	1·3638	1·3377		
2000 (635·82)	v	0·6011	0·5352	0·4668	0·3935	0·3532	0·3074	0·2489	0·2337	0·2161	0·1936		
	h	1832·5	1714·1	1596·1	1474·5	1409·2	1335·5	1240·0	1214·8	1184·9	1145·6		
	s	1·7660	1·7055	1·6384	1·5603	1·5139	1·4576	1·3783	1·3564	1·3300	1·2945		
2500 (668·13)	v	0·4784	0·4244	0·3678	0·3061	0·2710	0·2294	0·1686	0·1484				
	h	1826·2	1706·1	1585·3	1458·4	1387·8	1303·6	1176·8	1132·3				
	s	1·7389	1·6775	1·6088	1·5273	1·4772	1·4127	1·3073	1·2687				
3000 (695·36)	v	0·3966	0·3505	0·3018	0·2476	0·2159	0·1760	0·0984					
	h	1819·9	1698·0	1574·3	1441·8	1365·0	1267·2	1060·7					
	s	1·7163	1·6540	1·5837	1·4984	1·4439	1·3690	1·1966					
3206·2 (705·40)	v	0·3703	0·3267	0·2806	0·2288	0·1981	0·1583						
	h	1817·2	1694·6	1569·8	1434·7	1355·2	1250·5						
	s	1·7080	1·6452	1·5742	1·4874	1·4309	1·3508						
3500	v	0·3381	0·2977	0·2546	0·2058	0·1762	0·1364	0·0806					
	h	1813·6	1689·8	1563·3	1424·9	1340·7	1224·9	780·5					
	s	1·6968	1·6336	1·5615	1·4723	1·4127	1·3241	0·9615					
4000	v	0·2943	0·2581	0·2192	0·1743	0·1462	0·1052	0·0287					
	h	1807·2	1681·7	1552·1	1406·8	1314·4	1174·8	763·8					
	s	1·6795	1·6154	1·5417	1·4482	1·3827	1·2757	0·9347					
4500	v	0·2602	0·2273	0·1917	0·1500	0·1226	0·0798	0·0276					
	h	1800·9	1673·5	1540·8	1388·4	1286·5	1113·9	753·5					
	s	1·6640	1·5990	1·5235	1·4253	1·3529	1·2204	0·9235					
5000	v	0·2329	0·2027	0·1696	0·1303	0·1036	0·0593	0·0268					
	h	1794·5	1665·5	1529·5	1369·5	1256·5	1047·1	746·4					
	s	1·6499	1·5839	1·5066	1·4034	1·3231	1·1622	0·9152					
5500	v	0·2106	0·1825	0·1516	0·1143	0·0880	0·0463	0·0262					
	h	1788·1	1657·0	1518·2	1349·3	1224·1	985·0	741·3					
	s	1·6369	1·5699	1·4908	1·3821	1·2930	1·1093	0·9090					

* Abridged from "Thermodynamic Properties of Steam," by Joseph H. Keenan and Frederick G. Keyes. Copyright, 1937, by Joseph H. Keenan and Frederick G. Keyes. Published by John Wiley & Sons, Inc., New York.

ANSWERS TO PROBLEMS

1.1 (a) $1\cdot98 \times 10^6$ ft lb$_f$; (b) $2\cdot655 \times 10^6$ ft lb$_f$.

1.2 (a) $3\cdot995$ lb$_m$/hp h; (b) $29\cdot75$ lb$_m$/hp h; (c) $4\cdot75$ lb$_m$/hp h;
(d) $2\cdot08$ lb$_m$/hp h.

1.3 (a) $0\cdot412$ lb$_m$/hp h; (b) $2\cdot375$ lb$_m$/hp h; (c) $0\cdot497$ lb$_m$/hp h;
(d) $0\cdot605$ lb$_m$/hp h; (e) $0\cdot713$ lb$_m$/hp h; (f) $2\cdot28 \times 10^{-5}$ lb$_m$/hp h.

1.4 (a) $9\cdot6$ lb$_m$/lb$_f$; (b) $0\cdot953$ lb$_m$/lb$_f$; (c) $0\cdot542$ lb$_m$/lb$_f$.

1.5 (a) $5\cdot37$ hp; (b) $5\cdot09$ hp; (c) $0\cdot564$ lb$_m$/hp h.

2.1 (a) (i) $1\cdot0$ lb$_m$ ft/pdl s^2; (ii) $1\cdot0$ g$_m$ cm/dyne s^2;
(iii) $1\cdot0$ kg$_m$ m/N s^2; (iv) $1\cdot0$ slug ft/lb$_f$ s^2;
(v) $4\cdot17 \times 10^8$ lb$_m$ft/lb$_f$h^2; (vi) $8\cdot425 \times 10^7$ ton$_m$ mile/pdl year^2.
(b) $32\cdot174$ pdl; 10^5 dyne.

2.2 497 lb$_f$.   **2.3** (a) 8910 cm/s^2; (b) $203\cdot6$ cm/s^2.

2.4 (a) 100 lb$_m$ ft/c s^2; (b) $1c = 3\cdot11$ lb$_f$; (c) numerically m is $3\cdot125\ w$.

2.5 (a) $29\cdot2$ ft/s^2; (b) 172 lb$_f$.

2.6 $14\cdot8$ psia.   **2.7** (a) $0\cdot293$ psi; (b) 548 ft.

2.8 225 psia; $1\cdot23$ psia.   **2.9** $12\cdot25$ in.; $75\cdot58\%$.

3.1 15 ft lb$_f$.   **3.2** (a) 28 in. lb$_f$; (b) 24 in. lb$_f$; (c) -4 in. lb$_f$; 0.

3.3 $7\cdot47$ ft lb$_f$.

3.4 (a) 50 ft lb$_f$; -50 ft lb$_f$; (b) 1863 ft lb$_f$; -1863 ft lb$_f$;
(c) 100 ft lb$_f$; -100 ft lb$_f$; (d) 0; (e) 0.

3.5 -760 ft lb$_f$; $-26,880$ ft lb$_f$; 0; 0.

3.6 (a) $+0\cdot75$ ft lb$_f$; (b) $+32\cdot4$ ft lb$_f$; (c) $1587\cdot6$ ft lb$_f$;
(d) $-1620\cdot75$ ft lb$_f$.

3.7 (a) 720 ft lb$_f$; (b) 720 ft lb$_f$.   **3.8** $99\cdot1$ hp.

3.9 (a) 100 psi/inch; (b) $0\cdot763$ in^2.   **3.10** 415 hp.

3.11 (i) Sketch;

(ii) $$W = \frac{n}{n-1}\, p_1 V_{sw}\left[1 - \frac{c}{100}\left\{\left(\frac{p_2}{p_1}\right)^{\frac{1}{n}} - 1\right\}\right]\left[1 - \left(\frac{p_2}{p_1}\right)^{\frac{n-1}{n}}\right];$$

(iii) -311 ft lb$_f$/cycle; (iv) $22\cdot6$ hp.

3.12 1068 ft lb$_f$.

3.13 (i) Sketch; (ii) $p_m = \dfrac{p_1}{100}\left[a + (a + c)\ln\dfrac{100 + c}{a + c}\right] - p_e$

(iii) $39\cdot8$ psi; (iv) 2320 ft lb$_f$/cycle; (v) $18\cdot3$ hp.

3.14 $+6300$ ft lb$_f$.

3.15 (a) Sketch; (b) (i) -216 ft lb$_f$; (ii) 0; (iii) $-59\cdot1$ ft lb$_f$; (iv) 0;
(v) $275\cdot1$ ft lb$_f$.

3.16 -6800 ft lb$_f$.

3.17 1282 ft lb$_f$.

3.18 $108\cdot4$ hp.

3.19 (a) $33\cdot5$ ton$_f$ ft; (b) $19,400$ hp; (c) $-1\cdot98 \times 10^7$ ft lb$_f$/min.

3.20 $0\cdot788$ lb$_f$ in.; $0\cdot01$ hp.

3.21 (a) 3720 ft lb$_f$; (b) -420 ft lb$_f$.

CHAPTER 4

4.1   (a) 636·8°F; (b) −15°C; (c) 30·2°F; (d) 565·6°C; (e) 270°C.
4.2   73°.
4.3   (a) 24·27°C; (b) See pages 64 and 65.
4.4   (a) $t = 0·492p − 460$; (b) 69°F.

CHAPTER 5

5.1   (a) 1·8 Btu; (b) 252 calories.
5.2   (i) +1·6 Btu; (ii) −1·6 Btu; (iii) 0.
5.3   (i) +32 Btu; (ii) +1.6 Btu; (iii) −33·6 Btu; (iv) 0.
5.4   (i) +1·6 Btu; (ii) −33.6 Btu; (iii) +32 Btu; (iv) 0.
5.5   0.

5.6

	(a)	(b)	(c)	(d)	(e)	(f)	(g)	(h)
Q	−	0	+	+	0	0	0	0
W	0	+	0	−	−	−	0	−

5.7

	(a)	(b)
Q	0	−0·1 Btu
W	0	0

5.8

	(a)	(b)	(c)
Q	0	−	−
W	0	0	0

CHAPTER 6

6.1   (a) −23,350 ft lb_f; (b) 778 ft lb_f/Btu; 1400 ft lb_f/Chu;
     (c) +30 Btu in each vessel.
6.2   (a) +425 ft lb_f; −575 ft lb_f; (b) −425 ft lb_f; (c) 778 ft lb_f/Btu;
     (d) (i) +0·74 Btu; (ii) −0·74 Btu; (e) 0
6.3   778 ft lb_f/Btu.
6.4   −8 Btu.
6.5   (a) −; (b) −; (c) +; (d) +; (e) +; (f) +; (g) 0; (h) +.
6.6   −0·1 Btu.
6.7   (a) 0; (b) −; (c) −.
6.8   (i) −4000 ft lb_f; (ii) +4000 ft lb_f; (iii) 0.
6.9   0.   **6.10**   0.
6.11   (a) −17·9 Btu; (b) +27·1 Btu.
6.12   (a) +72·3 Btu; (b) −8·0 Btu; (c) 0.

6.13

	Q	W	ΔE
(i)	0	−	+
(ii)	0	0	0

6.14

	Q	W	ΔE
(i)	0	−	+
(ii)	0	0	0

6.15

	Q	W	ΔE
(a)	0	+	−
(b)	0	+	−
(c)	−	0	−

6.16   (a) −108·3 Btu; 0; 228 Btu; 0; (b) −100 Btu;
     (c) +108·3 Btu; +220 Btu; −228 Btu; −100·3 Btu.
6.17   (a) 0; (b) −45 Btu; (c) 30 Btu; −15 Btu.
6.18   −4·16 Btu.
6.19   (a) 13 Btu; 13 Btu; −19 Btu; (b) −3 Btu; −1 Btu. The process
     is not cyclic; the system is not restored to its initial state because
     chemical reaction has occurred.

CHAPTER 7

7.1 (a) 0; (b) +11·58 Btu.

7.2 (a) +16 Btu; (b) −10 Btu.

7.3 (a) 6·52 Btu/lb$_m$; (b) −565·8 Btu; (c) −584 Btu.

7.4 130·6 Btu/lb$_m$.

7.5 Proof. **7.6** Proof. **7.7** Proof.

7.8 (a) 180 Btu/lb$_m$; (b) 64 Btu; (c) (i) −85·5 Btu;
(ii) −120 Btu. No. Only $(Q - W)$ may be evaluated.

7.9 (a) 0·155 Btu/lb$_m$ °F; 0·217 Btu/lb$_m$ °F; (b) proof;
(c) 595·3°F; 8·57 Btu; 105·5 psia.

7.10 0·47 Btu/lb$_m$ °F; 0·543 Btu/lb$_m$ °F.

7.11 (a) 30·2°F; (b) +3630 ft lb$_f$.

CHAPTER 8

8.1 (a) 37 Btu; (b) +3·07 Btu. **8.2** −20·89 Btu.

8.3 1718 ft/s.

8.4 (a) −99·8 Btu/lb$_m$; (b) −104·04 Btu/lb$_m$.

8.5 (a) 409 ft/s; (b) 879·3 Btu/lb$_m$.

8.6 (a) 1192 Btu/lb$_m$; (b) 54·6 ft/s; 171 ft/s.

8.7 +3·7 Btu/lb$_m$.

8.8 63·6 ft/s; 625 ft/s; 2·89 lb$_m$/s.

8.9 (a) 1582 ft/s; (b) 545 ft/s; (c) 0; (d) 44·1 Btu/lb$_m$; (e) 5·2 hp;
(f) 1100 Btu/lb$_m$; 1100 Btu/lb$_m$; 1055·9 Btu/lb$_m$.

8.10 3542 lb$_m$. **8.11** 1033 Btu/lb$_m$.

8.12 18,670 Btu/lb$_m$. **8.13** −796 Btu/lb$_m$ mixture.

CHAPTER 9

9.1 (a) $v_f = 0.01614$ ft³/lb$_m$; (b) $v_g = 6.466$ ft³/lb$_m$; (c) $t_f = 212$°F;
(d) $t_g = 212$°F; (e) $t = 212$°F; (f) $h_{fg} = 885.4$ Btu/lb$_m$;
(g) $h_g = 1150.4$ Btu/lb$_m$; (h) $u_f = 453.2$ Btu/lb$_m$;
(i) $v = 11.441$ ft³/lb$_m$; $h = 1380.9$ Btu/lb$_m$; $u = 1253.7$ Btu/lb$_m$;
(j) $t = 607.2$°F; $v = 0.522$ ft³/lb$_m$; (k) $p = 154.6$ psia;
$u = 1215$ Btu/lb$_m$.

9.2 Sketch.

9.3 (a) 1118·6 Btu/lb$_m$; 1041·7 Btu/lb$_m$; 1·661 ft³/lb$_m$;
(b) 1130·3 Btu/lb$_m$; 1053·4 Btu/lb$_m$; 0·6095 ft³/lb$_m$.

9.4 566·1 psia; 10·734 lb$_m$; 0·0745 ft³/lb$_m$; 5529 Btu; 5445 Btu.

9.5 (a) 0·405 lb$_m$; 464 Btu; 431·9 Btu;
(b) +52 Btu; +42·8 Btu; +9·2 Btu; +52 Btu.

9.6 (a) 7 ft³/lb$_m$; 292·71°F; 0·976; 1077·5 Btu/lb$_m$; 1155·2 Btu/lb$_m$;
(b) 63·2 psia; +30·8 Btu/lb$_m$; +26·6 Btu/lb$_m$; +26·6 Btu/lb$_m$;
61·68 psia.

9.7 (a) 0·0503 ft³; (b) $m_f = 0.99833$ lb$_m$; $m_g = 0.00167$ lb$_m$;
(c) 728·3°F; (d) 644·9 Btu.

9.8 18·93 lb$_m$. **9.9** 0·967.

9.10 0·919; no. ($h_1 < h_g$ at 15 psia).

9.11 (a) 0·970; (b) no. ($h_1 < h_g$ at 14·7 psia).

9.12 (a) 1·242; (b) 2810 ft lb$_f$; (c) −0·62 Btu. **9.13** 0·898.

9.14 (a) −20 Btu/lb$_m$; (b) −20·03 Btu/lb$_m$.

9.15 (a) 2850 ft/s; (b) 2·055 lb$_m$/s; (c) 76·2 lb$_m$/s.

9.16 0·881; 3·15 ft². **9.17** (a) 60 psia; (b) 3·12 lb$_m$.

9.18 798 lb$_m$; 0·834. **9.19** +5·72 Btu.

CHAPTER 10

10.1 24·9%; 60·1 Btu.
10.2 21,200 Btu/min; 16,960 Btu/min.
10.3 (a) 54·1%; (b) 6970 Btu/s; 5330 hp.
10.4 (a) 1129·6 Btu/lb$_m$; (b) 108·6 Btu/lb$_m$; (c) 976 Btu/lb$_m$;
(d) 45 Btu/lb$_m$; (e) 9·6%.
10.5 (a) 1560°F; (b) 210·7 Btu/lb$_m$; (c) 65·3 Btu/lb$_m$; (d) 23·6%.
10.6 280·7 Btu; 2·97; 3·97.
10.7 (a) 177 Btu/s; 141·6 Btu/s; (b) 265·5 lb$_m$/min.
10.8 4·74; 14,580 Btu/h.
10.9 (a) 0·86 lb$_m$/min; (b) 2440 Btu/h; (c) 27·7 Btu/lb$_m$;
(d) 75·07 Btu/lb$_m$; 0·945; (e) 3·84.
10.10 1·81.

CHAPTER 11

11.1 (a) 45%; (b) (i) 2·22; (ii) 4·78 hp; (c) 1·22.
11.2 84·5, 826; 311·8, 0; −31·9, −537·7; −76·1, 0 Btu/lb$_m$;
$\Sigma w = 288\cdot3$ Btu/lb$_m$; 34·9%.
11.3 0, 826; 350·8, 0; 0, −537·7; −62·5, 0 Btu/lb$_m$;
$\Sigma w_x = 288\cdot3$ Btu/lb$_m$; 34·9%.
11.4 Possible according to the First Law ($\Sigma Q = \Sigma W$). Impossible according to the Second Law (PMM2).
11.5 Proof.

CHAPTER 12

12.1 (a) 32·9%; (b) 7·82 Btu; 5·25 Btu. (c) 3·04; 29 hp.
12.2 16·67%; 200°F; 90°F.
12.3 18·64 hp.
12.4 63·5%.
12.5 6·31 kWh.
12.6 (a) 37·7 Btu/s; 3·81; (b) 12·3; 4·34 hp.
12.7 224 hp.
12.8 Claim not valid ($\eta_{max} = 31\cdot5\%$).
12.9 (a) 4290 Btu; 5940 Btu; (b) 300 Btu; 1950 Btu.

CHAPTER 13

13.1 (a) 0·2 Btu/°F abs; (b) 0·0865 Btu/lb$_m$ °F abs;
(c) 0·086 Btu/lb$_m$ °F abs.
13.2 (a) $s_g = 1\cdot6350$ Btu/lb$_m$ °F abs; (b) $s_f = 0\cdot1326$ Btu/lb$_m$ °F abs;
(c) $s = 1\cdot4897$ Btu/lb$_m$ °F abs; (d) $s = 2\cdot0434$ Btu/lb$_m$ °F abs.
13.3 (a) 0·875; 281·01°F; 1·5026 Btu/lb$_m$ °F abs;
(b) 138·7 psia; 3·508 ft³/lb$_m$; 1131·2 Btu/lb$_m$.
(c) 247·31 psia; 1·6383 ft³/lb$_m$; 1025·2 Btu/lb$_m$.
13.4 Sketch.
13.5 7·712 Btu/°F abs.
13.6 1·0963 Btu/lb$_m$ °F abs; 795·5 Btu/lb$_m$.
13.7 (a) 0·3297 Btu/lb$_m$ °F abs; 283·5 Btu/lb$_m$; (b) 101·4 Btu/lb$_m$;
(c) 182·1 Btu/lb$_m$; 182·1 Btu/lb$_m$;
(d) 165·4 Btu/lb$_m$; 165·4 Btu/lb$_m$.
13.8 (a) 327·8°F; 258·6°F; (b) 2320 ft lb$_f$; (c) 0·005 Btu/°F abs;
(d) 3·66 Btu.
13.9 (a) 450·9°F; (b) 152·4 Btu/lb$_m$; (c) 179·8 Btu/lb$_m$;
(d) 152·4 Btu/lb$_m$; (e) 179·8 Btu/lb$_m$.

13.10   (*a*) -18 Btu; (*b*) $+0 \cdot 0284$ Btu/lb$_m$ °F abs.

13.11   (*a*) $78 \cdot 4$ Btu/lb$_m$; (*b*) $123 \cdot 9$ Btu/lb$_m$; (*c*) $63 \cdot 2\%$.

13.12   Check.

13.13   (*a*) $+843 \cdot 0$ Btu/lb$_m$, 0; 0, $+188 \cdot 3$ Btu/lb$_m$; $-674 \cdot 3$ Btu/lb$_m$, 0;
          0, $-19 \cdot 6$ Btu/lb$_m$; (*b*) $\Sigma w_x = 168 \cdot 7$ Btu/lb$_m = \Sigma q$; (*c*) 20%.

13.14   (*a*) $+1017 \cdot 3$ Btu/lb$_m$, 0; 0, $+188 \cdot 3$ Btu/lb$_m$; $+829 \cdot 0$ Btu/lb$_m$, 0;
          0, ≈ 0; (*b*) $\Sigma w_x = 188 \cdot 3$ Btu/lb$_m = \Sigma q$; (*c*) $\eta_{\text{Rankine}} = 18 \cdot 5\%$;
          $\eta_R = 20\%$.

13.15   (*a*) Proof; (*b*) $-1 \cdot 23$ Btu/lb$_m$.

13.16   (*a*) $0 \cdot 946$; $312 \cdot 7$ Btu/lb$_m$; (*b*) $-2 \cdot 5$ Btu/lb$_m$; (*c*) $24 \cdot 0\%$; $24 \cdot 2\%$.

13.17   (*a*) $0 \cdot 9$; $-27 \cdot 4$ Btu/lb$_m$; (*b*) $0 \cdot 179$; (*c*) $+130 \cdot 5$ Btu/lb$_m$;
          (*d*) $4 \cdot 76$; $5 \cdot 39$.

13.18   (*a*) $0 \cdot 933$; 2280 ft/s; (*b*) 2165 ft/s; $0 \cdot 944$; $+0 \cdot 0139$ Btu/lb$_m$ °F abs;
          (*c*) $A_a/A_b = 0 \cdot 939$.

13.19   (*a*) $1 \cdot 5272$ Btu/lb$_m$ °F abs; $1 \cdot 6119$ Btu/lb$_m$ °F abs;
          $0 \cdot 5287$ Btu/lb$_m$ °F abs; $0 \cdot 5664$ Btu/lb$_m$ °F abs.

          (*b*) Irreversible; Δs exceeds $\displaystyle\int \frac{dQ}{T}$ in each case.

          (*c*) $+826$ Btu/lb$_m$; 0; $-727 \cdot 7$ Btu/lb$_m$; 0; 12%;
          (*d*) $-0 \cdot 122$ Btu/lb$_m$ °F abs; (*e*) 0; $21 \cdot 86\%$.

13.20   (*a*) Proof; (*b*) $+0 \cdot 01705$ Btu/°F abs; (*c*) $+0 \cdot 0168$ Btu/°F abs;
          (*d*) $+0 \cdot 020$ Btu/°F abs.

13.21   (*a*) $+0 \cdot 0552$ Btu/lb$_m$ °F abs; 0; (*b*) $+0 \cdot 0139$ Btu/lb$_m$ °F abs; 0;
          (*c*) $+0 \cdot 01705$ Btu/°F abs; 0; (*d*) $+0 \cdot 2110$ Btu/°F abs; 0;
          (*e*) $+0 \cdot 070$ Btu/°F abs; 0.

CHAPTER 14

14.1   (i)

pv	$452 \cdot 3$	$449 \cdot 0$	$435 \cdot 5$		
pv/T	$0 \cdot 596$	$0 \cdot 591$	$0 \cdot 573$		

      (ii)

pv	$690 \cdot 8$	$690 \cdot 0$	$686 \cdot 0$	$626 \cdot 0$	$295 \cdot 2$
pv/T	$0 \cdot 595$	$0 \cdot 595$	$0 \cdot 592$	$0 \cdot 540$	$0 \cdot 255$

      (iii)

pv	$1227 \cdot 0$	$1227 \cdot 0$	$1226 \cdot 4$	$1218 \cdot 0$	$1189 \cdot 8$
pv/T	$0 \cdot 595$	$0 \cdot 595$	$0 \cdot 595$	$0 \cdot 591$	$0 \cdot 578$

      Units: p, psia; v, ft^3/lb$_m$; T, °F abs.

14.2   (i) $0 \cdot 1$ Btu/lb$_m$; (ii) $29 \cdot 8$ Btu/lb$_m$.

14.3   (i) $-0 \cdot 18$°F; $-66 \cdot 7$°F.

14.4   Check.

14.5 $0 \cdot 1815$ lb$_m$; $0 \cdot 00623$ lb mole.

14.6   (i) $2 \cdot 655$ lb$_m$; (ii) $2 \cdot 672$ lb$_m$. Answer (ii): steam is not an ideal gas.

14.7   (*a*) $37 \cdot 5$ lb$_m$; 177 psia; $1 \cdot 6$ ft^3/lb$_m$; $61 \cdot 8$ ft lb$_f$/lb$_m$°F abs;
          (*b*) $0 \cdot 2885$ Btu/lb$_m$ °F; $0 \cdot 2090$ Btu/lb$_m$ °F; (*c*) $139 \cdot 3$ psia;
          (*d*) -1098 Btu; -1514 Btu; -1098 Btu.

14.8   Sketch.

14.9 $72 \cdot 9$ psia; 870°F; $+40 \cdot 5$ Btu; $+141 \cdot 4$ Btu.

14.10   (i) $12 \cdot 95$ ft^3/lb$_m$; 46°F; 0; (ii) 0; 1336 hp.

14.11 $2 \cdot 445$ lb$_m$; 360 psia; 0; $-186{,}000$ ft lb$_f$; -239 Btu;
          $-0 \cdot 272$ Btu/°F abs.

14.12   (*a*) (i) $10 \cdot 54$ ft^3/lb$_m$; 110 °F; $+0 \cdot 075$ Btu/lb$_m$ °F abs.
            (ii) $+61 \cdot 7$ Btu/lb$_m$; $+46 \cdot 3$ Btu/lb$_m$.
          (*b*) (i) $0 \cdot 566$ ft^3/lb$_m$; 110°F; $+0 \cdot 075$ Btu/lb$_m$ °F abs.
            (ii) $15 \cdot 4$ Btu/lb$_m$; 0.

14.13   (i) 104°F; 204°F; (ii) $1 \cdot 177$; (iii) $-0 \cdot 182$ Btu; $-0 \cdot 101$ Btu.

14.14   (a) $-99\cdot3$ Btu/lb$_m$; (b) $-83\cdot9$ Btu/lb$_m$; (c) $84\cdot5\%$.

14.15   (a) $469°$F; (b) 97 hp.

14.16   (a) (i) $1376°$F; (ii) $1\cdot133$ ft^2; (b) $-222\cdot8$ Btu/lb$_m$.

14.17   (a) $40°$F; $0\cdot0022$ Btu/$°$F abs; (b) $20°$F; $+9\cdot37$ Btu;
   (c) $20°$F; $-10\cdot87$ Btu.

14.18   (i) $0\cdot216$ lb$_m$; (ii) $-2\cdot67$ Btu; (iii) $8\cdot97$ psia.

14.19   (i) $19\cdot03$ psia; (ii) $0\cdot0266$ lb$_m$.

14.20   (i) $7\cdot2$; (ii) $-77\cdot4$ ft lb$_f$; $+0\cdot002$ Btu.

14.21   (i) $90\cdot3$ ft lb$_f$/lb$_m°$F abs; $0\cdot406$ Btu/lb$_m°$F; (ii) $32\cdot5°$F; 1320 ft/s;
   (iii) $2\cdot57$ in^2; $1\cdot12$ in^2.

14.22   (a)

$$V = \sqrt{2g_0 R \frac{\gamma}{\gamma-1} \cdot T_1 \left[1 - \left(\frac{p}{p_1}\right)^{\frac{\gamma-1}{\gamma}} \right]}$$

$$A = \dot{m}\sqrt{\frac{\gamma-1}{\gamma} \cdot \frac{RT_1}{2g_0}} \cdot \frac{(r)^{\frac{\gamma-1}{\gamma}}}{rp_1 \sqrt{1-(r)^{\frac{\gamma-1}{\gamma}}}} \quad \text{where } r = \frac{p}{p_1}$$

(b) Plot.

(c) $\dfrac{p}{p_1} = \left(\dfrac{2}{\gamma+1}\right)^{\frac{\gamma}{\gamma-1}}$; $V = \sqrt{2g_0 \dfrac{\gamma}{\gamma+1} RT_1}$.

(d) Proof.

14.23   (i)

	1	2	3	4
p, (psia)	100	50	$7\cdot57$	$15\cdot14$
T, ($°$F abs)	960	960	560	560
V, (ft^3)	1	2	$3\cdot84$	$7\cdot68$
S, Btu/$°$F abs	S_1	$S_1 + 0\cdot0134$	$S_1 + 0\cdot0134$	S_2

(ii) $41\cdot7\%$; $5\cdot35$ Btu; (iii) $12\cdot6$ hp.

14.24   (i) Sketch; (ii) $\eta = 1 - \left(\dfrac{1}{r}\right)^{\gamma-1} \cdot \dfrac{\lambda^\gamma - 1}{\gamma(\lambda-1)}$;

(iii) $59\cdot6\%$; (iv) $T_2 = 1000°$F; $T_3 = 1730°$F; $T_4 = 492°$F;
   (v) $104\cdot3$ Btu/lb$_m$.

14.25   (i) Sketch; (ii) $\eta = 1 - \left(\dfrac{1}{r}\right)^{\gamma-1}$; (iii) $47\cdot4\%$;

(iv) $W_\mathrm{x} = R \cdot \dfrac{\gamma}{\gamma-1}[(r)^{\frac{\gamma-1}{\gamma}} - 1][T_3(r)^{\frac{1-\gamma}{\gamma}} - T_1]$;

(v) $W_\mathrm{x} = 86\cdot1$ Btu/lb$_m$; (vi) Answers would be the same.

14.26   (i) Sketch; (ii) $t_1 = 100°$F; $t_2 = 495°$F; $t_3 = 1400°$F; $t_4 = 803°$F;
   (iii) $22\cdot3\%$; (iv) $48\cdot5$ Btu/lb$_m$.

14.27   (a) (i) $100\cdot7$ ft lb$_f$/lb$_m$ $°$F abs; (ii) $1\cdot445$; (iii) 73 Btu/lb$_m$;
   $-13\cdot7$ Btu/lb$_m$; (b) (i) $1\cdot253$; (ii) $12\cdot35$ ft^3/lb$_m$; $289\cdot5$ Btu/lb$_m$;
   $152\cdot2$ Btu/lb$_m$; (iii) $0\cdot555$ Btu/lb$_m$ $°$F; $0\cdot425$ Btu/lb$_m$ $°$F;
   (c) $1\cdot496$; (d) -254 Btu; $+152$ Btu; (e) -541 Btu.

14.28   (a) (i) $100\cdot7$ ft lb$_f$/lb$_m$ $°$F abs; (ii) $1\cdot477$; (iii) $71\cdot2$ Btu/lb$_m$;
   $-15\cdot5$ Btu/lb$_m$; (b) (i) $1\cdot477$; (ii) $12\cdot35$ ft^3/lb$_m$; $227\cdot2$ Btu/lb$_m$;
   $89\cdot9$ Btu/lb$_m$; (iii) $0\cdot4$ Btu/lb$_m$ $°$F; $0\cdot2707$ Btu/lb$_m$ $°$F; (c) $1\cdot496$;
   (d) -254 Btu; $+10$ Btu; (e) -390 Btu.

14.29

	(i)	(ii)
V_2 ft/s	479	479
$\dot{Q}$ Btu/s	2198	2287

14.30 3·83; 4040 hp; 4080 hp.

CHAPTER 15

15.1 (i) $p_{CO} = 2\cdot01$ psia; $p_H = 27\cdot99$ psia; (ii) 100 ft³; 50 ft³/lb$_m$;
(iii) $V_{CO} = 6\cdot46$ ft³; $V_H = 90\cdot04$ ft³; (iv) $n_{CO} = 0\cdot0357$ moles;
$n_H = 0\cdot497$ moles; (v) 411 ft lb$_f$/lb$_m$ °F abs; 2·121 Btu/lb$_m$ °F;
1·592 Btu/lb$_m$ °F; 1·332.

15.2 (i) 590°F; (ii) $+1114$ Btu/lb$_m$; $+836$ Btu/lb$_m$;
$+1\cdot1103$ Btu/lb$_m$ °F abs; (iii) 1672 Btu.

15.3 (i) 590°F; (ii) $+1114$ Btu/lb$_m$; $+836$ Btu/lb$_m$;
$+1\cdot1103$ Btu/lb$_m$ °F abs; (iii) 1672 Btu.

15.4 (a) 0·496 ft³; (b) (i) 25·24 psia (ii) 0·236 Btu/lb$_m$ °F;
0·153 Btu/lb$_m$ °F; 1·541; (c) 5·36 psia; $+2\cdot08$ Btu;
$+0\cdot54$ Btu; 0·024 Btu/lb$_m$ °F abs; (d) 4·59 psia;
$+1\cdot93$ Btu; $+0\cdot00212$ Btu/°F abs; $-0\cdot00212$ Btu/°F abs.

15.5 (i) 60°F; (ii) $p_{air} = 13\cdot77$ psia; $p_{CH_4} = 1\cdot23$ psia;
(iii) 0·0303 Btu/lb$_m$ °F abs.

15.6 (a) (i) 60°F; (ii) $p_{CO} = 10$ psia; $p_H = 15$ psia; (iii) 17·97 ft³/lb$_m$;
(iv) $m_{CO} = 0\cdot2515$ lb$_m$; $m_H = 0\cdot0271$ lb$_m$;
(v) $n_{CO} = 0\cdot00898$ lb mole; $n_H = 0\cdot01346$ lb mole;
(vi) 124·3 ft lb$_f$/lb$_m$° F abs; 0·616 Btu/lb$_m$ °F; 0·456 Btu/lb$_m$ °F;
1·351; (b) 60°F; 12·5 psia; (c) 60°F; 12·5 psia.

15.7 276°F; 1·98 lb$_m$.

15.8 (a) (i) $p_a = 25\cdot45$ psia; $p_s = 4\cdot55$ psia; (ii) 9·93 ft³/lb$_m$;
(iii) 109·7 Btu/lb$_m$ (datum 32°F); (b) as (a).

15.9 (a) $m_a = 1\cdot014$ lb$_m$; $m_s = 0\cdot571$ lb$_m$; (b) 74·3°F; 3·7 psia.

15.10 (i) 5·22 psia; (ii) 2·87 lb$_m$; (iii) 4834 Btu; (iv) $-6\cdot143$ Btu/°F abs.

15.11 617·1 Btu/lb$_m$; 0·476.

15.12 (i) $p_a = 14\cdot465$ psia; $p_s = 0\cdot235$ psia; (ii) 13·67 ft³/lb$_m$;
(iii) 22·4 Btu/lb$_m$; (iv) $-14\cdot8$ Btu/lb$_m$; (v) 0·02381 Btu/lb$_m$ °F abs.

15.13 (i) 0·99; (ii) 70·7 grains/lb$_m$; (iii) 0·463; (iv) 65·5°F; (v) 57°F.

15.14 0·463; 0·463; 0·472.

15.15 (a) 67°F; 0·00026 lb$_m$; (b) 66°F; 0·00022 lb$_m$.

15.16 (a) 0·00443 lb$_m$/lb$_m$ air; 0·00443 lb$_m$/lb$_m$ air; (b) 0·82;
(c) -570 Btu/min.

15.17 (a) 0·0179 lb$_m$/lb$_m$ air; 0·0053 lb$_m$/lb$_m$ air; (b) 1·0;
(c) -1366 Btu/min; $\dot{m}_{H_2O} = 0\cdot72$ lb$_m$/min.

15.18 (i) 0·0032 lb$_m$ H$_2$O/lb$_m$ dry air; (ii) 134°F;
(iii) $+24\cdot9$ Btu/lb$_m$ mixture.

15.19 0·6; 329 Btu/lb$_m$; 0·218 lb$_m$.

15.20 Plot. **15.21** Yes. **15.22** 2400 ft.

CHAPTER 16

16.1

(a) 3·38 lb$_m$;	Products	CO$_2$	H$_2$O	SO$_2$	
	m lb$_m$	3·08	1·26	0·04	
	n lb mole	0·07	0·07	0·000625	
(b) 14·57 lb$_m$;	Products	CO$_2$	H$_2$O	SO$_2$	N$_2$
	m lb$_m$	3·08	1·26	0·04	11·19
	n lb mole	0·07	0·07	0·000625	0·4

16.2   (a) $15 \cdot 13$; $n_{CO_2} = 0 \cdot 0702$; $n_{H_2O} = 0 \cdot 0789$; $n_{N_2} = 0 \cdot 415$ lb mole;
         (b) $V_{fuel} = 0 \cdot 00463$ in³; $V_{air} = 41 \cdot 7$ in³.

16.3   (i) $n_{H_2O} = 0 \cdot 080$; $n_{CO_2} = 0 \cdot 041$; $n_{CO} = 0 \cdot 029$; $n_{N_2} = 0 \cdot 366$ lb mole;
         (ii) CO_2, $9 \cdot 4\%$;   CO, $6 \cdot 7\%$; N_2, $83 \cdot 9\%$.

16.4   (i) $13 \cdot 5$;   (ii) $24 \cdot 1\%$;   (iii) 3260 ft³/min.

16.5   (i) $n_{CO_2} = 0 \cdot 07$; $n_{SO_2} = 0 \cdot 000625$; $n_{O_2} = 0 \cdot 0422$; $n_{N_2} = 0 \cdot 559$;
         $n_{H_2O} = 0 \cdot 0907$ lb mole;   (ii) $1 \cdot 632$ lb$_m$;   (iii) $120 \cdot 1°F$.

16.6 CO_2, $14 \cdot 4\%$; O_2, $6 \cdot 06\%$; N_2, $79 \cdot 54\%$.

16.7   (i) $n_{CO} = 9 \cdot 84 \times 10^{-5}$ lb mole; $n_{O_2} = 4 \cdot 92 \times 10^{-5}$ lb mole;
         (ii) $-121,060$ Btu/lb mole CO;   (iii) $9 \cdot 8$ psia;
         (iv) $-121,532$ Btu/lb mole CO.

16.8   (a) Plot;   (b) $+47,974$ Btu/lb mole CO;   (c) $940°F$.

16.9   (i) Sketch;   (ii) $-19,133$ Btu/lb$_m$ octane;
         (iii) $-19,081$ Btu/lb$_m$ octane; $-19,135$ Btu/lb$_m$ octane;
         (iv) $-19,165$ Btu/lb$_m$ octane.

16.10 $0 \cdot 205$ Btu/lb$_m$ °F.

16.11 $2982°F$.

16.12   4348 Btu/lb$_m$ CO.

16.13   (a) (i) $-671,076$ Btu/lb mole C_2H_6;
           (ii) $+671,076$ Btu/lb mole C_2H_6;
           (iii) 22,369 Btu/lb$_m$ C_2H_6;   20,426 Btu/lb$_m$ C_2H_6;
         (b) $10,057°F$.

16.14   (a) (i) $-671,076$ Btu/lb mole C_2H_6;
           (ii) $+671,076$ Btu/lb mole C_2H_6;
           (iii) 22,369 Btu/lb$_m$ C_2H_6;   20,426 Btu/lb$_m$ C_2H_6;
         (b) $3070°F$.

16.15   (a) $156 \cdot 7$ Btu/ft³; $148 \cdot 8$ Btu/ft³;
         (b) $153 \cdot 7$ Btu/ft³ of wet gas; $146 \cdot 1$ Btu/ft³ of wet gas.

16.16   (i) 95%;   (ii) 97%.

16.17   (a) Proof;   (b) (i) $\overline{LCV} = 17,200$ Btu/lb$_m$; $q_1 = 13,520$ Btu/lb$_m$;
         $m\bar{c}_p(t - t_0) = 3130$ Btu/lb$_m$; $q_u = 550$ Btu/lb$_m$;   (ii) $78 \cdot 6\%$.

16.18   (a) 454 hp;   (b) $18 \cdot 9\%$.

16.19   51,983 Btu/lb$_m$ H_2.

INDEX